EATING DISORDERS IN THE 21ST CENTURY

NEW DEVELOPMENTS IN ANOREXIA NERVOSA RESEARCH

EATING DISORDERS IN THE 21ST CENTURY

Additional books in this series can be found on Nova's website
under the Series tab.

Additional e-books in this series can be found on Nova's website
under the e-book tab.

EATING DISORDERS IN THE 21ST CENTURY

NEW DEVELOPMENTS IN ANOREXIA NERVOSA RESEARCH

CARLA GRAMAGLIA
AND
PATRIZIA ZEPPEGNO
EDITORS

New York

For permission to use material from this book please contact us:
Telephone 631-231-7269; Fax 631-231-8175
Web Site: http://www.novapublishers.com

NOTICE TO THE READER

The Publisher has taken reasonable care in the preparation of this book, but makes no expressed or implied warranty of any kind and assumes no responsibility for any errors or omissions. No liability is assumed for incidental or consequential damages in connection with or arising out of information contained in this book. The Publisher shall not be liable for any special, consequential, or exemplary damages resulting, in whole or in part, from the readers' use of, or reliance upon, this material. Any parts of this book based on government reports are so indicated and copyright is claimed for those parts to the extent applicable to compilations of such works.

Independent verification should be sought for any data, advice or recommendations contained in this book. In addition, no responsibility is assumed by the publisher for any injury and/or damage to persons or property arising from any methods, products, instructions, ideas or otherwise contained in this publication.

This publication is designed to provide accurate and authoritative information with regard to the subject matter covered herein. It is sold with the clear understanding that the Publisher is not engaged in rendering legal or any other professional services. If legal or any other expert assistance is required, the services of a competent person should be sought. FROM A DECLARATION OF PARTICIPANTS JOINTLY ADOPTED BY A COMMITTEE OF THE AMERICAN BAR ASSOCIATION AND A COMMITTEE OF PUBLISHERS.

Additional color graphics may be available in the e-book version of this book.

Library of Congress Cataloging-in-Publication Data

ISBN: 978-1-63117-551-0

Library of Congress Control Number: 2014934030

Published by Nova Science Publishers, Inc. † New York

Contents

Preface

Eating disorders and anorexia nervosa are relevant psychiatric problems and often represent a serious challenge to patients, families and clinicians as well. There are several questions surrounding anorexia nervosa – about its etiology, maintaining factors, best treatment approach – which still lack a definite answer. Anorexia is often puzzling and difficult to understand, for patients - who may have a poor insight into the reasons and meaning of their disorder – and for their close ones – who may feel powerless and hopeless facing a disorder they can not figure out. Clinicians themselves may have very different approaches towards this disorder. While the Diagnostic and Statistical Manual for Mental Disorders (DSM) criteria for anorexia nervosa are focused on somatic and behavioral issues, available treatments range from cognitive-behavioral to psychodynamic ones, and may be used together or in different phases of the disorder. Moreover, what is surprising for anorexia is the fixation with body weight, which seems to be shared by patients (who want to loose it), parents (who want it to increase) and clinicians (who consider a body mass index >17.5 a requirement for recovery).

What about weight restored patients, with their fear of weight gain and body image distortion under control, but still inhabited by the same anger, competition, omnipotence, orality typical of anorexia? What if a patient is not >17.5 on BMI but she is no longer anorexic in her "mind"?

One may argue that if patients regain a normal BMI they are likely to have solved – or to be on the way to solve – the conflicts underlying anorexia. Anyway sometimes patients eat their way out of the hospital and it is not unusual to see them lose all the weight they had put on or experiencing a psychological breakdown after discharge from inpatient or residential treatments. This is no news, as well as the fact that the anorexic symptom has a meaning that goes far beyond body weight. Anyway, we may provocatively say that psychiatrists seem a little bit "eating disordered" in this focusing on bodily issues for the diagnosis of anorexia and in this "obsession" with BMI when describing recovery. Why?

Of course, criteria are needed, both for diagnosis and recovery, and anorexia is a psychosomatic disorder whose "somatic" issues must not be neglected. But shouldn't we ask ourselves about the meaning of this unique characteristic of anorexia? Aren't we colluding (or identifying) with the anorexic family, when (oversimplifying) the alarming physical condition of the very low weight patient obtains the result to elicit worry about the body and not (or less) about the wounded psyche hidden inside?

There is a lot to reflect about as regards anorexia. We hope that the contributions included in this volume may help the reader to find interesting hints about theoretical, clinical and research issues.

References

American Psychiatric Association. *Diagnostic and Statistical Manual for Mental Disorders–IV Edition, Text Revision*. Washington DC, 2000.

Bruch H. *Eating Disorders: Obesity, Anorexia Nervosa and the Person Within*. New York Basic Books, 1973.

Nordbø RH, Espeset EM, Gulliksen KS, Skårderud F, Holte A. The meaning of self-starvation: qualitative study of patients' perception of anorexia nervosa. *Int J Eat Disord* 2006;39(7):556-64.

Skårderud F. Eating one's words, part I: 'Concretised metaphors' and reflective function in anorexia nervosa--an interview study. *Eur Eat Disord Rev* 2007;15(3):163-74.

In: New Developments in Anorexia Nervosa Research
Editors: Carla Gramaglia and Patrizia Zeppegno

ISBN: 978-1-63117-551-0
© 2014 Nova Science Publishers, Inc.

Chapter 1

Ego-Syntonicity and Eating Disorders

María Roncero[1], Conxa Perpiñá[1,2] and Amparo Belloch[1]
[1]Universidad de Valencia
[2]Ciber Fisiopatología Obesidad y Nutrición (CIBEROBN),
Instituto de Salud Carlos III

Abstract

The present chapter deals with the ego-syntonicity that characterizes all Eating Disorders (EDs), but mainly Anorexia Nervosa. Many ED patients identify themselves with their disorder to the point of considering it their "lifestyle", which suggests that these patients value their symptoms as rational and desirable, in spite of their unpleasant consequences. The identification with the disorder might be associated with the patients' low insight and low motivation to change, two characteristics that make them especially resistant to treatment and cause high rates of therapy withdrawal. Despite the importance of ego-syntonicity and ego-dystonicity in both EDs psychopathology and treatment, there are few studies about this topic. The main aim of this chapter is to review studies about ego-syntonicity and ego-dystonicity in EDs, providing the latest studies, advances, and measures related to these concepts. In doing so, we first highlight different definitions of ego-syntonicity and its counterpart, ego-dystonicity, with a special emphasis on the most comprehensive definition, provided by Purdon, Cripps, Faull, Joseph, and Rowa (Purdon, Cripps, Faull, Joseph, Rowa, 2007). Second, we will focus on ED ego-syntonicity and ego-dystonicity as two different but related multidimensional constructs. From our point of view, this approach allows a more adequate understanding of the ambivalence ED patients typically feel about their symptoms. Third, we examine the low insight and treatment resistance found in EDs, analyzing the association between low motivation to change and the ego-syntonicity/ego-dystonicity of eating-intrusive and repetitive thoughts about appearance, diet and exercise in these patients. And finally, we discuss the need for studies that take into account patients' appraisal of ego-syntonicity about their symptoms, in order to provide the opportunity to design more tailored treatments that will increase patients' motivation and adherence.

Introduction

Eating Disorders are complex and difficult for lay people, and even professionals, to understand. Patients are usually young, good students, and in some cases even bright. They do not understand why their parents push them into therapy: "What is wrong with my eating habits?" They do not complain about their evident loss of weight. They may complain or feel worried because their ability to concentrate on their studies has deteriorated, and they feel pressured by their parents, who refuse to leave them alone. However, to any external observer it is obvious that their eating patterns are not normal, sometimes hidden, and produce an important alteration in their body shape. EDs can cause physical and psychical deterioration and even be lethal, and what is difficult for lay people, but also professionals, to understand is that EDs are a "self-imposed" disease ("*Refusal* to maintain body weight at or above a minimally normal weight for age and height" Criteria A of Anorexia Nervosa in DSM-IV American Psychiatric Association, APA, 1994, unfortunately reformulated in DSM-5, APA 2013). In Bruch's words, their "relentless pursuit of thinness" (Bruch, 1978) is amazing, despite their emaciation or life risk, and what can be more important that one's own life? Again in Bruch's words, Anorexia Nervosa is a "desperate struggle for a self-respecting identity". As this disease is complex and puzzling, it is understandable that the therapeutic alliance with these patients and their treatment are difficult and quite taxing for their therapists, which is why it is necessary to look for more efficient methods to help these young people. Keeping in mind that the difficulties and barriers in ED treatment are highly complex, in the present chapter we will focus on one psychopathological construct that has not been studied in depth to date: the ego-syntonicity/dystonicity of ED symptoms.

Ego-Syntonicity and Ego-Dystonicity: A Multidimensional Concept

Prior to addressing the issue of ego-syntonicity and ego-dystonicity in EDs, it is necessary to define both constructs, bearing in mind that there is no consensus about their definitions.

Some of the definitions of ego-syntonicity are: "*Acceptable to the aims of the ego*" (The American Heritage Medical Dictionary, 2007); "*Describing those elements of a person's behavior, thoughts, impulses, drives, and attitudes that are acceptable to him or her and are consistent with the total personality*" (Mosby's Medical Dictionary, 8th edition, 2009); "*Consistent with one's sense of self, as opposed to ego-alien or dystonic, foreign to one's sense of self*" (Gale Encyclopedia of Medicine, 2008). Regarding ego-dystonicity, the medical dictionaries describe this concept as follows: "*Repugnant to or at variance with the aims of the ego*" (The American Heritage Medical Dictionary, 2007); "*Describing elements of a person's behavior, thoughts, impulses, drives, and attitudes that are unacceptable to him or her and cause anxiety. Also called ego-alien, self-alien*" (Mosby's Medical Dictionary, 8th edition, 2009); "*Denoting aspects of a person's thoughts, impulses, and behavior that are felt to be repugnant, distressing, unacceptable, or inconsistent with the self-conception*" (Dorland's Medical Dictionary for Health Consumers, 2007).

The term ego-dystonicity is described in the DSM-IV (American Psychiatric Association, 2000); regarding Obsessive Compulsive Disorder (OCD), this manual specifically characterizes it as follows: *"The intrusive and inappropriate quality of the obsessions has been referred to as ego-dystonic. This refers to the individual's sense that the content of the obsession is alien, not within his or her own control, and not the kind of thought that he or she would expect to have"*. This definition is no longer included in the Obsessive Compulsive Disorder diagnostic features in the DSM-5.

Despite the different approaches to define ego-dystonicity, the descriptions share some characteristics. In the case of ego-syntonicity, they point out the aspects of acceptability and coherence with one's self. The ego-dystonicity definitions include other elements, such as unacceptability, repugnancy, inconsistency, and conflict. In this sense, Purdon, et al. (Purdon, Cripps, Faull, Joseph, Rowa, 2007) postulate a broad characterization of ego-dystonicity based on the most important aspects of the different definitions and theoretical perspectives of the development of obsessions. *"An ego-dystonic thought is one that is perceived as having little or no context within one's own sense of self or personality. That is, the thought is perceived, at least initially, as occurring outside the context of one's morals, attitudes, beliefs, preferences, past behavior and/or one's expectations about the kinds of thoughts one would or should experience. The thought gives rise to considerable emotional distress and is resisted"*. In this definition, the authors identify the following dimensions: Degree of consistency with morals, beliefs, values, and attitudes; Degree of consistency with preferences and past behavior; Degree of consistency with one's sense of what is rational; and Emotional reaction and resistance.

Purdon et al. (Purdon, Cripps, Faull, Joseph, Rowa, 2007) designed the Ego-Dystonicity Questionnaire (EDQ) to measure the aforementioned dimensions of ego-dystonicity, considering ego-syntonicity as the opposite extreme of ego-dystonicity. Belloch, Roncero, and Perpiñá (Belloch, Roncero, Perpiñá, 2012) adapted the EDQ to Spanish samples (EDQ-r), and it was reduced to 27 items grouped in three factors: Undesirability of thought and rejection of it coming true; Irrationality and incoherence with personality; and Immorality and/or Inconsistency of thought with morals or ethics. Furthermore, they developed the Ego-Syntonicity Questionnaire-ESQ (*Cuestionario de Egosintonía*; Belloch, Roncero, Perpiñá, 2012), which includes 27 items with the opposite meanings to the EDQ-r. Again, items were grouped into three factors: Desirability of thought; Rationality and coherence with personality; and Morality/consistency of thought with moral/ethics. Although related, ego-dystonicity and ego-syntonicity were best conceived as two separate dimensions of both eating-related intrusive thoughts and unwanted intrusive thoughts with contents analogous to clinical obsessions. In other words, the authors found that the same thought, impulse, or image may be considered ego-dystonic, but also ego-syntonic, which suggests that in spite of the unpleasantness or distress caused by these thoughts, individuals do not consider them to be completely "ego-alien".

Ego-Dystonicity and Ego-Syntonicity in Eating Disorders

Many individuals with EDs, especially those suffering from Anorexia Nervosa (AN), put considerable effort into keeping their symptoms, such as maintaining their low weight and thinness, under control. This happens regardless of the risk of severe, life-threatening complications and even in the case of bothersome symptoms such as dizziness, hunger, or concentration difficulties, since these symptoms are interpreted as a positive sign of control over their desired weight and thinness (Roncero, Belloch, Perpiñá, Treasure, 2013). This extreme behavior can be explained based on the idea that the disorder brings meaning to a self that is full of dissatisfaction and disgust, as some authors have claimed. In this sense, Bruch (Bruch, 1973) suggests that Anorexia Nervosa is not simply a problem of weight, but it is caused by a failure in the development of identities or definitions of the self. The ED emerges as an attempt to find a sense of self and compensate for a lack of identity that produces feelings of weakness and incompetence. For this reason, adolescents would focus on their physical aspect, trying to achieve a sense of control and a sense of self. Similarly, Crisp (Crisp, 1980), in his book *Anorexia Nervosa: Let me be*, defines AN as resulting from an existential crisis during adolescence in a situation of immaturity and personal insecurity. Toro (Toro, 1996) suggests that the origin of EDs could be explained as a patients' attempt to compensate for personal dissatisfaction and frustration, insecurity and low self-esteem through achieving what they consider a sort of "perfection" in their physical appearance. Thus, self-realization would be associated with thinness and physical appearance. The same idea was defended by Vandereycken and Hoek (Vandereycken, Hoek, 1992), who place the self as the key element in ED, postulating that ED patients would achieve a triumphant self through their physical appearance.

In EDs, the identification with the disorder is so marked that patients do not recognize their illness; they are not aware of or they deny the severity of their physical state or the risks of their eating patterns. Patients value their attitudes and behaviors as rational, defending them as a *"way of life"* that others simply do not understand. This fact is clearly reflected on pro-anorexia and pro-bulimia web pages, where one can find photos that motivate patients to achieve thinness, tricks to fast and lose weight without others realizing it, and narratives or poems (Abbate Daga, Gramaglia, Pierò, Fassino, 2006). The typical themes include aspects such as controlling their bodies and their lives, power, and perfection (Norris, Boydell, Pinhas, Katzman, 2006). To ED patients, their disorder becomes their only source of identity. It is precisely this quality, the ego-syntonicity, that distinguishes ED from other mental disorders, such as OCD (Bastiani, Altemus, Pigott, Rubenstein, Weltzin, Kaye, 1996; Holden, 1990). In most cases, obsessions in OCD are characterized as ego-dystonic-threatening to the self-, whereas the ED preoccupations are precisely characterized as over-valued ideas - coherent with the desired self-. This positive evaluation and the identification with the disorder would be a critical factor, not only in the patient's lack of insight about her/his abnormal eating pattern or emaciated figure, but in the maintenance of the disorder (Schmidt, Treasure, 2006).

Even though ED patients frequently feel "happy" about their illness, and secure and proud of their achievements, it is very common for them to feel ambivalent about change or recovery. Not every aspect of the ED is positively appreciated by patients; there are two sides to the coin. As an example, we can see how some patients describe two inner voices, one encouraging them to continue with the disorder, and the other encouraging them to leave it behind. Bulik and Kendler's chronic patient (Bulik, Kendler, 2000) asserts that "*a life without an eating disorder would be a life without an identity*". This patient described that she sometimes had rational moments when she admitted the destructiveness of the thoughts and the disorder, but other times she felt like she should achieve the goal of the ED; she could not imagine doing away with the disorder, but only managing the symptoms. Serpell, Treasure, Teasdale, and Sullivan (Serpell, Treasure, Teasdale, Sullivan, 1999) carried out a qualitative study in which 18 Anorexia Nervosa patients wrote two letters to their disorder, one as a friend and one as an enemy. The most significant themes that arose in the letters were that the disorder helps them to feel safe and secure, to feel in control of their lives, and to perceive themselves as more attractive and special or even superior to others. In the letters addressing the AN as an enemy, the most frequent themes were feeling upset by constant thoughts of food, feeling controlled by food, the loss of relationships, and feeling controlled by the AN. Differences between AN and Bulimia Nervosa (BN) have been found in the pros and cons appraised about the disorder: for AN, the perceived advantages of the illness were the safety, structure, specialness, and communication of emotions, whereas for BN patients, the advantage was the ability to eat and still stay slim (Gale, Holliday, Troop, Serpell, Treasure, 2006).

Regarding ED symptoms, even though some of them are uncomfortable (e.g. feeling cold or dizziness), it can often be observed that they are positively valued by patients, since they are interpreted as evidence of controlling their bodies and losing weight (Shafran, Fairburn, Nelson, Robinson, 2003). However, other symptoms are experienced as quite unpleasant, such as problems with concentration or mood lability, and motivate the search for treatment (Garfinkel Garner, 1982). An example of these symptoms can be found in the unwanted and repetitive intrusive thoughts, images and/or impulses about eating-related contents, or Eating Disorder Intrusive Thoughts (EDITs). Studies carried out with the Eating-related Intrusive Thoughts Inventory (*Inventario de Pensamientos Intrusos Alimentarios,* INPIAS; Perpiñá, Roncero, Belloch, 2008) show a continuum from non-clinical individuals to ED patients in the experience of EDITs: ED patients obtain higher scores on the EDITs' frequency, negative emotional consequences, dysfunctional appraisals, and thought control strategies, compared to non-clinical groups, groups at risk of ED, and recovered patients (Perpiñá, Roncero, Belloch, Sánchez-Reales, 2011; Roncero, Perpiñá, Belloch, 2010; Roncero, 2011). EDITs fit the characterization of an ego-dystonic thought formulated by Purdon et al. (Purdon, Cripps, Faull, Joseph, Rowa, 2007, p. 200), since patients appraise these thoughts as unpleasant and bothersome, and they are not a direct sign of control, but quite the opposite, as patients can feel overwhelmed by their inability to keep them under control and by their interference in their daily activities (Fairburn, 2008; Woolrich, Cooper, Turner, 2008). However, EDITs can also be ego-syntonic, since their contents are consistent with the person's values, personality structure, explicit feelings, and/or desired self-view, and patients appraise these thoughts as helping to remind them of their goal and motivating them (Woolrich, Cooper, Turner, 2008).

When the EDQ-r and ESQ were completed by a non-clinical population focusing on the most unpleasant EDIT, the findings showed that the EDIT was rated as both ego-syntonic and ego-dystonic, since it was assessed as undesirable, but also rational and coherent with their own personality. When they were compared based on the content, EDITs about appearance and dieting were evaluated as more ego-dystonic and less ego-syntonic than the exercising

EDITs, both in general and across the three ego-dystonicity dimensions. These results are coherent with the dual nature of intrusive cognitions about dieting and appearance: on the one hand, having a thin appearance is a valued social sign of beauty and success; on the other, the effort most people must make to achieve these goals could be a source of distress or the goal might be unattainable (Knauss, Paxton, Alsaker, 2007). In contrast, doing regular exercise is usually conceived of as a sign of self-care for good health and attainable, and a thought that reminds us of the need to do exercise might not be experienced as clearly ego-dystonic (Belloch, Roncero, Perpiñá, 2012; LePage, Crowthera, 2010). When ED patients completed the EDQ-r and ESQ, they valued their most upsetting EDIT as rational and coherent, but they also appraised it as undesirable, which suggests that this thought was not completely ego-syntonic or ego-dystonic. There were no significant differences among ED subtypes (Roncero, Belloch, Perpiñá, Treasure, 2013). This result could be a reflection of the ambivalence that characterizes these disorders (e.g., Bulik, Kendler, 2000; Serpell, Treasure, Teasdale, Sullivan, 1999).

The study carried out by Roncero et al. (Roncero, Belloch, Perpiñá, Treasure, 2013) also found that the more the EDIT caused interference with the patient's activity, the more ego-syntonic (rational, desirable and moral) and the less ego-dystonic it was. However, one might expect that the more interference caused by the intrusive thought, the more ego-dystonic it would be, and the greater the desire to get the thought out of one's mind. One explanation for this result would be that the interference indicates that the patient's mind is frequently occupied by the EDIT, which usually denotes an increased severity of the disorder and a lower level of insight about the disorder. Another interesting finding was that when the EDIT is assessed as ego-syntonic, patients will try to do what the EDIT tells them, whereas when the EDIT is assessed as ego-dystonic, patients try to keep the thought under control by using strategies such as avoiding (i.e., anxiety strategies) and suppressing the thought. Finally, the ego-syntonicity and ego-dystonicity of the thought was found to be one of the factors that mediate between the EDITs' interference and how patients manage them, i.e. the thought control strategies.

Other authors have examined the ego-dystonicity and ego-syntonicity of repetitive preoccupations and rituals related to ED. Mazure, Halmi, Sunday, Romano, and Einhorn (Mazure, Halmi, Sunday, Romano, Einhorn, 1994), in their Yale Brown Cornell Eating Disorder Scale, included two additional items evaluating the ego-syntonicity/ego-dystonicity (*consistency/inconsistency with their personality*) of preoccupations and rituals related to ED. In a study with 40 women with an ED diagnosis, these authors found that more than half rated their eating-related preoccupations (28 women) and rituals (25 women) as ego-syntonic, whereas 10 women rated their preoccupations as ego-dystonic, and 6 others rated their rituals in this way. Similar results were also found in recovered ED patients and restrained-eating control subjects (Sunday, Halmi, 2000).

In sum, ED symptoms are not always considered completely ego-syntonic or ego-dystonic by ED patients, which would agree with Purdon et al. (Purdon, Cripps, Faull, Joseph, Rowa, 2007). Regarding the Obsessive-Compulsive Disorder, these authors suggest that a given obsession (e.g., avoiding contamination) can be syntonic with some valued aspects of the self (e.g., protecting others from diseases) and simultaneously dystonic with others (e.g., the excessiveness and/or irrationality of the concern). The clinical implications of these suggestions for ED might be that the therapist should assess the appraisals that patients ascribe to their symptoms, including the ego-syntonicity and ego-dystonicity. The rationality and normality of thoughts could be confronted through cognitive discussion, and psycho-education and a review of pros and cons might be useful (Vitousek, Watson, Wilson, 1998). Fairburn (Fairburn, 2008) posits the utility of remarking on the negative aspects of symptoms in order to make patients aware of the implications of being on a diet.

Ego-Syntonicity: A Barrier in Eating Disorders Treatment

Sometimes patients feel desperate and go to therapy, and although it might seem that they are seeking recovery, in many cases they are unwilling to gain an ounce of weight and reluctant to make any substantial change. They resent having lost their jobs or their friends, or they lament the harm their illness has caused to the family. The dysfunctional identification of ED patients with their disorder, as well as the ego-syntonicity of many of their symptoms, makes these patients ambivalent and reluctant to undergo treatment (e.g., Vandereycken, 2006). This vicious cycle is considered a key element in the maintenance of ED (Fairburn, Shafran, Cooper, 1999; Schmidt, Treasure, 2006), making it essential to dedicate efforts to enhancing the motivation for treatment (Treasure, Schmidt, 2001; Vitousek, Watson, Wilson, 1998) and relapse prevention.

Throughout recent decades, many efforts have focused on studying the mechanism involved in the motivation to change in EDs. As a result, various instruments have been specifically designed to evaluate motivation in EDs, such as the *Anorexia Nervosa Stages Of Change Questionnaire* (ANSOCQ; Rieger, Touyz, Beumont, 2002), the *Bulimia Nervosa Stages Of Change Questionnaire* (BNSOCQ; Martinez, Castro, Bigorra, Morer, Calvo, Vila, Toro, Rieger, 2007), *Motivational Stages of Change for Adolescents Recovering from an Eating Disorder* (MSCARED; Gusella, Butler, Nichols, Bird, 2003), the *Decisional Balance* scale (DB; Cockell, Geller, Linden, 2002), and the *Attitudes Towards Change in Eating Disorders* (ACTA; Beato-Fernández, Rodríguez-Cano, 2003).

One approach in the study of motivation in EDs proposes that, similar to addiction disorders, ED patients advance through the stages of change described by Prochaska and DiClemente (Prochaska, DiClemente, 1982): *Precontemplation*, the patient does not admit to having a problem; *Contemplation*, the patient admits the problem but is ambivalent about change; *Preparation/Determination*, getting ready to change; *Action*, when change starts; *Maintenance*, the change has been achieved; *Relapse*, regression to previous stages (not included in the original article).

The above-mentioned model is the basis of Motivational Interviewing (MI), an approach to overcome the resistance to change (Miller, Rollnick, 2002) that has been applied to ED patients and their caregivers with promising results (e.g., Cooper, Todd, Wells, 2009; Price-Evans, Treasure, 2011; Treasure, Schmidt, 2001; Waller, Cordery, Corstorphine, Hinrichsen, Lawson, Mountford, Russell, 2007). Studies about motivation to change in ED patients indicate that positive beliefs about ED decrease throughout the stages of change (Blake, Turnbull, Treasure, 1997; Rieger, Touyz, Beumont, 2002). Moreover, studies point out that the motivation varies across ED subtypes and ED symptoms (Casasnovas, Fernández-Aranda, Granero, Krug, Jiménez-Murcia, Bulik, Vallejo-Ruiloba, 2007; Geller, Zaitsoff, Srikameswaran, 2005). AN patients are more likely to be in a *Precontemplation* or

Contemplation stage when they arrive to the clinic, whereas BN patients are more likely to be in the *Action* stage (Blake et al., 1997; Ward, Troop, Todd, Treasure, 1996). Patients in the *Action* stage at the beginning of treatment would achieve a better therapeutic alliance and higher improvement on binge symptoms than patients who begin in the *Contemplation* stage (Franko, 1997; Treasure, Katzman, Schmidt, Troop, Todd, de Silva, 1999). In a longitudinal study with adolescents with BN, motivation to change predicted improvement on the bulimia scale (EDI-2) and binges (Castro-Fornieles, Bigorra, Martinez-Mallen, Gonzalez, Moreno, Font, Toro, 2011). In other studies, higher motivation to change has been associated with lower ED symptomatology (Beato-Fernández, Rodríguez-Cano, 2003; Zaitsoff, Taylor, 2009).

Regarding the association between motivation to change and the ego-syntonicity of ED symptoms, one study utilized the ACTA, based on Prochaska and DiClemente's model, and the ESQ and EDQ-r to measure the ego-syntonicity and ego-dystonicity of eating related intrusive thoughts (Roncero, 2011). In ED patients, the stages of *Precontemplation* and *Contemplation* were associated with the ego-syntonicity of EDITs, and the *Precontemplation* stage was also negatively related to Irrationality of thought (Ego-dystonicity factor). This specific stage, *Precontemplation*, has been used as an indicator of denial of illness in ED patients (Vandereyken, 2006). This result indicates that patients with low insight and low motivation to change would be more likely to evaluate their upsetting intrusive thoughts as rational and coherent with their personality. The same analysis carried out in women recovered from ED indicated that the *Maintenance* stage was negatively associated with the ego-syntonicity of EDITs, which is coherent with the result found in currently ill ED patients.

Future Studies and Research Directions

Studies about ego-syntonicity and ego-dystonicity suggest that symptoms experienced by ED patients are not completely ego-syntonic or ego-dystonic. Moreover, ego-syntonicity has been associated with early stages of motivation to change. In this sense, future studies should investigate to what extent the ego-syntonicity and ego-dystonicity of ED symptoms, including intrusive thoughts, predict treatment response. Results suggest that the ego-syntonicity of EDITs could be taken as an indirect indicator of low insight, which is very important in designing effective treatments, depending on the stage of change (Treasure, Ward, 1997). However, it is noteworthy that, as some authors point out, motivation to change can sway, even in the same session (Treasure, Schmidt, 2001; Waller, Cordery, Corstorphine, Hinrichsen, Lawson, Mountford, Russell, 2007).

It would be interesting to evaluate the ego-syntonicity and ego-dystonicity of other symptoms, such as restrictive food intake, calorie counting, or excessive exercising at different stages of change, and find out to what extent ego-syntonicity and ego-dystonicity are associated or influenced by other variables such as comorbidity or specific personality dimensions.

Ego-syntoncity and ego-dystonicity studies would also help to understand similarities and differences between EDs and other disorders, such as OCD. OCD has been found to be highly comorbid in ED patients (Bastiani, Altemus, Pigott, Rubenstein, Weltzin, Kaye, 1996; Matsunaga, Miyata, Iwasaki, Matsui, Fujimoto, Kiriike,1999; Rubenstein, Altemus, Pigott,

Hess, Murphy, 1995; von Ranson, Kaye, Weltzin, Rao, Matsunaga, 1999). In fact, ED and OCD patients experience thoughts, impulses and intrusive and repetitive images, as well as preoccupations about feared stimuli that generate negative affect. In both cases, patients carry out compensatory behaviors in order to reduce anxiety (Lawson, Lockwood, Waller, 2004). It is interesting to note that our results are in line with those found by Purdon et al. (Purdon, Cripps, Faull, Joseph, Rowa, 2007) regarding OCD obsessions, as these authors suggest that the association between ego-dystonicity and the severity of OCD may not be linear.

In conclusion, understanding how patients appraise their symptoms is essential to discerning the nature of ED, which in turn will help to design tailored and effective treatments. This proposal is particularly urgent given the severity of ED, the denial of the disorder, and the resistance and poor treatment outcomes, especially in AN, where only around 50% of patients fully recover from the disorder (Steinhausen, 2002]. All these studies show that the fight against the ambivalence of ED patients is a fight against part of their identities. Therefore, trying to "convince" patients in a rational way is, by itself, clearly insufficient and ineffective. In this sense, studies about the ego-syntonicity and ego-dystonicity of symptoms, perhaps combined with emotion management approaches, could be a promising line of research in the ED field.

Acknowledgments

This study was supported by the Spanish Ministerio de Investigación, Ciencia e Innovación (PSI2009-10957) (PSI2010-18340) and Conselleria d'Educació, Cultura i Esport. Generalitat Valenciana, Valencia, Spain (PROMETEO/2013/066).

References

Abbate Daga, G., Gramaglia, C., Pierò, A., Fassino, S., (2006). Eating disorders and the Internet: Cure and curse. *Eating and Weight Disorders 11*, 68–71

American Heritage Medical Dictionary, (2007). Houghton Mifflin Harcourt. Retrieved July 20, 2013, from Dictionary.com website: http://dictionary.reference.com/browse/

American Psychiatric Association, (1994). *Diagnostic and statistical manual of mental disorders (4th ed.)*. Washington, DC: APA.

American Psychiatric Association, (2000). *Diagnostic and statistical manual of mental disorders (4th ed., text rev.)*. Washington, DC: APA.

American Psychiatric Association, (2013). *Diagnostic and statistical manual of mental disorders (5th ed.)*. Arlington, VA: American Psychiatric Publishing.

Anderson, K. N., Anderson, L. E., & Glanze, W. D., (2009). *Mosby's Medical Dictionary*. Elsevier.

Bastiani, A. M., Altemus, M., Pigott, T. A., Rubenstein, C., Weltzin, T. E., Kaye, W. H., (1996). Comparison of obsessions and compulsions in patients with anorexia nervosa and obsessive compulsive disorder. *Biological Psychiatry 39*, 966-969.

Beato-Fernández, L., Rodriguez-Cano, T., (2003). Attitudes towards change in eating disorders (ACTA). Development and psychometric properties. *Actas Españolas de Psiquiatría 31*, 111-119.

Belloch, A., Roncero, M., Perpiñá, C., (2012). Ego-Syntonicity and Ego-Dystonicity associated with upsetting intrusive cognitions. *Journal of Psychopathology & Behavioral Assessment 34*, 94–106.

Blake, W., Turnbull, S., Treasure, J., (1997). Stages and processes of change in eating disorders: Implications for therapy. *Clinical Psychology & Psychotherapy 4*, 186-191.

Bruch, H., (1973). *Eating disorders. Obesity, anorexia nervosa and the person within*. New York: Basic Books.

Bruch, H., (1978). *The golden cage: The enigma of anorexia nervosa*. New York: Vintage/Random House.

Bulik, C. M., Kendler, K. S., (2000). "I am what I (don't) eat": Establishing an identity independent of an eating disorder. *American Journal of Psychiatry 157*, 1755-1760.

Casasnovas, C., Fernández-Aranda, F., Granero, R., Krug, I., Jiménez-Murcia, S., Bulik, C. M., Vallejo-Ruiloba, J., (2007). Motivation to change in eating disorders: Clinical and therapeutic implications. *European Eating Disorders Review 15*, 449-456.

Castro-Fornieles, J., Bigorra, A., Martinez-Mallen, E., Gonzalez, L., Moreno, E., Font, E., Toro, J., (2011). Motivation to change in adolescents with bulimia nervosa mediates clinical change after treatment. *European Eating Disorders Review 19*, 46-54.

Cockell, S. J., Geller, J., & Linden, W., (2002). The development of a decisional balance scale for anorexia nervosa. *European Eating Disorders Review 10*, 359-375.

Cooper, M. J., Todd, G., Wells, A., (2009). *Treating bulimia nervosa and binge eating. An integrated metacognitive and cognitive therapy manual*. New York: Routledge.

Crisp, A. H., (1980). *Anorexia nervosa. Let me be*. London: Academic Press.

Dorland's Medical Dictionary for Health Consumers., (2007). Saunders. Elsevier, Inc. Retrieved July 20, 2013, from Dictionary.com website: http://dictionary.reference.com/browse/

Fairburn, C. G., (2008). Eating disorders: The transdiagnostic view and the cognitive behavioral therapy. In C. Fairburn (Ed.). *Cognitive behavior therapy and eating disorder*. New York: Guilford Press.

Fairburn, C. G., Shafran, R., Cooper, Z., (1999). A cognitive behavioural theory of anorexia nervosa. *Behaviour Research and Therapy 37*, 1-13.

Franko, D. L., (1997). Ready or not? Stages of change as predictors of brief group therapy outcome in bulimia nervosa. *Group 21*, 39-45.

Gale, C., Holliday, J., Troop, N. A., Serpell, L., Treasure, J., (2006). The pros and cons of change in individuals with eating disorders: A broader perspective. *International Journal of Eating Disorders 39*, 394-403.

Garfinkel, P. E., Garner, D. M., (1982). *Anorexia nervosa: A multidimensional perspective*. New York: Brunner/Mazel.

Geller, J., Zaitsoff, S. L., Srikameswaran, S., (2005). Tracking readiness and motivation for change in individuals with eating disorders over the course of treatment. *Cognitive Therapy and Research 29*, 611-625.

Gusella, J., Butler, G., Nichols, L., Bird, D., (2003). A brief questionnaire to assess readiness to change in adolescents with eating disorders: Its applications to group therapy. *European Eating Disorders Review 11*, 58-71.

Holden, N. L., (1990). Is anorexia-nervosa an obsessive-compulsive disorder? *British Journal of Psychiatry 157*, 1-5.

Knauss, C., Paxton, S. J., Alsaker, F. D., (2007). Relationships amongst body dissatisfaction, internalisation of the media body ideal and perceived pressure from media in adolescent girls and boys. *Body Image 4*, 353-360.

Lawson, R., Lockwood, R., Waller, G., (2004). Compulsive features in the eating disorders: A role for trauma? *International Journal of Eating Disorders 35*, 295-300.

LePage, L. E., Crowthera, J. H., (2010). The effects of exercise on body satisfaction and affect. *Body Image 7*, 124-130.

Martinez, E., Castro, J., Bigorra, A., Morer, A., Calvo, R., Vila, M., Toro, J., Rieger, E., (2007). Assessing motivation to change in bulimia nervosa: The bulimia nervosa stages of change questionnaire. *European Eating Disorders Review 15*, 13-23.

Matsunaga, H., Miyata, A., Iwasaki, Y., Matsui, T., Fujimoto, K., Kiriike, N., (1999). A comparison of clinical features among Japanese eating-disordered women with obsessive-compulsive disorder. *Comprehensive Psychiatry 40*, 337-342.

Mazure, C. M., Halmi, K. A., Sunday, S. R., Romano, S. J., Einhorn, A. M., (1994). The yale-brown-cornell eating disorder scale - development, use, reliability and validity. *Journal of Psychiatric Research 28*, 425-445.

Miller, W. R., Rollnick, S., (2002). *Motivational interviewing: Preparing people for change.* New York: Guilford Press.

Norris, M. L., Boydell, K. M., Pinhas, L., Katzman, D. K., (2006). Ana and the internet: A review of pro-anorexia websites. *International Journal of Eating Disorders 39*, 443-447.

Olendorf, D., Jeryan, C., Boyden, K. (2008). *Gale Encyclopedia of Medicine.* The Gale Group, Inc.

Perpiñá, C., Roncero, M., Belloch, A., (2008). Intrusiones sobre trastornos alimentarios en población general: Desarrollo y validación del Inventario de Pensamientos Intrusos Alimentarios (INPIAS). *Revista de Psicopatología y Psicología Clínica 13*, 187-203.

Perpiñá, C., Roncero, M., Belloch, A., Sánchez-Reales. (2011). Eating-related Intrusive Thoughts Inventory: exploring the dimensionality of eating disorder symptoms. *Psychological Reports 109*, 108-126.

Price-Evans, K., Treasure, J. (2011). The use of motivational interviewing in anorexia nervosa. *Child and Adolescent Mental Health 16*, 65-70.

Prochaska, J. O., Diclemente, C. C., (1982). Trans-theoretical therapy - toward a more integrative model of change. *Psychotherapy-Theory Research and Practice 19*, 276-288.

Purdon, C., Cripps, E., Faull, M., Joseph, S., Rowa, K., (2007). Development of a measure of egodystonicity. *Journal of Cognitive Psychotherapy 21*, 198-216.

Rieger, E., Touyz, S. W., Beumont, P. J. V., (2002). The anorexia nervosa stages of change questionnaire (ANSOCQ): Information regarding its psychometric properties. *International Journal of Eating Disorders 32*, 24-38.

Roncero, M., (2011). Los trastornos de la conducta alimentaria y el espectro obsesivo-compulsivo: Intrusiones mentales, egodistonía y creencias. Unpublished Doctoral dissertation. University of Valencia.

Roncero, M., Belloch, A., Perpiñá, C., Treasure, J., (2013). Ego-syntonicity and ego-dystonicity of eating-related intrusive thoughts in patients with eating disorders. *Psychiatry Research 208*, 67-73.

Roncero, M., Perpiñá, C., Belloch, A., (2010). Obsesividad e intrusiones alimentarias en pacientes con trastornos alimentarios y en la población general. *Revista de Psicopatología y Psicología Clínica 15*, 101-113.

Rubenstein, C. S., Altemus, M., Pigott, T. A., Hess, A., Murphy, D. L. (1995). Symptom overlap between ocd and bulimia-nervosa. *Journal of Anxiety Disorders 9*, 1-9.

Schmidt, U., & Treasure, J., (2006). Anorexia nervosa: Valued and visible. A cognitive-interpersonal maintenance model and its implications for research and practice. *British Journal of Clinical Psychology 45*, 343-366.

Serpell, L., Treasure, J., Teasdale, J., Sullivan, V., (1999). Anorexia nervosa: Friend or foe? *International Journal of Eating Disorders 25*, 177-186.

Shafran, R., Fairburn, C. G., Nelson, L., Robinson, P. H., (2003). The interpretation of symptoms of severe dietary restraint. *Behaviour Research and Therapy 41*, 887-894.

Steinhausen, H. C., (2002). The outcome of anorexia nervosa in the 20th century. *American Journal of Psychiatry 159*, 1284-1293.

Sunday, S. R., Halmi, K. A., (2000). Comparison of the Yale-Brown-Cornell Eating Disorders Scale in recovered eating disorder patients, restrained dieters, and nondieting controls. *International Journal of Eating Disorders 28*, 455–459.

Toro, J., (1996). *El cuerpo como delito: Anorexia, bulimia, cultura y sociedad*. Barcelona: Ariel.

Treasure, J. L., Katzman, M., Schmidt, U., Troop, N., Todd, G., de Silva, P., (1999). Engagement and outcome in the treatment of bulimia nervosa: First phase of a sequential design comparing motivation enhancement therapy and cognitive behavioural therapy. *Behaviour Research and Therapy 37*, 405-418.

Treasure, J., Schmidt, U., (2001). Ready, willing and able to change: Motivational aspects of the assessment and treatment of eating disorders. *European Eating Disorders Review 9*, 4-18.

Treasure, J., Ward, A., (1997). A practical guide to the use of motivational interviewing in anorexia nervosa. *European Eating Disorders Review 5*, 102-114.

Vandereycken, W., (2006). Denial of illness in anorexia nervosa - A conceptual review: Part 1 diagnostic significance and assessment. *European Eating Disorders Review 14*, 341-351.

Vandereycken, W., Hoek, H. W. (1992). Are eating disorders culture-bound syndromes. En A. Halmi (Ed). *Psychobiology Treatment of Anorexia Nervosa and Bulimia Nervosa*. Washington, DC: American Psychiatric Press

Vitousek, K., Watson, S., Wilson, G. T., (1998). Enhancing motivation for change in treatment-resistant eating disorders. *Clinical Psychology Review 18*, 391-420.

von Ranson, K. M., Kaye, W. H., Weltzin, T. E., Rao, R., Matsunaga, H., (1999). Obsessive-compulsive disorder symptoms before and after recovery from bulimia nervosa. *American Journal of Psychiatry 156*, 1703-1708.

Waller, G., Cordery, H., Corstorphine, E., Hinrichsen, H., Lawson, R., Mountford, V., Russell, K., (2007). *Cognitive behavioral therapy for eating disorders. A comprehensive treatment guide*. New York: Cambridge University Press.

Ward, A., Troop, N., Todd, G., Treasure, J., (1996). To change or not to change - 'how' is the question? *British Journal of Medical Psychology 69*, 139-146.

Woolrich, R. A., Cooper, M. J., Turner, H. M., (2008). Metacognition in patients with anorexia nervosa, dieting and non-dieting women: A preliminary study. *European Eating Disorders Review 16*, 11-20.

Zaitsoff, S. L., Taylor A., (2009). Factors related to motivation *European Eating Disorders Review 17*, 227-33.

In: New Developments in Anorexia Nervosa Research
Editors: Carla Gramaglia and Patrizia Zeppegno

ISBN: 978-1-63117-551-0
© 2014 Nova Science Publishers, Inc.

Chapter 2

Transdisciplinary Approach for Anorexia Nervosa

*Javier Oltra-Cucarella[1], Raúl Espert[2,3], Verónica Guillén[3,4]
and Pablo Duque[5,6]*

[1]Diagrama Foundation, Murcia, Spain
[2]Unit of Neuropsychology. Hospital Clinic Universitario, Valencia, Spain
[3]Faculty of Psychology, University of Valencia, Spain
[4]Unit of Eating Disorders, PREVI Center of Psychology,
Valencia, Spain
[5]Hospital Virgen Macarena, Sevilla, Spain
[6]iNeuro Association, Sevilla, Spain

Abstract

Eating disorders (ED) are complex and severe illnesses in which eating behavior is abnormal mainly as a consequence of the patient's dramatic will to control their body and weight. Anorexia Nervosa (AN) can lead to death in up to 10% of the cases, and ¼ of people affected by AN suffer the illness chronically. Continued binge behaviors or vomiting and purgative behavior seen in Bulimia Nervosa affect not only physically those who suffer this disorder, but also impact their quality of life through their daily living. Both severe physical and psychological consequences of ED affect not only those diagnosed with the illness, but their families and social structures too. In the first section of this chapter, a review of different actual evidence-based psychological treatment programmes will be made. Among them, special attention will be given to the Fairburn, Cooper and Shafran's (2003) model as its effectiveness has been empirically demonstrated and replicated consistently in previous research. The second section will provide an up-to-date review of the neuroendocrinology functioning in AN in order to help the readers understand one the most severe physical consequences of ED. The final part of the chapter will review neuropsychological impairments seen in AN with a special focus on executive impairments including both previous and recent research, as well as a summary of neuropsychological tests and tasks used both in clinical practice and in research for assessing cognitive functioning in order to help readers understand the patient's performance on the tasks included in neuropsychological assessment.

Introduction

Anorexia Nervosa (AN) is characterized by the presence of a marked reduction in body weight and a refusal to maintain it within normal ranges (American Psychiatric Association, 2000). This weight loss is accompanied by an extreme fear to regain it even though this condition causes severe physical impairments. Females with AN show a distorted vision of their own body and feel obese, when reality is totally different (Rutsztein, 1997). In fact, AN represents the highest rates of mortality within psychiatric diseases, maybe because of the complex clinical course and the dysfunctional behaviors that these patients develop and that cause both severe starvation and extreme low weight. Frequently, females with AN need hospital admission and long-lasting treatments.

Eating Disorders are diseases with high social relevance, especially in the population at very high risk: young females in developed and developing Countries (Peláez, Labrador, Raich, 2005). According to Fairburn (2004), the prevalence of the ED has increased 2 to 5-fold during the last decades. According to the National Health Institute (Insalud, 1995), the American Psychiatric Association (DSM-IV-TR, APA, 2000) and recent epidemiological studies it is estimated that the prevalence of AN falls between 0.5-1% (Hoek, 2003), with a ratio 1:9 between males and females. Data about AN show a heterogeneous course with both short-lasting cases requiring a brief intervention, who fully recover after one single episode (tipically young females with brief prior history), and long-lasting cases requiring multidisciplinary approaches and intensive cares. Some people with AN show a fluctuating weight gain followed by relapses and some suffer chronic impairments during years. This progressive starvation leads to a severely malnourished state with up to a 50% weight loss, whereas in other cases weight can be stable with 20-25% weight loss.

Clinical Features

The most typical and striking manifestations are related with both restrictive dieting and purges, but there exists another set of behaviors in AN. We will divide them in behavioral, emotional, cognitive and biological features.

Regarding behavioral features, fasting and dieting are the core feature of the illness: they range from eating insufficient amounts of food, eating "light" food, avoiding food (especially those categorized as forbidden). These females exercise excessively, abuse laxatives and diuretics and/or provoke vomiting to empty their stomach. Abnormal eating behaviors like hiding food, cutting it into very small pieces or eating very slowly, as well as ritualistic and repetitive behaviors such as weighing repetitively or using the mirror for body checking are frequent. They can also show hyperactivity or excessive study, sleep reductions or lack of interest about sex. All these features lead to both social and familiar isolation. Regarding emotional features, they can cause changes in their mood and irritability. Comorbid depressive symptomatology is common, with emotional lability, crying, sadness, apathy, feelings of guilt or suicide ideations that can lead to suicide attempts. It is difficult for these females to relax and feel comfortable. They feel anxious about food, their body, their clothes or their weight, which can lead to develop a phobia or a generalized stress disorder. Social anxiety is also common, with both fear and avoiding behaviors.

Regarding biological features, AN is one the psychopathological diseases that causes the highest number of organic imbalances. Besides an extreme thinness caused by starvation, patients may have dry and cold skin, limp hair, alopecia and fragile nails (Turón, 1997; Glorio et al., 2000). As the disease progresses, there can be severe physical consequences such as electrolytic and vital signs imbalance (hypotension, bradycardia, hypothermia), infections, consciousness impairments, convulsions, dehydration, liver or kidney dysfunction, arrhythmia, as well as metabolic changes that can lead to death.

Explanatory Models of AN

Among several AN explanatory models, this chapter will focus on the model proposed by Fairburn, Cooper and Shafran (1998; 2003). These authors affirm that there is a high need for self-control at the beginning of the AN. This need comes from patients' perfectionism, personal inefficacy feelings and low self-esteem. The question is, then: *why to get control through food intake*? The answer is easy: because it rewards with immediate results. Other areas in their lives are not under their exclusive control. Besides, the results of their control over food intake have a powerful effect on other people such as their families. Through food intake, they can counteract the effects of puberty. Moreover, the value of body shape in the current culture should be considered.

According to Fairburn's explanatory model, once AN has established, the food restriction maintains through three feedback mechanisms:

- First of all, food restriction increases both self-control and self-value feelings. This strategy is rapidly successful, thus becoming a powerful reward (success, pride, power). This, in turn, helps facing other problems (about family, friends or sexual relations). It also has to be acknowledged that there exists a great resistance to change such rewarding behaviors. Hence, initially the disease has an almost egosyntonic profile and the personal identity focused on *being anorectic* reinforces itself.
- Second, starvation itself reinforces restriction and causes several physiological and psychological changes. Beside, hunger and satiety are seen as enemies. Intense hunger is perceived as a threat to self-control, and the feeling of satiety as a failure of control. This, in turn, increases the worry about food and eventually leads to a narrowing of interests: the tendency to use control over the food as a measure of self-control and self-value is exaggerated.
- Third, the extreme worry about weight and body shape also reinforces the starvation. As already described, in western societies the idea that a thin shape equals self-control and self-esteem is common (and it is also extending to non-western cultures).
- All the issues described above are accompanied by confirmatory processing biases. AN patients show an attentional and interpretative bias toward all the information related to food, weight and body shape. This bias leads to an attentional

hypervigilance and confirmatory behaviors. Lately, this hypervigilance may become aversive, and eventually causes avoidant behaviors. During this process, the rate of weight loss may decrease, which may be interpreted as a failure.

To make that model more comprehensive, Fairburn et al. (2003) re-elaborated their model through the *transdiagnostic theory* perspective also including Bulimia Nervosa (BN). Its core approach is that ED share the same underlying general psychopathology and those patients move between ED diagnoses (crossover). The transdiagnostic theory, a re-elaboration of previous ideas (Fairburn, Marcus, Wilson, 1993), affirms that there are common mechanisms involved in the maintenance of AN, BN and atypical ED. Four maintaining mechanisms are recognized that are common to all ED, although the authors underscore the differences in their expression in females with AN and females with BN:

1. The Perfectionism, Especially Higher in AN

Perfectionism is related to the over-evaluation of the striving for, and the achievement of, personally demanding standards despite adverse consequences, together with a self-evaluation in which self-value is judged according to the efforts to achieve their goals and success is judged on the basis of achieving them. Perfectionism is not only involved in their efforts for controlling food, weight and body shape, but also in other domains such as work, sports, etc. This pathological way of fighting for perfection is accompanied by a fear of failure (which in this kind of patients means eating or gaining weight), attention focused on performance, obsessiveness (repetitive calories counting, weight testing) and self-criticism from evaluations negatively biased to their performance.

2. Low Self-Esteem

Low self-esteem is related to the negative global vision of oneself. This does not mean that these patients think negatively, but their low self-esteem depends on a pervasive vision of themselves that is part of their permanent identity. These negative judgments are independent of their achievements. Low self-esteem prevents change by two different mechanisms: first, patients' despair about personal capacity to change impacts their trust in treatment. Second, these patients are extremely decided to achieve goals related to over-valued domains such as food control, weight and body shape, which makes change especially difficult.

3. Irritability and Mood Intolerance

Mood intolerance is related to the incapacity of coping with certain emotional states, generally adverse (anxiety, depression, anger, etc.). In some cases, mood intolerance may be related to any intense emotion, even positive (for instance, excitement). This intolerance may be caused by their intense emotional experience, or maybe by their extreme sensibility to emotions. Instead of coping with emotions, they get involved in dysfunctional behaviors aimed at modulating mood (hyperactivity, self-harm or substance abuse) in order to reduce the consciousness of emotion, although at a high personal cost.

4. Interpersonal Difficulties

Interpersonal difficulties may intensify patients' feeling of losing control which is especially hard for individuals who do not want to lose control. In a recent paper focusing on interpersonal difficulties in AN, Carter, Kelly and Norwood (2012) found that patients showed difficulties with submissiveness, non-assertiveness and social inhibition compared to healthy controls. Moreover, they found that levels of social inhibition predicted treatment non-completion.

The relevance of this model, integrating every aspect concerned with ED comprehension, is clear. Moreover, the transdiagnostic theory has the advantage of offering common intervention strategies for the treatment of ED.

The Transdiagnostic Approach

As already described, one the most relevant current approaches to AN is the *transdiagnostic theory* proposed by Fairburn, Cooper, Shafran (2003). These authors suggest there is a shared central cognitive distortion in all ED, characterized by an over-value of eating behavior, weight control and body shape. The transdiagnostic approach is characterized by: (1) it is designed to be sensible to all forms of ED irrespective of time since onset of symptomatology; (2) the correct diagnosis is irrelevant for treatment; (3) it is design to be applied in patients with typical ED and can be developed by both male and female therapists, (4) there are two versions, one lasting 20 sessions and another lasting 40 sessions. The latter is recommended for severe underweighted patients (BMI<17.5). Contents are shared by both versions, and both start with two weekly sessions; one difference is that the longest version includes strategies focused on weight restoration to stabilize patients' condition; (5) the treatment is completely individualized. The transdiagnostic approach is structured in a four-step process:

1) I - Initial: 4-8 weeks. Focused on hooking the patient into the treatment programme. Each case is formulated gathering all the information needed for an intervention focused on behavior modification.
2) II: 1-3 weeks. Progress is reviewed in detail. The barriers to change are identified, and then the contribution of each of the four maintaining mechanisms (food restriction, starvation, extreme worry about weight and body shape, and confirmatory processing biases) is evaluated. Once that information is obtained, an extended and reviewed formulation is created together with the patient's help.
3) III: 13-15 weeks. This is the longest part of the treatment and is based on the reviewed formulation. The modification of the psychopathology of ED is emphasized, while other processes identified during the formulation are addressed and the four maintaining mechanisms are modulated.

4) IV: variable duration. The goal is to assure that changes are long-lasting and to end the treatment process.

Since the Nineties, several approaches related to Virtual Reality have consolidated as treatment interventions (Hodges et al., 1993, 1995, 1996; North, North Coble, 1996, 1997; Glantz et al., 1996, 1997; Riva et al., 1999). We think that, given the importance of body image in ED, one of the core components and main goals in the treatment of ED (and particularly, AN), should be an intervention focused on body image distortions (Perpiñá, Botella, Baños, 2000). Slade and Russell (1973) found that relapses (weight loss) were related to the severity of body image distortions at discharge in those patients who successfully ended the treatment. Several authors (Bruch, 1962; Button, 1986; Strobe, Bowen, Preble, 1985) found that improvements in clinical symptomatology were temporary unless they were accompanied by body image distortion treatment in hospitalized AN in-patients. In this sense, CBT has proved effective for improving cognitive, affective, perceptive and behavioral components of body image distortion (Butters, Cash, 1987; Cash, Grant, 1995; Cash, Lavalle, 1997; Dworkin, Kerr, 1987; Raich et al., 1997; Rosen, et al., 1989;). Perpiñá et al. (1999) compared the efficacy of both Virtual Reality (VR) and traditional interventions for treating body image distortions in patients suffering with either AN or BN. These authors found that patients improved significantly after the intervention, but those treated using VR showed greater improvements in variables such as general psychopathology, eating psychopathology and body image distortion measured with the Body Image Automatic Thoughts Questionnaire, the Body Attitudes Test and the Eating Attitudes Test, EAT-40 (Perpiñá, 1999; Marco, 2000). Moreover, the results achieved were maintained over time and even improved both at six (Marco, 2000) and twelve months follow-up (Perpiñá, Marco, Botella, Baños, 2002).

Neuroendocrine Mechanisms Involved in Anorexia Nervosa

Anorexia nervosa (AN) is a complex multi-factorial disease that involves not only psychological but also neurobiological mechanisms. Although patients with AN almost uniformly exhibit complex psychological disturbances, it is still likely that biological factors play a role in the initiation and development of the disorder. This section will review the molecular etiology of AN and the experimental biological context with emphasis on molecular systems controlling food intake and body weight, with especial focus on neuroendocrine hunger regulatory systems.

Human studies related to AN can be grouped into six main categories: (1) Hunger neurohormonal regulatory systems (leptin, cortisol, estrogens, NPY, ghrelin, cholecystokinin (CCK) and some neurohormonal axes). (2) Systems related to mental disorders (serotonin, brain-derived neurotrophic factor (BDNF), norepinephrine (NE), glutamate (NMDA) receptor and SK3 channel, KCCN3). (3) Feeding motivation- and reward-related systems (opioids, OPRD1, cannabinoids (anandamide (AEA), THC, CBR1), dopamine, DRD2, DRD3, DRD4, catecholamine-O-methyltransferase (COMT). (4) Systems regulating energy metabolism (uncoupling proteins 2 and 3 (UCP2 and UCP3). (5) Neuroendocrine systems with emphasis on sex hormones (estrogen receptor-β (ESR2). (6) The immune system and inflammatory response (tumor necrosis factor-alpha (TNF-α)) (Rask-Andersen et al., 2010).

Among the six mechanisms previously described, we will focus especially on the neuroendocrine factors linked to AN. The psychiatric approach of AN has its basis in a strong psychological component of the disease. The rates of depression and obsessive compulsive disorder are higher than in healthy population. Disturbed self-image and anxiety are common. Moreover, mortality due to suicide and psychoactive substance abuse has also been described in AN patients (Papadopoulos et al., 2009). Mortality due to both natural and unnatural causes in patients with AN is six-fold higher than in AN-unaffected persons. AN has been associated with personality traits such as perfectionism and obsessionality (Kaye et al., 1998). Psychological factors along with accompanying endocrine changes have been suggested as one of the underlying causes of AN. For example, AN patients often do rigorous exercise regime characterized by hyperactivity, and linked to personality traits like obsessionality and anxiety. It has been proposed that hyperactivity is caused by activation of hypothalamic-pituitary-adrenal (HPA) axis, linked to leptin deficiency and reinforced by the release of glucocorticoids (Baranowska et al., 2008).

Studies about the molecular risk factors underlying obesity have yielded significant insights about the mechanisms that regulate energy balance and consumption. One of the factors most frequently linked to food intake regulation is leptin, a hormone released by adipocytes and that induces satiety via receptors in the arcuate nucleus. The discovery of leptin in 1994 was a milestone in unraveling the signal cascade regulating eating behavior. Activation of leptin receptors leads to release of anorexigenic peptides, and this response can precipitate abnormally diminished consummatory behavior in AN. A consequence of extremely low body fat store is low plasma levels of leptin both in the fed state as well as during the night, where the nocturnal rise is abolished. Furthermore, the levels of the soluble leptin receptor are highly elevated in AN, resulting in an even lower free leptin index (Misra et al., 2004). Studies in animals and human beings have shown that low concentrations of leptin are partly responsible for starvation-induced changes in neuroendocrine axes, including low reproductive, thyroid, and insulin-like growth factor hormones. Disease states such as exercise-induced hypothalamic amenorrhoea and anorexia nervosa are also associated with low concentrations of leptin and a similar spectrum of neuroendocrine abnormalities (Chan, Mantzoros, 2005).

Another endocrine factor involved in this pathology is ghrelin, an orexigenic peptide produced mainly in the stomach (but also in hypothalamus). Gherlin is released into the bloodstream and the central nervous system to bind to its growth hormone secretatogue receptor (GHSR), mostly present in the arcuate nucleus of the hypothalamus (Olzewski et al., 2008). Paradoxically, high levels of this peptide have been found in AN patients, probably due to a compensatory mechanism to try to stimulate appetite during food restriction period (Schnaider et al., 2008; Usdan et al., 2008). A review of the current literature shows that leptin may have therapeutic potentials in promoting restoration of menstrual cycles in weight restored patients, reducing motor restlessness in severely hyperactive patients, and preventing osteoporosis in chronic patients. Ghrelin and endocannabinoids exert orexigenic effects which may facilitate nutritional restoration. Leptin and endocannabinoids may exert antidepressive and anxiolytic effects. Finally, monitoring serum concentration of leptin may be useful in order to prevent refeeding syndrome (Støving, et al., 2009).

Cholecystokinin (CCK) is another endocrine mechanism involved in AN that serves as a peripheral signal decreasing appetite via receptors in the CNS. CCK is a hormone secreted into the duodenum from cells of the mucosal epithelium. It stimulates digestion of lipids and proteins in the small intestine and functions as a satiety signal through CCK receptors in the CNS and via the vagus nerve (de Krom et al., 2006).

Anorexia causes reduced levels of reproductive hormones, changes in thyroid hormones and higher levels of other hormones (for example, cortisol). It is possible that hypercortisolism may underlie some aspects of this disturbance. Prolonged exposure to elevated corticosteroids has been shown to be associated with impairments in cognition, particularly learning and memory due to the fact that these impairments may be mediated in part by effects on the hippocampus, a brain structure dense with corticosteroid receptors and the site of long term-potentiation. In addition, corticosteroids are known to affect cellular glucose metabolism in the body. Seed et al. (2002), found that a sample of 20 patients was significantly impaired on tasks of attention, long-term memory and working memory.

Hypothalamic-pituitary-gonadal (HPG) is the neuroendocrine axis most frequently involved in AN and may manifest clinically as a delay in the onset of puberty. The characteristic of the malfunctioning of HPG axis is the hypogonadotropic hypogonadism. This means that the pituitary is not sending the appropriate commands to operate the ovarian cycle, leading to a decrease in the secretion of LH and FSH hormones and, consequently, to a decrease in the levels of oestradiol (Bruni et al., 2011). A number of specific biochemical or developmental pathways—abnormalities in the classical or membrane-bound forms of estrogen receptors, in co-activators for estrogen, in thyroxine receptors, in steroid metabolizing enzymes, in quantitative trait loci, in perinatal androgenization, and in processes of puberty—could converge to produce an abnormal response to estrogen and the onset of anorexia nervosa (Young, 2010). Specifically, estrogens upregulate adult hippocampal neurogenesis (via cell proliferation) and synaptic protein levels in the hippocampus in a time- and dose-dependent manner. Low levels of estradiol facilitate spatial working memory and contextual fear conditioning while high levels of estradiol impair spatial working memory, spatial reference memory and contextual fear conditioning. Thus, low levels of estrogens in AN could explain some cognitive disturbances in this patients (Barha and Galea, 2010; Frick et al., 2010).

Growth hormone (GH) dysfunction is manifested in a more visible manner. The earlier it occurs the more pronounced the delay of growth is. This demonstrates that, although there are high GH levels, there is also a resistance to insulin. This means that either the binding of the hormone to the receptor is altered or that the union is not giving the consequences that should be given normally. Moreover, it has also been reported that there is a decrease in insulin secretion, which also affects GH (Misra et al., 2003; Facelli et al., 2010).

The hypothalamic-pituitary-thyroid (HPT) axis function is usually altered in patients with AN. Both normal TSH and low T3 (which is the more active hormone at peripheral level) levels may be found in AN.

Hypothalamic-pituitary-adrenal (HPA) is another neuroendocrine axis involved in AN. The adrenal gland reacts to the situation of anorexia facing it as a stressful situation. Generally, hypercortisolism is manifested as an increase in basal levels of cortisol rhythm and urinary free cortisol along with an increase in half-life of cortisol.

Thus, based on previous research it could be concluded that disturbances on hormonal axes, found in patients with AN, may explain some of behavioral and cognitive disturbances associated to this disease.

Neuropsychological Functioning in Anorexia Nervosa

Neuropsychological research has highlighted the existence of subtle impairments affecting several cognitive domains in Anorexia Nervosa (AN). In order to identify the cognitive status of each patient, neuropsychological assessment is one of the necessary steps both in clinical practice and in research. This section will summarize some of the tests most frequently used to assess cognition in AN and will focus on some recent research on executive functioning.

Neuropsychological Assessment

As in many other diseases, neuropsychological tests are used by clinicians and researchers in order to identify the functioning of different cognitive domains. Neuropsychological assessment is based on suspicions about cognitive impairments. General explorations using wide batteries without relation to the cognitive characteristics of a specific disease are not the best way to look for cognitive impairments. As cognition status is inferred in part from performance on tests and batteries, it is necessary to choose the most adequate tasks with high sensibility and specificity.

Cognitive impairments in AN have been reported in the last years. Many different tests have been used in previous research, some of them being statistically normalized and some being experimental tasks. Lower scores do not imply invariably that impairments in general cognitive functioning do exist. One specific task measuring one cognitive domain may be affected by functioning in other domains. Thus, cognitive tasks warn about the possibility that one cognitive function –or its association with other functions– may be impaired.

The core cognitive domains identified in neuropsychological literature are related to measures of central coherence and specific domains within the executive functioning, including executive attention and tasks assessing *Theory of Mind*. Two review papers (Oltra-Cucarella, Espert and Rojo, 2012; Jáuregui-Lobera, 2013) reported the same findings, indicating that there is no consensus neither about cognitive impairments in AN nor whether those impairments are a consequence of the disease or underlying factors.

When reviewing scientific literature, two approaches may be identified for assessing cognitive functioning in AN: 1) neuropsychological tests for assessing single domains (although performance in one specific test will always be affected by other cognitive domains), and 2) cognitive batteries.

The former group includes tests such as the Wisconsin Card Sorting Test, the Iowa Gambling Task, the Trail Making Test, the Stroop Test, the Rey-Osterrieth Complex Figure, the Embedded Figure Test, the Brixton Test or the Symbol Digit Modalities Test as the most commonly used tasks.

Table 1. Neuropsychological tests used in Anorexia Nervosa research

Tasks	Works
Wisconsin Card Sorting Test	Tchanturia et al., 2004; Fassino et al., 2002; Fagundo et al., 2012; Tchanturia et al., 2012; Gillber et al., 2007; Roberts et al., 2007; Steinglass et al., 2006; Wilsdon and Wade, 2006
Iowa Gambling Task	Fagundo et al., 2012; Lindner et al., 2012; Guillaume et al., 2010; Salvador et al., 2010; Brogan et al., 2010; Bosanac et al., 2007; Tchanturia et al., 2007; Cavedini et al., 2006
Trail Making Test	Roberts et al., 2007; Holliday et al., 2005; Oltra-Cucarella et al., 2013
Rey-Osterrieth Complex Figure	Zuchova et al., 2013; Favaro et al., 2012; Roberts et al., 2013; Andrés-Perpiñá et al., 2011; Alvarado-Sánchez et al., 2009; Lopez et al., 2008a; Lopez et al., 2008b; Oltra-Cucarella et al., 2013
Embedded Figure Test	Roberts et al., 2013; Lopez et al., 2008a; Lopez et al., 2008b
Stroop Test	Kingston et al., 1996; Steinglass et al., 2006; Kemps et al., 2010; Van den Eynde et al., 2012; Oltra-Cucarella et al., 2013
Brixton Spatial Anticipation Test	Lounes et al., 2011; Roberts et al., 2007; Tchanturia et al., 2004
Block Design	Lopez et al., 2008a
CatBat task	Roberts et al., 2007; Holliday et al., 2005
Digit Symbol Test	Pieters et al., 2004; Palaziduo et al., 1990
Haptic Illusion	Roberts et al., 2007; Holliday et al., 2005; Tchanturia et al., 2004
Verbal Fluency test	Stedal et al., 2013; Tchanturia et al., 2004

Tasks	Works
RAVELLO PROFILE	Fagundo et al., 2012; Fowler et al., 2006; Fassino et al., 2002
Baron-Cohen's "Reading the mind in the Eyes" task (RME)	Tapajoz et al., 2013; Russell et al., 2009
Cantab	Galimberti et al., 2012; Roberts et al., 2007; Fowler et al., 2006
Faux Pas Test	Tapajoz et al., 2013
Sentence Completion Task	Lopez et al., 2008a; Lopez et al., 2008b
Homograph Reading Test (HRT)	Lopez et al., 2008a; Lopez et al., 2008b
Tower of London	Lindner et al., 2012; Alvarado-Sánchez et al., 2009;
Affective Priming paradigm	Cserjési, 2009
Cognitive Drug Research (CDR)	Bosanac, 2007
Cognitive Flexibility Scale (CFS)	Lounes et al., 2011
Detail and Flexibility Questionnaire (DFlex)	Roberts et al., 2011
Happé's cartoon task	Russell et al., 2009; Tchanturia et al., 2004
Letter n-back paradigm	Lao-Kaim et al., 2013
Luria word recall test	Gillberg et al., 2007
Matching Familiar Figures Test (MFFT)	Southgate et al., 2008
Uses of common objects test (UCOT)	Wilsdon and Wade, 2006
WAIS	Gillberg et al., 2007
Wechsler Memory Scale-Revised	Oltra-Cucarella et al., 2013
Novel risk taking measure (Bets 16)	Butler and Montgomery, 2005
Stroop Test emotional	Redgrave et al., 2008; Fassino et al., 2002
Symbol-Digit Modalities Test	Oltra-Cucarella et al., 2013; Palazidou et al., 1990

The latter group includes batteries such as the Ravello Profile or the CANTAB (Table 1; Table 2). The Ravello Profile includes several tasks such as the Rey-Osterrieth Complex Figure; verbal fluency tests, Trail Making Test, Tower of London and the Color Word interference tests from the D-KEFS; Vocabulary and Matrix subtests from the Wechsler Adult Intelligence Scale; and the Brixton Spatial Anticipation and the Hayling Sentence Completion tests from the Brixton and Hayling Test.

One of the cognitive domains investigated in AN is the Theory of Mind (ToM), defined as "the ability to make inferences about others' mental state, behavior, knowledge, motivations, and beliefs" (Tchanturia et al., 2004a). Tasks for assessing ToM are those such as the Reading the Mind in the Eyes test, the Faux Pas Test and Happé Stories test. The Reading the Mind in the Eyes test assesses the ability to interpret how other individuals feel by presenting pictures of their eyes. In the Happé stories, the examinee must interpret both what other individuals feel and also what they think. This test assesses both hot executive functions and cold executive functions (Zalazo and Müller, 2007). Related to the hot executive functions, another task widely used is the Iowa Gambling Task, in which how emotions modulate executive functioning is assessed.

To assess both cognitive and motor inhibitory systems, tasks such as the Stroop test and Go/no-Go tests have been used, more frequently in binge-purging AN and bulimia nervosa (Kemps and Wilsdon, 2010), maybe because an inhibitory deficit is suspected to underlie bulimic behaviors.

To test for central coherence, tests such as the Rey-Osterrieth Complex Figure, the Block design task, the Object Assembly task and the Matching Familiar Figures Test have been used. These tests assess both cognitive domains such as spatial cognition, perception, organization, planning or praxis, and the time needed to perform the tasks.

Working memory, a complex system in which several cognitive domains are integrated, has also been studied in AN using tasks such as the N-back paradigm. This task assesses both the attentional-inhibitory and the working memory processes, as both are necessary to perform the task.

Neuropsychological Functioning in Anorexia Nervosa

Executive Functions

Among the most significant neuropsychological impairments in AN, Executive Functioning (EF) has been given attention especially during the last years (Cavedini et al., 2006; Wilsdon and Wade, 2006). EF includes different capacities with separate functions. However, although several works also identified impairments on cognitive domains different to EF (Lena, Fiocco and Leyenaar, 2004; Oltra-Cucarella et al., 2012, 2013), none of them investigated how EF may impact performance on tasks measuring these cognitive domains. This section will summarize some knowledge and recent findings about that topic.

The category Executive Functioning (or Executive Functions) includes several capacities responsible for organizing, planning, deciding or supervising behaviors, inhibiting irrelevant stimuli or behaviors, or even facilitating the systems adaptation to the changes that occur in the environment by allowing behavioral modification. Some of these capacities are decision making, set-shifting and inhibition, which will be detailed along this section. Previous research has shown that the impairments in EF are a core symptomatology in AN, by means of tasks for which participants must use cognitive capacities such as decision making, cognitive flexibility, set-shifting or behavioral inhibition. However, the impact of impaired EF on verbal memory functioning has not been investigated so far. In the attempt to fill this gap of knowledge, we will describe data from a recent work about this issue.

1. Decision Making

Decision making (DM) is a cognitive ability related to the capacity to choose successfully among several possibilities in an adaptive way (Tchanturia et al., 2007). For making the best decision it is necessary to evaluate all the possibilities and choose the most adequate one in order to get the expected results (Clark, Cools and Robbins, 2004). When DM has been studied in ED using the Iowa Gambling Task (IGT), results showed that females with AN have troubles for choosing the options that give them back future rewards. They perform the task in a way that rewards immediately, thus getting much less benefits than they actually could get (Cavedini et al., 2006; Tchanturia et al., 2007). This immediate reward has been associated with the reward these females feel when they refuse to intake food or when they control their environment despite the future damage this behavior will cause.

2. Set-Shifting

It is related to the capacity of moving back and forth between several tasks, mental operations or response criteria (Roberts et al., 2007). Impairments in set-shifting may appear in two ways: on one hand there may be perseverative behaviors as a consequence of inflexibility. On the other hand, it can manifest as cognitive inflexibility in the form of rigid and narrow thinking styles when facing problems or performing tasks. In AN, set-shifting has been explored using neuropsychological tasks such as the Wisconsin Card Sorting Test (Gillberg et al., 2007; Steinglass et al., 2006, Wilsdon and Wade, 2006), the Trail Making Test (Kingston et al., 1996; Oltra-Cucarella et al., 2013; Pendleton-Jones et al., 1991; Stedal et al., 2012; Steinglass et al., 2006; Tchanturia et al., 2004), the CANTAB battery (Fowler et al., 2006) or the Brixton Test (Tchanturia et al., 2004).

Impairments have been found in set-shifting using the TMT (Kingston et al, 1996; Pendleton-Jones et al., 1991; Stedal et al., 2012; Tchanturia et al., 2004), the WCST (Steinglass et al., 2006; Wilsdon and Wade, 2006) and the Brixton Test (Tchanturia et al., 2004). However, other authors found no difference between females with AN and healthy controls using the WCST (Gillberg et al., 2007) or the TMT (Oltra-Cucarella et al., 2013; Steinglass et al., 2006).

3. Inhibition

It is related to the capacity to stop a future plan or a current action. It is a control action internally generated for regulating the information processing and regulating oneself. The task most frequently used for assessing inhibition in AN is the Stroop Task, both in its classical version (Kingston et al., 1996; Oltra-Cucarella et al, 2013; Pedleton-Jones et al., 1991; Steinglass et al., 2006) and in its modified version including elements related to food and body shape (Ben-Tovim, Walker, Fok, and Yap, 1989; Ben-Tovim and Walker, 1991; Green,

Wakeling, Elliman and Rogers, 1998). Using the classical Stroop task, only Oltra-Cucarella et al. (2013) found lower performance in the AN group when compared to a healthy control group, while Kingston et al. (1996), Pendleton-Jones et al. (1991) and Steinglass et al. (2006) found that participants with AN and healthy controls performed similarly. Regarding the Stroop – modified version including items about weight and body shape, Ben-Tovim et al. (1989) found that participants with AN took longer to complete the task when items were related to food (but not to body shape), whilst Ben-Tovim and Walker (1991) found that females with AN took longer to complete the task when items related both to food and body shape were used. Green et al. (1998) found that, when items related to food were used, patients with AN took significantly longer to complete the task only when they were underweight. On the contrary, when their weight was restored, performance of both groups was comparable. When items related to body shape were used, patients with AN took significantly longer to complete the task both when they were underweight as well as after one week of therapy, but performance of both groups was comparable after 12 weeks of therapy. It seems that the Stroop – modified task is more useful when items are related to body shape compared to those related to food (Dobson and Dozois, 2004).

In general, it seems that there is a marked impairment in EF among patients with AN affecting set-shifting and inhibition which could be intrinsic to the disease and not a consequence of BMI decreases (Roberts et al., 2007).

4. Verbal Memory

It is related to the capacity to learn new information across several learning series and recall it after a delay. Verbal memory has been studied in AN using different measures such as lists (California Verbal Learning Test, Rey Auditory Verbal Learning Test) and stories (Logical Memory subtest from the Wechsler Memory Scale). As impaired performance on verbal memory tasks has inconsistently been found, there is no consensus in the literature about whether verbal memory impairments are part of AN or, conversely, are an artifact of the severity of symptomatology. Two factors could explain this inconsistency. On one hand, several authors (Bayless et al., 2002, Bosanac et al., 2007, Chui et al., 2008, Kingston et al., 1996 and Pendleton-Jones et al., 1991) found that patients with AN performed significantly worse than the healthy control group on tasks measuring verbal memory. On the contrary, others (Connan et al., 2006, Fowler et al., 2006, Gillberg et al., 2007, Seed et al., 2002) found no difference between groups. On the other hand, in those works that found differences between groups, the profile of verbal memory impairments is difficult to explain. For example, Bayless et al. (2002), Chui et al. (2008) and Pendleton-Jones et al. (1991) found a significantly lower delayed recall in their patients with AN, but Bosanac et al. (2007) and Kingston et al. (1996) found that their participants with AN performed significantly lower in tasks measuring immediate recall but were comparable to the healthy control group in the delayed recall tasks. Seed et al. (2002) did not find significant differences in the amount of items recalled after a delay, but found a higher percentage of errors in the AN group. However, as we will explain in the next section, those differences might be accounted for by another factor, namely the executive functioning.

Is Verbal Memory Independent of Executive Functioning in AN?

In one recent research (Oltra-Cucarella et al., 2013), our group compared an underweight AN group (BMI<17), a weight-restored AN group (BMI>17) and a healthy control group. We found that patients with AN performed significantly worse than healthy controls in tasks measuring speed of processing information, inhibition and delayed recall. However, as different tasks measuring verbal memory were used and there were no relationships between them, data let us conclude that executive functioning might be affecting performance on delayed recall tasks. We measured delayed recall using both a list learning tasks and a logical memory task. The list learning task was the *Test de Aprendizaje Verbal España-Complutense* (TAVEC; Benedet and Alejandre, 1998), the Spanish adaptation of the California Verbal Learning Test (CVLT). The TAVEC includes two lists of 16 words from four semantic categories. List A is presented out loud across 5 learning trials. Memory is tested both in a free and a cued manner to obtain both an index of learning and the way the examinees benefit from semantic clustering. Then List B serves as an interference material. In the final part, a recognition task including both all the words from List A and List B and several distractors is performed.

Regarding the logical story task, one of the stories from the Logical Memory subtest of the Spanish version of the Wechsler Memory Scale – 3d Ed. (Wechsler, 1997) was used. In this task, a story containing 25 items was read out loud by the examiner and the examinee was required to reproduce all the information she was capable to recall in a free manner.

EF were assessed by means of tasks measuring inhibition (Stroop Test; Golden, 2005), impulsivity (Rey-Osterrieth Complex Figure – ROCF; Rey, 1987) and Speed of Information Processing (SIP; Symbol Digit Modalities Test - SDMT; Strauss et al., 2006).

In this work, we found that patients with AN performed significantly worse than healthy controls in immediate recall, thus supporting the findings reported by Kingston et al. (1996) and Bosanac et al. (2007). We also found that patients with AN performed significantly worse than healthy control subjects in the Logical Memory task supporting the findings reported by Bayless et al. (2002), Chui et al. (2008) and Pendleton-Jones et al. (1991). However, both the delayed recall task and the recognition task within the TAVEC showed that patients with AN had learnt the material correctly, supporting that their memory might not be affected. Thus, although we concluded that verbal memory impairments seemed to be a primary impairment in AN based on their relations with other cognitive domains, we suggested that differences in delayed recall on the Logical Memory test could be accounted for by EF in some way.

In another recent work carried out to test this hypothesis (Oltra-Cucarella et al., submitted for review), we studied how SIP, inhibition and impulsivity could affect delayed recall performance on the Logical Memory subtests from the WMS-III. We performed a hierarchical multiple regression to test which of the variables affected delayed recall and, if so, to what extent. Results showed that the tasks used for measuring impulsivity and SIP accounted for the 80% of the variance on the Logical Memory subtest from the WMS-III even when depressive symptomatology and BMI were controlled for, which indicates that impaired EF go beyond the specific cognitive abilities included under the Executive Functioning category and affect performance on other superior mental abilities such as verbal memory. Thus, we concluded that EF must be monitored in AN in order to test how they affect performance on other cognitive abilities and should be included in treatments carried out to improve cognitive functioning (Tchanturia et al., 2008).

Conclusion

This chapter offers a transdisciplinary approach to Anorexia Nervosa, covering its psychological, neuroendocrine and neuropsychological features. Eating Disorders are one of the most frequent and devastating diseases in young females, affecting several domains in their lives. When facing a patient with AN, clinicians must gather information regarding personality traits, affective state, as well as neuroendocrine, social and cognitive functioning, as all these areas are likely to be affected. We hope that this chapter will help the readers understand AN from different perspectives both for clinical practice and for future research.

References

Agras, W.S., Barlow, D.H., Chapin, H.N., Abel, G.G., Jackson, Leitenberg, H. (1974). Behaviour modification of anorexia nervosa. *Archives of general Psychiatry, 30*, 274-286

Alvarado-Sánchez, N., Silva-Gutiérrez, C., Salvador-Cruz, J. (2009). Visoconstructive deficits and risk of developing eating disorders. *The Spanish Journal of Psychology, 12*(2), 677-85.

American Psychiatric Association (2000). Manual diagnóstico y estadístico de los trastornos mentales. (DSM-IV-TR) (4ª ed. texto revisado) (*Diagnostic and statistic manual of mental disorders (4ª edición – Text Revised*). Barcelona: Masson.

American Psychiatric Association (2006). Practice guideline for the treatment of patients with eating disorders (3ª ed.). APA Practice Guidelines.www.psych.org.

Andrés-Perpiña, S., Lozano-Serra, E., Puig, O., Lera-Miguel, S., Lázaro, L., Castro-Fornieles, J. (2011). Clinical and biological correlates of adolescent anorexia nervosa with impaired cognitive profile. *European Child and Adolescent Psychiatry, 20*(11-12), 541-9.

Baranowska, B., Baranowska-Bik, A., Bik, W., Martynska, L., (2008). The role of leptin and orexins in the dysfunction of hypothalamo-pituitary-gonadal regulation and in the mechanism of hyperactivity in patients with anorexia nervosa. *Neuroendocrinology Letters, 29*, 37–40.

Barha, C.K., Galea L.A. (2010). Influence of different estrogens on neuroplasticity and cognition in the hippocampus. *Biochimica et Biophysica Acta, 1800*(10), 1056-67.

Bayless, J.D., Kanz, J.E., Moser, D.J., McDowell, B.D., Bowers, W.A., Andersen, A.E., Paulsen, J.S. (2002). Neuropsychological characteristics of patients in a hospital-based eating disorder program. *Annals of Clinical Psychiatry, 14*, 203–207.

Bell, C., Bulik, C., Clayton, P., Crow, S., Davis, D.M., DeMaso, D.R., Dogin, J., Fairburn, C.G., Fink, A.H., Fisher, M., Forman, S., Garner, D.M., Golden, N.H., Hagan, J., Kaplan, A.S., Katzman, D.K., Katzman, M.A., Keddy, D., Kottke, T.E., Kreipe, R., Lonegran, E., Motto, J.A., Mickley, D., Rubel, J.B., Schienholtz, M., Schyve, P.M., Sloan, R., Sokol, M., Sparrow, J., Strober, M., Stunkard, A., Suchinsky, R.T., Swanson, J., Treasure, J., Westermeyer, J., Wilfley, D., Wonderlich, S. (2000). Practice guideline for the treatment of patients with eating disorders (revision). *American Journal of Psychiatry, 157*(1), 1-39.

Benedet, M., Alejandre, M. (1998). TAVEC: Test de aprendizaje verbal Espan~ a-Complutense. Madrid, Spain: TEA Ediciones.

Ben-Tovim, D.I., Walker, M.K. (1991). Further evidence for the Stroop Test as a quantitative measure of psychopathology in eating disorders. *International Journal of Eating Disorders, 10*(5), 609-13.

Ben-Tovim, D.I., Walker, M.K., Fok, D., Yap, E. (1989). An adaptation of the Stroop Test for measuring shape and food concerns in eating disorders: a quantitative measure of psychopathology?. *International Journal of Eating Disorders, 8*, 681-7.

Bosanac, P., Kurlender, S., Stojanovska, L., Hallam, K., Norman, T., McGrath, C., Burrows, G., Wesnes, K., Manktelov, T., Olver, J. (2007). Neuropsychological Study of Underweight and "Weight-Recovered" Anorexia Nervosa Compared with Bulimia Nervosa and Normal Controls. *International Journal of Eating Disorders, 40*, 613–621.

Brogan, A., Hevey, D., Pignatti, R. (2010). Anorexia, bulimia, and obesity: shared decision making deficits on the Iowa Gambling Task (IGT). *Journal of the International Neuropsychological Society, 16*(4), 711-5.

Bruch, H. (1962). Perceptual and conceptual disturbances in anorexia nervosa. *Psychosomatic Medicine*, 24, 187-194.

Bruni, V., Dei, M., Morelli, C., Schettino, M.T., Balzi. D., Nuvolone, D. (2011). Body Composition Variables and Leptin Levels in Functional Hypothalamic Amenorrhea and Amenorrhea Related to Eating Disorders. *Journal of Pediatric and Adolescent Gynecology, 24*, 347-352.

Butler, G.K., Montgomery, A.M. (2005). Subjective self-control and behavioral impulsivity coexist in anorexia nervosa. *Eating Behaviors, 6*(3), 221-7.

Butters, J.W. & Cash, T.F. (1987). Cognitive behavioral treatment of women´s body image dissatisfaction. *Journal of Consulting and Clinical Psychology, 55*, 889-897.

Button, E. (1986). Body Size perception and response to in-patient treatment in anorexia nervosa. *International Journal of Eating Disorders*, 5, 617-629.

Calderoni, S., Muratori, F., Leggero, C., Narzisi, A., Apicella, F., Balottin, U., Carigi, T., Maestro, S., Fabbro, F., Urgesi, C. (2013). Neuropsychological functioning in children and adolescents with restrictive-type anorexia nervosa: an in-depth investigation with NEPSY-II. *Journal of Clinical and Experimental Neuropsychology, 35*(2), 167-79.

Carter, J.C., Kelly, A.C., Norwood, S.J. (2012). Interpersonal problems in anorexia nervosa: Social inhibition as defining and detrimental. *Personality and Individual Differences, 53*(3), 169–174.

Cash, T.F. Grant, J.R. (1995). Cognitive-Behavioral treatment of Body-Image disturbances. In V.B. Van Hasselt & M. Hersen (Eds.), *Sourcebook of psychological treatment manuals for adult disorders.* New York: Plenum Press.

Cash, T.F., lavallee, D. (1997). Cognitive-behavioral body image therapy: Extended evidence of the efficacy of a self-directed program. *Journal of Rational-Emotive and Cognitive-Behavior Therapy, 15*(4), 281-294.

Cavedini, P., Zorzi, C., Bassi, T., Gorini, A., Baraldi, C., Ubbiali, A., Bellodi, L. (2006). Decision-making functioning as a predictor of treatment outcome in anorexia nervosa. *Psychiatry Research, 145*, 179–187.

Chan, J.L., Mantzoros, C.S. (2005). Role of leptin in energy-deprivation states: normal human physiology and clinical implications for hypothalamic amenorrhoea and anorexia nervosa. *The Lancet, 366*(9479), 74-85.

Chui, H.T., Christensen, B.K., Zipursky, R.B., Richards, B.A., Hanratty, M.K., Kabani, N.J., Mikulis, D.J., Katzman, D.K. (2008). Cognitive function and brain structure in females with a history of adolescent-onset anorexia nervosa. *Pediatrics, 122*, 426–437.

Clark, L., Cools, R., Robbins, T.W. (2004). The neuropsychology of ventral prefrontal cortex: Decision-making and reversal Learning. *Brain and Cognition, 55*, 41–53.

Connan, F., Murphy, F., Connor, S.E.J., Rich, P., Murphy, T., Bara-Carill, N., Landau, S., Krljes, S., Ng, V., Williams, S., Morris, R.G., Campbell, I.C., Treasure, J. (2006). Hippocampal volumen and cognitive function in anorexia nervosa. *Psychiatry Research: Neuroimaging, 146*, 117–125.

Cserjési, R. (2009). Emotions, cognition, awareness and behavior in eating disorders. Comparison between obesity and anorexia nervosa. *Orv Hetil, 150*(24), 1135-43.

de Krom, M., Hendriks, J., Hillebrand, J., van Elburg, A., Adan, R., (2006). A polymorphism in the 3′ untranslated region of the CCK gene is associated with anorexia nervosa in Dutch patients. Psychiatr. Genet. 16, 239.

Dobson, K.S., Dozois, D.J.A. (2004). Attentional biases in eating disorders: A meta-analytic review of Stroop performance. *Clinical Psychology Review, 23*, 1001-1022.

Dworkin, S.K., Kerr, B. (1987). Comparison of interventions for women experiencing body image problems. *Journal of Counseling Psychology, 34*,136-140.

Fagundo, A.B., de la Torre, R., Jiménez-Murcia, S., Agüera, Z., Granero, R., Tárrega, S., Botella, C., Baños, R., Fernandez-Real, J.M., Rodriguez, R., Forcano, L., Fruhbeck, G., Gomez-Ambrosi, G., Tinahones, F.J., Fernandez-Garcia, J.C., Casanueva, F.F., Fernández-Aranda, F. (2012). Executive functions profile in extreme eating/weight conditions: from anorexia nervosa to obesity. *PLoS One, 7*(8):e43382.

Fairburn, C.G. & Wilson, G.T. (1993). *Binge eating: Nature, assessment, and treatment.* New York: Guilford Press.

Fairburn, C.G., Cooper, Z., Shafran, R. (2003). Cognitive behaviour therapy for eating disorders: a "transdiagnostic" theory and treatment. *Behaviour Research and Therapy, 41*, 509-528.

Fairburn, C.G., Shafran, R., Cooper, Z. (1998). A cognitive behavioural theory of anorexia nervosa. *Behavioural Research and Therapy, 37*, 1-17.

Fassino, S., Pieró, A., Daga, G.A., Leombruni, P., Mortara, P., Rovera, G.G. (2002). Attentional biases and frontal functioning in anorexia nervosa. *International Journal of Eating disorders, 31*(3), 274-83.

Favaro, A., Santonastaso, P., Manara, R., Bosello, R., Bommarito, G., Tenconi, E., Di Salle, F. (2012). Disruption of visuospatial and somatosensory functional connectivity in anorexia nervosa. *Biological Psychiatry, 72*(10), 864-70.

Fazeli, P.K., Lawson, E.A., Prabhakaran, R., Miller, K.K., Donoho, D.A., Clemmons, D.R., Herzog, D.B., Misra, M., Klibanski, A. (2010). Effects of Recombinant Human Growth Hormone in Anorexia Nervosa: A Randomized, Placebo-Controlled Study. *The Journal of Clinical Endocrinology & Metabolism, 95*, 4889–4897.

Ferro, A.M., Brugnolo, A., De Leo, C., Dessi, B., Girtler, N., Morbelli, S., Nobili, F., Rossi, D.S., Falchero, M., Murialdo, G., Rossini, P.M., Babiloni, C., Schizzi, R., Padolecchia, R., Rodriguez, G. (2005). Stroop interference task and single-photon emission tomography in anorexia: a preliminary report. International Journal of Eating Disorders, 38(4), 323-9.

Fowler, L. Blackwell, A., Jaffa, A., Palmer, R., Robbins, T.W., Sahakian, B.J., Dowson, J.H. (2006). Profile of neurocognitive impairments associated with female in-patients with anorexia nervosa. Psychological Medicine, 36, 517–527.

Frick, K.M. Fernandez, S.M. Harburger, S.M., Lauren L. (2010). A new approach to understanding the molecular mechanisms through which estrogens affect cognition. Biochimica et Biophysica Acta, 1800(10), 1045-55.

Galimberti, E., Martoni, R.M., Cavallini, M. C., Erzegovesi, S., Bellodi, L. (2012). Motor inhibition and cognitive flexibility in eating disorder subtypes. Progress in Neuro-Psychopharmacology & Biological Psychiatry, 36(2), 307-12.

Garner, D.M., Bemis, K.M. (1982). Anorexia Nervosa: a cognitive behavioral approach to AN. Cognitive Therapy and Research, 6, 123-150.

Garner, D.M., Vitousek K.M. Pike K.M. (1997).Cognitive-Behavioral Therapy for AN. In D.M. Garner & P.E. Garfinkel (eds), Handbook of treatment for eating disorders. New York: Guilford Press.

Gillberg, I.C., Rastam, M., Wentz, E., Gillberg, C. (2007). Cognitive and executive functions in anorexia nervosa ten years after onset of eating disorder. Journal of Clinical and Experimental Neuropsychology, 29(2),170-178.

Glantz, K., Durlach, N.L., Barnett, R.C, Aviles, W.A. (1997). Virtual reality (VR) and psychotherapy: opportunities and challenges. Presence, 6(1), 87-105.

Glantz, K., Durlach, N.L., Barnett, R.C., Aviles, W.A. (1996). Virtual reality (VR) and psychotherapy: from the physical to the social environment. Psychotherapy, 33(3), 464-473.

Glorio, R., Allevato, M., De Pablo, A., Abbruzzese, M., Carmona, L., Savarin, M., Ibarra, M., Busso, C., Mordoh, A., Llopis, C., Haas, R., Bello, M., Woscoff, A. (2000). Prevalence of cutaneous manifestations in 200 patients with eating disorders. International Journal of Dermatology, 39(5), 348-353.

Golden, C. J. (2005). Test de colores y palabras (Stroop). Madrid: TEA Ediciones.

Green, M.W., Wakeling, A., Elliman, N., A., Rogers, P.J. (1998). Impaired colour-naming of clinically salient words as a measure of recovery in anorexia nervosa. Behavioural and Cognitive Psychotherapy, 26, 53–62.

Grunwald, M., Ettrich, C., Busse, F., Assmann, B., Dähne, A., Gertz, H.J. (2002). Angle paradigm: a new method to measure right parietal dysfunctions in anorexia nervosa. Archives of Clinical Neuropsychology, 17(5), 485-96.

Guillaume, S., Sang, C.N., Jaussent, I., Raingeard, I., Bringer, J., Jollant, F., Courtet, P. (2010). Is decision making really impaired in eating disorders? Neuropsychology, 24(6), 808-12.

Hatch, A., Madden, S., Kohn, M.R., Clarke, S., Touyz, S., Gordon, E., Williams, L.M. (2010). In first presentation adolescent anorexia nervosa, do cognitive markers of underweight status change with weight gain following a refeeding intervention? International Journal of Eating Disorders, 43(4), 295-306.

Hodges, L.F., Bolter, J., Mynatt, E., Ribarsky, W., Van Teylingen, R. (1993). Virtual environments research at the Georgia Tech GVU Center. Presence, 2(3), 234-243.

Hodges, L.F., Rothbaum, B.O., Kooper, R., Opdyke, D., Meyer, T, North, M., de Graaff, J.J., Williford, J. (1995). Virtual environments for treating the fear of heights. *IEEE Computer, 28*(7), 27-34.

Hodges, L.F., Rothbaum, B.O., Watson, B., Kessler, G.D. Opdyke, D. (1996). The virtual airplane for fear of flying therapy. Paper presented alt the virtual reality annual international symposium-VRAIS 96, Los Alamitos, CA. In G. Riva, M. Bacchetta, M. Baruffi, S. Rinaldi, E. Molinari. (1999). Virtual reality based experiential cognitive treatment of anorexia nervosa. *Journal of Behavior Therapy and Experimental Psychiatry, 30,* 221-230.

Hoek, H. (2003). Review of the prevalence and Incidence of Eating Disorders. *International Journal of Eating Disorders, 34,* 383-396.

Holliday, J., Tchanturia, K., Landau, S., Collier, D., Treasure, J. (2005). Is impaired set-shifting an endophenotype of anorexia nervosa? *Amercan Journal of Psychiatry, 162*(12), 2269-75.

Instituto Nacional de la Salud (1995). *Protocolo de los trastornos del comportamiento alimentario.* Madrid: INSALUD. Secretaría General.

Jáuregui-Lobera I. Neuropsychology of eating disorders: 1995–2012. *Journal of Neuropsychiatric Disease and Treatment, 9,* 415–430.

Keel, P. Haedt, A. (2008). Evidence-Based Psychosocial Treatments for Eating Problems and Eating Disorders. *Journal of Clinical Child & Adolescent Psychology, 37* (1), 39-61 DOI: 10.1080/ 15374410701817832.

Kemps, E., Wilsdon, A. (2010). Preliminary evidence for a role for impulsivity in cognitive disinhibition in bulimia nervosa. *Journal of Clinical and Experimental Neuropsychology, 32*(5), 515–521.

Kingston, K., Szmukler, G., Andrewes, D., Tress, B., Desmond, P. (1996). Neuropsychological and structural brain changes in anorexia nervosa before and after refeeding. *Psychological Medicine, 26,* 15-28.

Lao-Kaim, N.P., Giampietro, V.P., Williams, S.C., Simmons, A., Tchanturia, K. (2013). Functional MRI investigation of verbal working memory in adults with anorexia nervosa. European Psychiatry, in press, doi: http://dx.doi.org/10.1016/j.eurpsy.2013.05.003.

Lena, S.M., Fiocco, A.J., Leyenaar, J.K. (2004). The Role of Cognitive Deficits in the Development of Eating Disorders. *Neuropsychology Review, 14*(2), 99–113.

Lindner, S.E., Fichter, M.M., Quadflieg, N. (2012). Decision-making and planning in full recovery of anorexia nervosa. *International Journal of Eating Disorders, 45*(7), 866-75.

Lopez, C.A., Tchanturia, K., Stahl, D., Treasure, J. (2008a). Central coherence in women with bulimia nervosa. *International Journal of Eating Disorders, 41*(4),340-7.

Lopez, C., Tchanturia, K., Stahl, D., Booth, R., Holliday, J., Treasure, J. (2008b). An examination of the concept of central coherence in women with anorexia nervosa. *International Journal of Eating Disorders, 41*(2), 143-52.

Lounes, N., Khan, G., Tchanturia, K. (2011). Assessment of cognitive flexibility in anorexia nervosa--self-report or experimental measure? A brief report. *Journal of the International Neuropsychological Society, 17*(5), 925-8.

Lovell, D. M., Williams, J. M., Hill, A.B. (1997). Selective processing of shape-related words in women with eating disorders, and those who have recovered. *British Journal of Clinical Psychology, 36*(3), 421-32.

Marco, J.H. (2000). *Tratamiento de las alteraciones de la Imagen Corporal en los Trastornos Alimentarios. Eficacia Diferencia de las técnicas de Realidad Virtual frente a las técnicas tradicionales (Treatment for body image distortions in ED. Efficacy of Virtual Reality over traditional techniques).* Tesis de Licenciatura. Universidad Mimeo: Universidad Jaime I. Castellón.

Misra, M., Miller, K.K., Almazan, C., Ramaswamy, K., Aggarwal, A., Herzog, D.B. (2004) Hormonal and body composition predictors of soluble leptin receptor, leptin, and free leptin index in adolescent girls with anorexia nervosa and controls and relation to insulin sensitivity. *Journal of Clinical Endocrinology & Metabolism, 89*, 3486–95.

Misra, M., Miller, K.K., Bjornson, J., Hackman, A., Aggarwal, A., Chung, J., Ott, M., Herzog, D.B., Johnson, D.B., Klibanski, A. (2003) Alterations in growth hormone secretory dynamics in adolescent girls with anorexia nervosa and effects on bone metabolism. Journal of Clinical Endocrinology & Metabolism, 88, 5615–5623.

Mizuta, I., Inoue, Y., Fukunaga, T., Ishi, R., Ogawa, A., Takeda, M. (2002). Psychological characteristics of eating disorders as evidenced by the combined administration of questionnaires and two projective methods: the Tree Drawing Test (Baum Test) and the Sentence Completion Test. *Psychiatry and Clinical Neurosciences, 56*(1), 41-53.

Nikendei, C., Funiok, C., Pfüller, U., Zastrow, A., Aschenbrenner, S., Weisbrod, M., Herzog, W., Friederich, H.C. (2011). Memory performance in acute and weight-restored anorexia nervosa patients. *Psychological Medicine, 41*(4), 829-38.

North, M.M., North, S.M., Coble, J.R. (1996). Effectiveness of virtual environment desensitization in the treatment of agoraphobia. *Presence, 5*(3), 127-132.

North, M.M., North, S.M., Coble, J.R. (1997). Virtual reality therapy for fear of flying. *American Journal of Psychiatry, 154*(1), 130.

Olszewski, P.K., Schioth, H.B., Levine, A.S. (2008). Ghrelin in the CNS: from hunger to a rewarding and memorable meal?. *Brain Research Reviews, 58*, 160–170.

Oltra-Cucarella, J., Espert, R., Rojo, L. (2012). Neuropsychology and anorexia nervosa. Cognitive and radiological findings. *Neurología, 27*(8), 504–510.

Oltra-Cucarella, J., Espert, R., Rojo, L., Jacas, C., Guillén, V., Moreno, S. (2013). Neuropsychological Impairments in Anorexia Nervosa: A Spanish Sample Pilot Study. *Applied Neuropsychology: Adult,* DOI: 10.1080/09084282.2013.782030.

Palazidou, E., Robinson, P., Lishman, W.A. (1990). Neuroradiological and neuropsychological assessment in anorexia nervosa. *Psychological Medicine, 20*(3), 521-7.

Papadopoulos, F.C., Ekbom, A., Brandt, L., Ekselius, L. (2009). Excess mortality, causes of death and prognostic factors in anorexia nervosa. *The British Journal of Psychiatry, 194*, 10–17.

Pelaez, M.A., Labrador, F.J., Raich, R. M. (2005). Epidemiología de los trastornos de la conducta alimentaria en España (Epidemiology of ED in Spain). In J. M. Mancilla (ed), *Trastornos de la Conducta Alimentaria en Iberoamérica.* Thompson Learning Iberoamérica.

Pendleton-Jones, B., Duncan, C.C., Brouwers, P., Mirsky, A.F. (1991). Cognition in eating disorders. *Journal of Clinical and Experimental Neuropsychology, 13*(5), 711-728.

Perpiñá, C. (1999). Trastornos alimentarios. Anorexia y Bulimia. (*Eating Disorders: Anorexia and Bulimia).* Madrid: UNED-FUE.

Perpiñá, C., Botella, C., Baños, R. M. (2000): *Imagen corporal en los trastornos alimentarios. Evaluación y tratamiento por medio de realidad virtual (*Body image in ED. Assessment and treatment using Virtual Reality*).* Valencia: Promolibro.

Pieters, G., Maas, Y., Hulstijn, W., Vandereycken, W., Probst, M., Peuskens, J., Sabbe, B. (2004). Differentiation of cognitive and motor aspects in a digit symbol substitution test in Anorexia nervosa patients, before and after weight restoration. *Psychopathology, 37*(5), 227-32.

Raich R.M., Mora, M., Marroquín, H., Pulido S.A., Soler, A. (1997), "Tratamiento cognitivo conductual de la insatisfacción corporal". *Análisis y modificación de conducta, 23*(89), 405-424.

Rask-Andersen, M., Olszewski, P.K., Levine, A.S., Schiötha, H.B. (2010). Molecular mechanisms underlying anorexia nervosa: Focus on human gene association studies and systems controlling food intake. *Brain Research Reviews, 62*, 147 -164.

Redgrave, G.W., Bakker, A., Bello, N.T., Caffo, B.S., Coughlin, J.W., Guarda, A.S., McEntee, J.E., Pekar, J.J., Reinblatt, S. P., Verduzco, G., Moran, T.H. (2008). Differential brain activation in anorexia nervosa to Fat and Thin words during a Stroop task. *NeuroReport, 19*(12), 1181-5.

Rey, A. (1987). *Test de copia de la figura compleja*. Madrid: TEA Ediciones

Riva, G., Bacchetta, M., Baruffi, M., Rinaldi, S., Molinari, E. (1999). Virtual reality based experiential cognitive treatment of anorexia nervosa. *Journal of Behavior Therapy and Experimental Psychiatry, 30*(3), 221–230.

Roberts, M.E., Barthel, F.M., Lopez, C., Tchanturia, K., Treasure, J.L. (2011). Development and validation of the Detail and Flexibility Questionnaire (DFlex) in eating disorders. *Eating Behaviors, 12*(3), 168-74.

Roberts, M.E., Tchanturia, K., Treasure, J.L. (2013). Is attention to detail a similarly strong candidate endophenotype for anorexia nervosa and bulimia nervosa? *The World Journal of Biological Psychiatry, 14*(6), 452-63.

Roberts, M.E., Tchanturia, K., Stahl, D., Southgate, L., Treasure, J. (2007). A systematic review and meta-analysis of set-shifting ability in eating disorders. *Psychological Medicine, 37*, 1075–1084.

Rose, M., Davis, J., Frampton, I., Lask, B. (2011). The Ravello Profile: development of a global standard neuropsychological assessment for young people with anorexia nervosa. *Clinical Child Psychology and Psychiatry, 16*(2), 195-202.

Rose, M., Frampton, I., Lask, B. (2012). A case series investigating distinct neuropsychological profiles in children and adolescents with anorexia nervosa. *European Eating Disorders Review, 20*(1), 32-8.

Rosen, J.C., Saltzberg, E., Srebnik, D.(1989). Cognitive behavior therapy for negative body image. *Behavior Therapy, 20*, 393-404.

Russell, T.A., Schmidt, U., Doherty, L., Young, V., Tchanturia, K. (2009). Aspects of social cognition in anorexia nervosa: affective and cognitive theory of mind. *Psychiatry Research, 168*(3), 181-5.

Rutsztein, G. (1997). El aspecto central de la anorexia nerviosa. Investigaciones en psicología. *Revista del Instituto de Investigaciones de la Facultad de Psicología Universidad de Buenos Aires, 1*, 103-128. ISSN 0329-5893.

Saldaña, C. (2001). Tratamientos psicológicos eficaces para el tratamiento de los trastornos del comportamiento alimentario (Effective psychological treatments for eating disorders). *Psicotema, 13(3)*, 381-92.

Salvador, J., Mestas, L., Gordillo, F., Arana, J.M., Meilán, J.J., Pérez, E., Carro, J. (2010). Decision-making in anorexia nervosa. *Revista de Neurología, 50*(11), 703-4.

Schneider, L.F., Monaco, S.E., Warren, M.P. (2008). Elevated ghrelin level in women of normal weight with amenorrhea is related to disordered eating. *Fertility and Sterility, 90*(1), 121-128.

Seed, J. A., McCue, P.M., Wesnes, K.A., Dahabra, S., Young, A.H. (2002).Basal activity of the HPA axis and cognitive function in anorexia nervosa. International Journal of Neuropsychopharmacology, 5, 17–25.

Slade, P.D., Russell, G.F.H. (1973). Awareness of body dimensions in AN: Cross sectional and longitudinal studies. *Psycological Medicine, 3*, 188-199.

Southgate, L., Tchanturia, K., Treasure, J. (2008). Information processing bias in anorexia nervosa. *Psychiatry Research, 160*(2), 221-7.

Stedal, K., Frampton, I., Landrø, N. I., Lask, B. (2012). An examination of the ravello profile--a neuropsychological test battery for anorexia nervosa. *European Eating Disorders Review, 20*(3), 175-81.

Stedal, K., Landrø, N.I., Lask, B. (2013). Verbal fluency in anorexia nervosa. *Eating and Weight Disorders, 18*(2), 151-6.

Stedal, K., Rose, M., Frampton, I., Landro, N.I., Lask, B. (2012). The Neuropsychological Profile of Children, Adolescents, and Young Adults with Anorexia Nervosa. *Archives of Clinical Neuropsychology, 27*(3), 329-337.

Steinglass, J., Walsh, T. (2006). Habit learning and anorexia nervosa: a cognitive neuroscience hypothesis. *International Journal of Eating Disorders, 39*(4), 267–275.

Steinglass, J.E., Walsh, B.T., Stern, Y. (2006). Set shifting deficit in anorexia nervosa. *Journal of the International Neuropsychological Society, 12*, 431–435.

Steinhausen, H. C (2002). The outcome of anorexia nervosa in the 20th century. *American Journal of Psychiatry*; 159(8): 1284-93.

Støving, R.K., Andries, A., Brixen, K., Flyvbjerg, A., Hørder, K., Frystyk, J. (2009). Leptin, ghrelin, and endocannabinoids: Potential therapeutic targets in anorexia nervosa. *Journal of Psychiatry Research, 43*, 671-679.

Strauss, E.A., Sherman E.M.S., Spreen, O. (2006). Compendium of Neuropsychological Tests: Administration, Norms and Commentary (3ª Ed). New York: Oxford University Press.

Strober, M., Bowen, E., Preble, J. (1985). Predictors of weight change in juvenile anorexia nervosa. *International Journal of Eating Disorders, 4*, 605-608.

Sunday, S.R., Halmi, K.A., Einhorn, A. (1995). The Yale–Brown–Cornell Eating Disorder Scale: a new scale to assess eating disorder symptomatology. *International Journal of Eating Disorders*, 18, 237–245.

Tapajóz Pereira de Sampaio, F., Soneira, S., Aulicino, A., Allegri, R.F. (2013). Theory of Mind in Eating Disorders and Their Relationship to Clinical Profile. *European Eating Disorders Review, in press*, DOI: 10.1002/erv.2247.

Tchanturia, K., Anderluh, M.B., Morris, R.G., Rabe-Hesketh, S., Collier, D.A., Sanchez, P., Treasure, J.L. (2004b). Cognitive flexibility in anorexia nervosa and bulimia nervosa. *Journal of the International Neuropsychological Society, 10*, 513–520.

Tchanturia, K., Davies, H., Lopez, C., Schmidt, U., Treasure, J., Wykes, T. (2008). Neuropsychological task performance before and after cognitive remediation in anorexia nervosa: a pilot case-series. *Psychological Medicine, 38*, 1371–1373.

Tchanturia, K., Davies, H., Roberts, M., Harrison, A., Nakazato, M., Schmidt, U., Treasure, J., Morris, R. (2012). Poor cognitive flexibility in eating disorders: examining the evidence using the Wisconsin Card Sorting Task. *PLoS One, 7*(1):e28331.

Tchanturia, K., Happé, F., Godley, J., Treasure, J., Bara-Carril, N., Schmidt, U. (2004a). 'Theory of mind' in Anorexia Nervosa. *European Eating Disorders Review, 12*, 361-366.

Tchanturia, K., Liao, P-C., Uher, R., Lawrence, N., Treasure, J., Campbell, I. C. (2007). An investigation of decision making in anorexia nervosa using the Iowa Gambling Task and skin conductance measurements. *Journal of the International Neuropsychological Society, 13*, 635–641.

Turón (1997). *Trastornos de la alimentación: anorexia nerviosa, bulimia y obesidad* (Eating disorders: anorexia nervosa, bulimia and obessity). Barcelona: Masson.

Usdan, L.S., Khaodhiar, L., Apovian, C. M. (2008). The endocrinopathies of anorexia nervosa. *Endocrine Practice, 14*, 1055–1063.

Van den Eynde, F., Samarawickrema, N., Kenyon, M., DeJong, H., Lavender, A., Startup, H., Schmidt, U. (2012). A study of neurocognition in bulimia nervosa and eating disorder not otherwise specified-bulimia type. *Journal of Clinical and Experimental Neuropsychology, 34*(1), 67–77.

Vandereycken, W., Meerman, R. (1984). Anorexia nervosa: Is prevention possible?. *International Journal of Psychiatry in Medicine, 3*, 15-24.

Vitousek, F.B. (2002). Cognitive-behavioral therapy for anorexia nervosa. In C.G. Fairburn y K.L. Brownell (Eds.), *Eating Disorders and Obesity: a comprehensive handbook (2nd ed)*. New York: Guildford Press. pp. 308-313.

Wechsler, D. (1997). Escala de Memoria Wechsler para Adultos (WMS-III) (3ª Ed). Madrid: TEA Ediciones.

Wilsdon, A., Wade, T.D. (2006). Executive functioning in anorexia nervosa: Exploration of the role of obsessionality, depression and starvation. *Journal of Psychiatric Research, 40*, 746–754.

Witt, E.D., Ryan, C., Hsu, L.K. (1985). Learning deficits in adolescents with anorexia nervosa. *Journal of Nervous and Mental Disease, 173*(3), 182-4.

Young, J.K. (2010). Anorexia nervosa and estrogen: Current status of the hypothesis. *Neuroscience & Biobehavioral Reviews, 34*, 1195-1200.

Zelazo, P., Müller, U. (2007). Executive function in typical and atypical development. In U. Goswami [ed.], *Handbook of Chilhood Cognitive Development*. Malden, MA: Blackwell Publishers Ltd.

Zuchova, S., Kubena, A.A., Erler, T., Papezova, H. (2013). Neuropsychological variables and clinical status in anorexia nervosa: relationship between visuospatial memory and central coherence and eating disorder symptom severity. *Eating and Weight Disorders, in press*, DOI: 10.1007/s40519-013-0062-7.

In: New Developments in Anorexia Nervosa Research
Editors: Carla Gramaglia and Patrizia Zeppegno

Chapter 3

Healthy Eating Obsession in Women with Anorexia Nervosa: A Case Control Study

Anna Brytek-Matera[*]

University of Social Sciences and Humanities, Campus in Katowice, Poland

Abstract

Introduction: Unhealthy fixation with healthy eating, called "orthorexia nervosa", was first developed by Bratman (1987) in the United States. Several studies investigated the prevalence of orthorexia nervosa in the general population but to our knowledge, there is no reported study involving the prevalence of orthorexia nervosa in people suffering from anorexia nervosa.

Objective: The purpose of the present study was two-fold. The first purpose was to assess whether anorexia nervosa is related to orthorexia nervosa tendency. The second purpose was to determine whether there is a relationship between orthorexia nervosa, body image and eating attitudes in outpatients with anorexia nervosa.

Methods: The sample consisted of 37 women diagnosed with anorexia nervosa (DSM-IV-TR, APA, 2000) and 48 women without a current eating disorder. We used the ORTO-15 test, the Multidimensional Body-Self Relations Questionnaire (MBSRQ) and the Eating Attitude Test (EAT-26).

Results: Among all participants, 37.8% of outpatients with anorexia nervosa and 22.9% of women without eating disorders presented a tendency towards orthorexia nervosa based on the cut-off of 35 for the ORTO-15 test. In women with anorexia nervosa, symptoms of orthorexia nervosa were negatively related to dieting (r = -.612; p < .01), fitness orientation (r = -.481; p < .01), overweight preoccupation (r = -.402; p < .05) and self-classified weight (r = -.402; p < .05).

Conclusion: The present study may increase psychological knowledge about eating-related problems and points out possible future research directions in eating psychology.

[*] Corresponding author: University of Social Sciences and Humanities, Campus in Katowice, Techników 9, 40-326 Katowice, Poland, Email: abrytek-matera@swps.edu.pl.

Keywords: Anorexia nervosa – orthorexia nervosa – body image – eating attitudes

Introduction

Orthorexia nervosa (ON) was described for the first time in the United States and contextually defined as a pathological fixation on healthy eating (Bratman, 1997; Bratman & Knight 2000). According to Bratman and Knight (2000) is characterized by: (a) spending an excessive amount of time (more than 3 hours per day) on thinking about looking for and preparing healthy food; (b) feeling superior to those with different eating habits; (c) following a particular health-food diet rigidly and engaging in compensatory restriction to make up for any dietary indiscretions; (d) associating self-esteem with adherence to the diet (feeling guilt and self-loathing when straying and self-satisfaction when complying), and (e) turning eating "properly" into the central focus of life, at the expense of other personal values, relationships, previously enjoyed activities, and sometimes physical health (Bratman & Knight, 2000; Gleaves, Graham, & Ambwani, 2013).

Orthorexia nervosa does not have any valid diagnostic criteria. It is not recognized as a mental disorder neither by the American Psychiatric Association (it is not listed in the DSM-5) nor by the World Health Organization (it is not present in ICD-10). The first diagnostic criteria for orthorexia nervosa were proposed by Bratman (1997) who created a short 10-item test (The Bratman's Orthorexia Test, Bratman & Knight, 2000), as a screening tool useful for early diagnosis. In Europe, Donini, Marsili, Graziani, Imbriale, and Cannella (2004, 2005) carried out the first empirical research aimed at measuring what was known as a "maniacal obsession about healthy and proper food" and developed a diagnostic instrument for this disorder, the ORTO-15 test. Characteristics of orthorexia nervosa based on the descriptions of Bratman (1997), Donini et al. (2005) and Mathieu (2005) were summarized by Vandereycken (2011) who listed the diagnostic criteria as following: (a) a strong preoccupation with "healthy eating" as manifested by the avoidance of all foods or ingredients considered by the subject to be "unhealthy" such as those containing preservatives or manmade food additives; (b) an unusual concern about one's own health; (c) significant distress or impairment in social, occupational or other important areas of functioning; (d) due to selective eating, malnutrition and weight loss can ensue and (e) the symptoms are not due to another mental disorder (e.g. hypochondriasis or anorexia nervosa) (Vandereycken, 2011).

The literature is not exactly clear about whether orthorexia nervosa is an eating disorder (at all), a variant of a currently recognized eating disorder or a separate disorder. Mac Evilly (2001) suggested that orthorexia nervosa was more aptly to be considered a risk factor for developing a future eating disorder (orthorexia may over time result in an eating disorder as the diet becomes more refined and compulsive), rather than an eating disorder itself and Cartwright (2004) indicated that orthorexia nervosa may precede anorexia nervosa or result from it.

Orthorexia nervosa and other eating disorders (mainly anorexia nervosa) share many similarities (see Figure 1) but also have several differences (see Figure 1). Figure 1 describes the similarities and differences between orthorexia nervosa and anorexia nervosa established on the basis of the whole descriptions given by Arusoĝlu, Kabakçi, Köksal, Kutluay, & Merdol, 2008; Baĝci Boci, Çamur, & Güler, 2007; Bartrina, 2007; Bratman, 1997; Bratman

& Knight, 2010; Catalina Zamora, Bote Bonaechea, García Sánchez, & Ríos Rial, 2005; Fidan, Ertekin, Işikay, & Kirpinar, 2010; Gleaves, Graham, & Ambwani, 2013; Mathieu, 2005, Ramacciotti et al., 2011. It is noteworthy that the parallels and differences between anorexia nervosa and orthorexia nervosa have not been empirically established (Gleaves, Graham, & Ambwani, 2013).

Besides similarities with anorexia nervosa, orthorexia nervosa also demonstrates an overlap with obsessive-compulsive disorder (Catalina Zamora et al., 2005; Bağci Boci, Çamur, & Güler, 2007; Donini et al., 2004). Time-consuming obsessions (thinking about eating in "correct" ways, planning detailed menus) and compulsive behaviours (spending excessive time selecting, preparing, and eating healthful foods in the "proper" manner) are common elements (Gleaves, Graham, & Ambwani, 2013).

Despite increasing research efforts there is a dearth of empirical data regarding the interrelation between anorexia nervosa and orthorexia nervosa. Several studies evaluated the prevalence of orthorexia nervosa among the general population (Donini et al., 2005; Ramacciotti et al., 2011) but to our knowledge, there is no reported study involving the prevalence of orthorexia nervosa among people suffering from anorexia nervosa. The purpose of the present study was two-fold: the first one was to assess whether anorexia nervosa is related to orthorexia nervosa tendency (a prevalence study) and the second one was to determine whether there are relationships between orthorexia nervosa, body image and eating attitudes in outpatients with anorexia nervosa (a correlation study).

Methods

Participants

Thirty-seven outpatients with anorexia nervosa, *diagnosed* by *DSM-IV*-TR criteria (APA, 2000), and 48 women without a current eating disorder participated in the study. The following criteria for inclusion were used:

(1) female recruitment only. Research indicates that anorexia nervosa is the most common of psychiatric disorders among young women, and also that females are more likely to be affected by eating disorders than males. The male-to-female ratio is assessed about 1:10 in adolescents and decreases to 1:20 during young adulthood (Kohn & Golden, 2001). Because of the infrequency of men with anorexia nervosa they were excluded from the current study;

(2) female recruitment only meeting criteria for anorexia nervosa as defined in the revised 4th edition of the Diagnostic and Statistical Manual of Mental Disorders (APA, 2000);

(3) female without a current eating disorder recruitment only if having an index of weight-for-height (BMI) not more greater than 25 kg/m^2, which is the principal cut-off point to overweight and mostly connected with obesity according to The World Health Organization;

(4) adult participants. The present study includes women aged at least 18 years of age, and at most 25 years of age;

(5) at least thirty subjects per group.

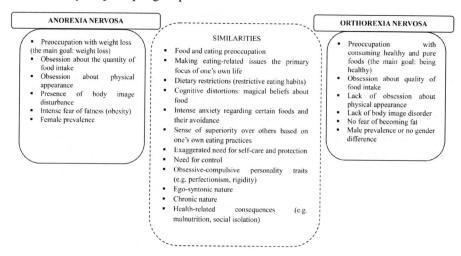

Figure 1. Characteristics of anorexia nervosa and orthorexia nervosa: similarities and differences between both disorders.

Both groups took part voluntarily in the study after informed consent was obtained. The study was approved by the local ethics committee. The average age of the two groups was 22.86 years ($SD = 4.03$) and 21.81 years ($SD = 1.68$) for the clinical and nonclinical samples, respectively. The mean duration of *eating-related problems was* 1.72 years ($SD = .41$) *in outpatients with anorexia nervosa*. The basic characteristics of the participants are shown in Table 1.

Materials

All participants completed the following questionnaires: the ORTO-15 test (Donini et al., 2005), the Multidimensional Body-Self Relations Questionnaire (MBSRQ) (Brown, Cash, & Mikulka, 1990; Cash, 2000) and the Eating Attitude Test (EAT-26) (Garner, Olmsted, Bohr, & Garfinkel, 1982).

The ORTO-15 test

As of now, three questionnaires have been developed to evaluate orthorexia nervosa: the Bratman's Orthorexia Test (Bratman & Knight, 2000), the ORTO-15 test (Donini et al., 2005) and the Eating Habits Questionnaire (Gleaves, Graham, & Ambwani, 2013).

Donini et al. (2004) were recognized as the pioneers in the field of orthorexia nervosa in Europe and created the ORTO-15 test. The ORTO-15 test is a self-report questionnaire that determines the prevalence of highly sensitive behaviour related to healthy and proper nutrition (orthorexia nervosa). It assesses an individual's obsessive attitudes related to the selection, purchase, preparation, and consumption of food that she/he considers to be healthy. The ORTO-15 is based on the short 10-item Bratman's questionnaire. It consists of 15 items (e.g., "Is the taste of food more important than the quality when you evaluate food?") with closed multiple-choice answers (from *always* to *never*). Items receiving a score of 1 correspond to an orthorexic tendency, while those with a score of 4 indicate normal eating habits. A total score below 40 or 35 (an alternative cut-off) indicates symptoms consistent with orthorexia nervosa. In the present study, the Cronbach's alpha internal consistency reliability was .48.

Table 1. Participant characteristics (N = 85)

	Clinical sample (AN) (*N* = 37)	Nonclinical sample (CG) (*N* = 48)
	Number of observation (No.) and percentage (%)	
Family situation		
Parents living together	20 (54.1%)	39 (81.3%)
Separated parents	3 (8.1%)	2 (4.2%)
Divorced parents	11 (29.7%)	4 (8.3 %)
Deceased father	1 (2.7%)	3 (6.3%)
Deceased mother	1 (2.7%)	0
Deceased parents	1 (2.7%)	0
Body satisfaction		
Yes	8 (21.6%)	20 (41.7%)
No	29 (78.4%)	28 (58.3%)
Intentional weight loss[*]		
Dieting	17 (45.9%)	15 (31.3%)
Physical exercise	17 (45.9%)	25 (52.1%)
Using laxatives	5 (13.5%)	1 (2.1%)
Vomiting	5 (13.5%)	0
Starvation	8 (21.6%)	1 (2.1%)

Note. AN = women with anorexia nervosa, CG = control group (women without a current eating disorder).
[*] *The participants* were asked to respond *yes* or *no* to five questions about intentional weight loss. The numbers in the table indicate the percentage of participants responding *yes*.

The Multidimensional Body-Self Relations Questionnaire (MBSRQ)

The Multidimensional Body-Self Relations Questionnaire (Brown et al., 1990; Cash, 2000) is a 69-item self-report questionnaire used for the evaluation of self-attitude aspects of body image. It contains two character measurements, an evaluation and an orientation, in the areas of appearance, fitness and health, as well as an orientation character measurement for illness. In addition, the MBSRQ is composed of three more subscales related to body areas satisfaction, overweight preoccupation, and self-classified weight. The *Appearance evaluation subscale* assesses feelings of physical attractiveness or unattractiveness, satisfaction or dissatisfaction with one's looks (e.g., "I like the way I look without my clothes on"). The *Appearance orientation subscale* measures the extent of investment in one's appearance (e.g., "It is important that I always look good"). The *Fitness evaluation subscale* evaluates feelings of being physically fit or unfit (e.g., "I easily learn physical skills"). The *Fitness orientation subscale* reflects the extent of investment in being physically fit or athletically competent (e.g., "My physical endurance is good"). The *Health evaluation subscale* involves feelings of physical health and/or the freedom from physical illness (e.g., "I am a physically healthy person"). The *Health orientation subscale* reflects the extent of investment in a physically healthy lifestyle (e.g. "Good health is one of the most important things in my life"). The *Illness orientation subscale* assesses the extent of reactivity to being or becoming ill (e.g., "At the first sign of illness, I seek medical advice"). The *Body areas satisfaction subscale* evaluates satisfaction or dissatisfaction with body areas and attributes (e.g., face, weight, overall appearance). The *Overweight preoccupation subscale* measures fat anxiety, dieting, weight vigilance and eating restraint (e.g., "I am on a weight-loss diet"). The *Self-classified weight subscale* assesses self-appraisal of weight from very underweight to very overweight (e.g., "I think I am …").

The MBSRQ uses a Likert type rating scale for each item ranging from *definitely disagree* (1) to *definitely agree* (5) with each statement. High scores indicate positive feelings and satisfaction, while low scores reflect a general dissatisfaction. Internal consistency for the subscales of the MBSRQ ranged from .70 to .91 for males and from .73 to .90 for females (Cash, 2000). The Polish version of the MBSRQ was translated by Schier (2009). In the present study, the Cronbach's alpha internal consistency reliability ranged from .48 to .62.

The Eating Attitude Test (EAT-26)

The Eating Attitude Test (EAT-26) (Garner et al., 1982) is a standardized self-report questionnaire intended to identify abnormal eating habits and concerns about weight. It consists of three scales: dieting, bulimia and food preoccupation and oral control. The *dieting scale* is related to avoidance of fattening foods and the preoccupation with being thinner (e.g., "I think about burning up calories when I exercise"). The *bulimia and food preoccupation scale* describes indications of bulimia and thoughts about food (e.g., "I have gone on eating binges where I feel that I may not be able to stop"). The *oral control scale* explores the self-control of eating and the perceived social pressure to gain weight (e.g., "I take longer than others to eat my meals"). The EAT-26 test consists of 26 items to be scored on a 6-point scale (from *always* to *never*). A total score at or above 20 is considered to be an indicator of a possible eating disorder problem.

The EAT-26 shows a satisfactory internal consistency (Garner et al., 1982). The Polish version of the EAT-26 was translated by Rogoza and Faber (2013). The *Cronbach's alpha coefficient for the total EAT-26 in the present study* was .70.

Statistical Analysis

The statistical analysis, focused on orthorexia nervosa, body image and eating attitudes variables, was carried out on the Statistical Package for the Social Sciences (SPSS version 19.0 for Windows). In the present study the *Student's t-test* for independent samples was used to determine whether women with anorexia nervosa and women without a current eating disorder had significantly different scores on the measured variables. The *Pearson's correlation coefficient* was used to investigate the relationship between orthorexia nervosa, body image and eating attitudes in outpatients with anorexia nervosa and women without a current eating disorder.

Results

Descriptive Statistics

The results indicated that there were no statistically significant differences in the ORTO-15 between the two groups ($t(83) = .125$, $p = .213$) (see Table 2).

The MBSRQ has revealed significant differences between the groups in terms of appearance evaluation ($t(83) = 4.28$, $p = .001$), fitness evaluation ($t(83) = 2.76$, $p = .007$), health evaluation ($t(83) = 2.86$, $p = .005$), overweight preoccupation ($t(83) = -4.79$, $p = .001$), and body areas satisfaction ($t(83) = 4.72$, $p = .001$) (see Table 2).

Table 2. Means and standard deviations for measured variables in outpatients with anorexia nervosa and women without a current eating disorder

Measure	Clinical sample (AN) $M \pm SD$	Nonclinical sample (CG) $M \pm SD$
ORTO-15	34.41 ± 4.78	35.60 ± 4.00
MBSRQ		
Appearance evaluation	$2.66 \pm .93^{***}$	$3.50 \pm .85$
Appearance orientation	$3.62 \pm .96$	$3.93 \pm .75$
Fitness evaluation	$3.03 \pm .98^{**}$	$3.62 \pm .96$
Fitness orientation	$3.21 \pm .84$	$3.46 \pm .87$
Health evaluation	$3.00 \pm .88^{**}$	$3.52 \pm .78$
Health orientation	$3.09 \pm .40$	$3.22 \pm .44$
Illness orientation	$3.00 \pm .89$	$3.32 \pm .71$
Overweight preoccupation	$3.79 \pm 1.00^{***}$	$2.80 \pm .94$
Self-classified weight	$2.98 \pm .69$	$3.01 \pm .30$
Body areas satisfaction	$2.57 \pm .82^{***}$	$3.31 \pm .61$
EAT-26	$27.42 \pm 18.69^{***}$	10.94 ± 10.18
Dieting	$17.92 \pm 11.36^{***}$	7.60 ± 7.38
Bulimia and food preoccupation	$5.14 \pm 5.30^{***}$	2.02 ± 3.00
Oral control	$4.36 \pm 4.59^{***}$	1.31 ± 1.76

Note. AN = women with anorexia nervosa, CG = control group (women without a current eating disorder), MBSRQ – the Multidimensional Body-Self Relations Questionnaire, EAT-26 – the Eating Attitude Test.
$** p < .01$; $*** p < .001$

We found *statistically significant differences* between each group on the total EAT-26 score ($t(82) = -5.17$, $p = 0.001$), dieting ($t(82) = -5.03$, $p = 0.001$), bulimia and food preoccupation ($t(82) = -3.41$, $p = 0.001$) as well as oral control ($t(82) = -4.20$, $p = 0.001$) (see Table 2).

Means and standard deviations for orthorexia nervosa, self-attitude aspects of body image and eating attitudes for women with and without a current eating disorder are presented in Table 2.

Prevalence

Among all participants, 37.8% of women with anorexia nervosa (N = 14) and 22.9% of women without eating disorders (N = 11) presented tendency towards orthorexia nervosa based on the cut-off of 35 for the ORTO-15 test.

Correlation Coefficients

The statistical analysis has shown that in clinical samples orthorexia nervosa tendency was significantly negatively correlated with dieting ($p < .01$), fitness orientation ($p < .01$), overweight preoccupation ($p < .05$) and self-classified weight ($p < .05$) (see Table 3).

Table 3. Correlations between orthorexia nervosa, eating attitudes and body image among outpatients with anorexia nervosa ($N = 37$)

Orthorexia nervosa (ORTO-15)
Dieting (EAT-26)
Fitness orientation (MBSRQ)
Overweight preoccupation (MBSRQ)
Self-classified weight (MBSRQ)

Note. EAT-26 – the Eating Attitude Test, MBSRQ – the Multidimensional Body-Self Relations Questionnaire.
* $p < .05$; ** $p < .01$.

Table 4. Correlations between orthorexia nervosa, eating attitudes and body image among women without a current eating disorder ($N = 48$)

Orthorexia nervosa (ORTO-15)
Dieting (EAT-26)
Fitness evaluation (MBSRQ)
Fitness orientation (MBSRQ)
Oral control (EAT-26)
Health orientation (MBSRQ)
Appearance evaluation (MBSRQ)
Health evaluation (MBSRQ)

Note. EAT-26 – the Eating Attitude Test, MBSRQ – the Multidimensional Body-Self Relations Questionnaire.
* $p < .05$; ** $p < .01$.

However, in women without a current eating disorder orthorexia nervosa tendency was negatively related to dieting ($p < .01$), fitness evaluation ($p < .05$), fitness orientation ($p < .05$), oral control ($p < .05$) health orientation ($p < .05$) appearance evaluation ($p < .05$) and health evaluation ($p < .05$) (see Table 4).

Conclusion

To our knowledge, this is the first study evaluating the prevalence of orthorexia nervosa among women with anorexia nervosa. The results revealed a higher frequency of orthorexia nervosa for outpatients with anorexia nervosa (37.8%) than for women without a current eating disorder (22.9%), based on the cut-off of 35 at the ORTO-15 test. This prevalence is definitely much higher than that found in studies focused on the German general population (1 to 2%; Barthels & Pietrowsky, 2012), the Italian general population (6.9%; Donini et al.), the Austrian female dieticians (12.8%; Kinzl, Hauer, Traweger, & Kiefer, 2006) and the Italian athletes (28% for female athletes; Segura-García et al., 2012). A previous work by Kinzl et al. (2006), suggested that individuals (in the study there were dieticians) with orthorexic behaviours experienced past eating disorders more frequently than people without orthorexic behaviours. The high prevalence of orthorexia nervosa in our clinical population may signify that both disorders often co-occur or may also mean that anorexia nervosa could develop into an orthorexia nervosa tendency.

In the present study we also examined the relationship between orthorexia nervosa, body image and eating attitudes in outpatients with anorexia nervosa. Our data supported the conclusion that orthorexia nervosa in women with anorexia nervosa, was negatively related to dieting, fitness orientation, overweight preoccupation and self-classified weight. Following the study results we might suppose that women with anorexia nervosa who tend to avoid eating fat and are more preoccupied with being thin have lower orthorexic tendencies, that as they do more exercise activities to enhance their fitness or be physically fit, their tendency towards orthorexia nervosa decreases. We might also suppose that as outpatients' concentration on dieting, eating restraint and weight vigilance (overweight preoccupation) increases, their level of orthorexic behaviours decreases.

Our results partially confirm recent research (Brytek-Matera, Krupa, Poggiogalle, & Donini, 2014) among the general population, which revealed that orthorexia nervosa was negatively associated with disordered eating behaviours. The same results were obtained in two American studies conducted by McInerney-Ernst (2011) and by Shah (2012). The Polish data (Brytek-Matera et al., 2014) indicate that orthorexia nervosa is negatively *linked* to *eating disorder-related behaviours and attitudes*: dieting, bulimic behaviours and thoughts about food as well as the control of eating and the perceived pressure from others to gain weight. Orthorexia nervosa could not be considered as a new eating disorder (it did not include the most characteristic symptoms of anorexia and bulimia nervosa such as preoccupation with weight loss, fear of becoming fat, overestimation of body size). Unlike eating disorders which involve obsessions about the quantity of food intake, orthorexia nervosa results from an obsession about quality of food intake (Bratman & Knight, 2000). However, some authors (Bartrina, 2007; Catalina Zamora et al., 2005; Mathieu, 2005) emphasized the similarities between orthorexia nervosa and other eating disorders: preoccupation with foods (e.g. rigid or restrictive eating habits, restrictions on the consumption of forbidden foods, malnutrition), experiencing symptoms of the disorder as ego-syntonic, and genetic predisposition to perfectionism and need for control.

In contrast to our results, Varga & Máté (2010) reported that symptoms of orthorexia nervosa were highly associated with the maladaptive eating attitudes and behaviors associated with anorexia nervosa among a population composed of university *students*.

A tendency for orthorexia nervosa appears to be connected to disordered *eating* and *related attitudes* (Fidan et al., 2010). The results of a previous research by Arusoğlu et al. (2008) suggest that orthorexic tendency could be related to abnormal eating attitudes (food preoccupation, dieting, slow eating, clandestine eating, body image for thinness, vomiting and laxative abuse as well as perceived social pressure to gain weight) and that obsessive-compulsive symptoms has a significant effect on orthorexic tendency in the general population. In addition, eating attitude was noted to be a good predictor of orthorexic tendency (Arusoğlu et al., 2008). The results of a previous work by Eriksson, Baigi, Marklund, & Lindgren (2008) suggest that *high level of internationalization* of Western norms on the slim body ideal were linked to a high tendency towards orthorexia nervosa as well as to a high awareness of Western appearance *ideals* in female fitness participants. In addition, a high social anxiety connected to appearance is associated with high orthorexia nervosa tendency (Eriksson et al., 2008). Orthorexia nervosa, as well as other eating disorders, seems to be connected with social pressures: the second are influenced by the thin ideal standard of beauty whereas the first is affected by the requirement for healthy living (Martins, Alvarenga, Vargas, Sato, & Scagliusi, 2011).

Our research study has some limitations. First, outpatients participants were receiving eating disorder treatment and, therefore, may not be representative of the population of individuals with anorexia nervosa. Second, we used only self-report measures. Third, people in the control group were not screened to exclude psychiatric disorders.

Although the number of publications on orthorexia nervosa has increased in the last decade, there is still relatively scant research on this topic. In the future, more research is needed to broaden the knowledge about the bio-psycho-social model of orthorexia nervosa, the kind of disorder it is (eating disorder, obsessive-compulsive disorder, mood disorder, anxiety disorder), its diagnostic criteria and its co-existence with other disorders.

Acknowledgments

The author thanks Magdalena Krupa and her team from the Polish National Center for Eating Disorders for putting a lot of effort into collecting the data. In addition, she thanks all the participants for their time and effort. The author is very grateful to Annick Obermann for her English correction.

References

Alvarenga, M. S., Martins, M. C., Sato, K. S., Vargas, S. V., Philippi, S. T. & Scagliusi, F. B. (2012). Orthorexia Nervosa Behavior in a Sample of Brazilian Dietitians Assessed by the Portuguese Version of ORTO-15. *Eating and Weight Disorders - Studies on Anorexia, Bulimia and Obesity, 17*(1), e29-35.

American Psychiatric Association. (2000). *Diagnostic and Statistical: Manual of Mental Disorders DSM-IV-TR (Text Revision)*. 4th edition. Washington, DC: American Psychiatric Press.

Arusoğlu, G., Kabakçi, E., Köksal, G. & Merdol, T. K. (2008). Orthorexia Nervosa and Adaptation of ORTO-11 into Turkish. *Türk Psikiyatri Dergisi, 19*(3), 283-291.

Bağci Bosi, A. T., Camur, D. & Güler, C. (2007). Prevalence of Orthorexia Nervosa in Resident Medical Doctors in the Faculty of Medicine (Ankara, Turkey). *Appetite, 49*(3), 661-766.

Barthels, F. & Pietrowsky, R. (2012). Orthorectic Eating Behaviour - Nosology and Prevalence Rates. *Psychotherapie Psychosomatik Medizinische Psychologie, 62*(12), 445-499.

Bartrina, J. A. (2007). Ortorexia o la obsesión por la dieta saludable. *Archivos Latinoamericanos de Nutrición, 57*(4), 313-315.

Bratman, S. (1997). Health Food Junkie: Obsession with Dietary Perfection Can Sometimes Do More Harm Than Good, Says One who Has Been There. *Yoga Journal, 136*, 42-46.

Bratman, S. & Knight, D. (2000). *Health Food Junkies. Orthorexia Nervosa: Overcoming the Obsession with Healthful Eating.* New York: Broadway Books.

Brown, T. A., Cash, T. F. & Mikulka, P. J. (1990). Attitudinal body image assessment: Factor analysis of the Body-Self Relations Questionnaire. *Journal of Personality Assessment, 55*, 135-144.

Brytek-Matera, A., Krupa, M., Poggiogalle, E., & Donini, L.M. (2014). Adaptation of the ORTO-15 test to Polish women and men. *Eating and Weight Disorders - Studies on Anorexia, Bulimia and Obesity.* DOI 10.1007/s40519-014-0100-0.

Cash, T. F. (2000). *The multidimensional Body-Self Relations Questionnaire. MBSRQ User's Manual.* 3rd Revision. Norfolk Virgina: Old Dominion University.

Cartwright, M. M. (2004). Eating Disorder Emergencies: Understanding the Medical Complexities of the Hospitalized Eating Disordered Patient. *Critical Care Nursing Clinics of North America, 16*(4), 515-530.

Catalina Zamora, M. L., Bote Bonaechea, B., García Sánchez, F. & Ríos Rial, B. (2005). Ortorexia nerviosa. ¿Un nuevo trastorno de la conducta alimentaria? *Actas Españolas de Psiquiatría, 33*(1), 66-68.

Donini, L. M., Marsili, D., Graziani, M. P., Imbriale, M. & Cannella, C. (2004). Orthorexia Nervosa: A Preliminary Study with a Proposal for Diagnosis and an Attempt to Measure the Dimension of the Phenomenon. *Eating and Weight Disorders - Studies on Anorexia, Bulimia and Obesity, 9*(2), 151-157.

Donini, L. M., Marsili, D., Graziani, M. P., Imbriale, M. & Cannella, C. (2005). Orthorexia Nervosa: Validation of a Diagnosis Questionnaire. *Eating and Weight Disorders - Studies on Anorexia, Bulimia and Obesity, 10*, e28-32.

Eriksson, L., Baigi, A., Marklund, B. & Lindgren, E. C. (2008). Social Physique Anxiety and Sociocultural Attitudes Toward Appearance Impact on Orthorexia Test in Fitness Participants. *Scandinavian Journal of Medicine & Science in Sports, 18*(3), 389-394.

Fidan, T., Ertekin, V., Işikay, S. & Kirpinar I. (2010). Prevalence of Orthorexia among Medical Students in Erzurum, Turkey. *Comprehensive Psychiatry, 51*(1), 49-54.

Garner, D. M., Olmsted, M. P., Bohr, Y. & Garfinkel, P. E. (1982). The Eating Attitudes Test: Psychometric Features and Clinical Correlates. *Psychological Medicine, 12*(4), 871-878.

Graham, E., Gleaves, D. H. & Ambwani, S. (2004). Measuring "Orthorexia": Development of the Eating Habits Questionnaire. *International Journal of Educational and Psychological Assessment, 12*(2), 1-18.

Kinzl, J. F., Hauer, K., Traweger, C. & Kiefer, I. (2006). Orthorexia Nervosa in Dieticians. *Psychotherapy and Psychosomatics*, 75(6), 395-396.

Kohn, M. & Golden, N. H. (2001). Eating disorders in children and adolescents: epidemiology, diagnosis and treatment. *Paediatric Drugs*, 3(2), 91-99.

Mac Evilly, C. (2001). The Price of Perfection. *Nutrition Bulletin*, 26(4), 275-276.

Martins, M. C. T., Alvarenga, M. S., Vargas, S. V. A., Sato, K. S. C. J. & Scagliusi, F. B. (2011). Ortorexia nervosa: reflexões sobre um novo conceito. *Revista de Nutrição*, 24(2), 345-357.

Mathieu, J. (2005). What is Orthorexia? *Journal of the American Dietetic Association*, 105(10), 1510-1512.

McInerney-Ernst, E. M. (2011). *Orthorexia Nervosa: Real Construct or Newest Social Trend?* Dissertation. University of Missouri-Kansas City.

Ramacciotti, C. E., Perrone, P., Coli, E., Burgalassi, A., Conversano, C., Massimetti, G. & Dell'Osso, L. (2011). Orthorexia Nervosa in the General Population: A Preliminary Screening Using a Self-Administered Questionnaire (ORTO-15). *Eating and Weight Disorders - Studies on Anorexia, Bulimia and Obesity*, 16(2), e127-130.

Rogoza, R. & Faber, K. (2013, May). Estymacja rozpowszechnienia problemu zaburzeń odżywiania za pomocą polskiej wersji kwestionariusza EAT-26 [*Estimating the Prevalence of Eating Disorders Using the Polish Adaptation of the EAT-26*]. Oral presentation presented at the 22nd General Polish Conference on Developmental Psychology, Gdańsk.

Schier, K. (2009). *Piękne brzydactwo. Psychologiczna problematyka obrazu ciała i jego zaburzeń.* Warszawa: SCHOLAR.

Segura-García, C., Papaianni, M. C., Caglioti, F., Procopio, L., Nisticò, C. G., Bombardiere, L., Ammendolia, A., Rizza, P., De Fazio, P. & Capranica, L. (2012). Orthorexia Nervosa: a Frequent Eating Disordered Behavior in Athletes. *Eating and Weight Disorders - Studies on Anorexia, Bulimia and Obesity*, 17(4), e226-233.

Shah, S. M. (2012). *Orthorexia Nervosa: Healthy Eating or Eating Disorder?* Master Thesis. Eastern Illinois University.

Vandereycken, W. (2011). Media Hype, Diagnostic Fad or Genuine Disorder? Professionals' Opinions about Night Eating Syndrome, Orthorexia, Muscle Dysmorphia, and Emetophobia. *Eating Disorders*, 19(2), 145-155.

Varga, M. & Máté, G. (2010). Eating disturbances in orthorexia nervosa. XIII annual meeting of the European Association for Consultation-Liaison Psychiatry and Psychosomatics (EACLPP) XXVIII European Conference on Psychosomatic Research (ECPR): A selection of the best abstracts submitted. *Journal of Psychosomatic Research*, 68, 672-673.

In: New Developments in Anorexia Nervosa Research
Editors: Carla Gramaglia and Patrizia Zeppegno

ISBN: 978-1-63117-551-0
© 2014 Nova Science Publishers, Inc.

Chapter 4

Expressed Emotion in Anorexia Nervosa

Carla Gramaglia[*] *and Patrizia Zeppegno*[†]
Institute of Psychiatry, Department of Translational Medicine,
Università del Piemonte Orientale "Amedeo Avogadro", Novara, Italy

Abstract

Although the role of family dynamics in the development and possibly maintenance of anorexia nervosa has been widely acknowledged (Bruch, 1973; Selvini Palazzoli, 2006; Minuchin, 1978) for a long time, the concept of expressed emotion in this disorder has not received much attention. This is surprising, considering the concept of "anorexic family" suggested by Minuchin (1978), i.e. the entanglement between anorexia and family dynamics, especially after the onset of the eating disorder itself.

The concept of expressed emotion was first developed to measure the emotional temperature of the family. With more detail, it is a marker of the intensity of the emotional response to a stressful situation like having an ill relative. At first, the focus of expressed emotion research was on schizophrenic families (Brown, 1972), according to the clinical observation that schizophrenic patients' outcome significantly correlated with the features of the social group patients returned to after inpatient or residential treatment. It was observed that sometimes it was inadvisable for patients to return to their own families, since families' expressed emotion played a relevant role as far as relapse and disease course and outcome are concerned.

Our aim is to describe the concept of expressed emotion, its measures and the main findings of the current literature about this construct in anorexia nervosa.

[*] Carla Gramaglia e-mail: carla.gramaglia@gmail.com.
[†] Patrizia Zeppegno e-mail: patrizia.zeppegno@med.unipmn.it.

Abbreviations

AESED	Accommodation and Enabling Scale for Eating Disorders
AN	Anorexia Nervosa
ANBN	Anorexia and Bulimia Nervosa
AOU	Azienda Ospedaliera Universitaria
BN	Bulimia Nervosa
BDSEE	Brief Dyadic Scale of Expressed Emotion
CC	Critical Comments
CF	Cystic Fibrosis
CFI	Camberwell Family Interview
CFT	Conjoint Family Therapy
CSE	Caregiving Self-Efficacy
DSM-III-R	Diagnostic and Statistical Manual of Mental Disorders III-Revised
ECHO	Expert Carers Helping Others
EDE	Eating Disorder Examination Interview
EDE-Q	Eating Disorders Examination Questionnaire
EDI-2	Eating Disorder Inventory-2
EDNOS	Eating Disorder Not Otherwise Specified
EDs	Eating Disorders
EE	Expressed Emotion
EOI	Emotional Over-Involvement
FBT	Family Based Treatment
FMSS	Five Minute Speech Sample
FQ	Family Questionnaire
HADS	Hospital Anxiety and Depression Scale
HOS	Hostility
LEE	Level of Expressed Emotion Scale
NICE	National Institute for Clinical Excellence
POS	Positive Remarks
SCFI	Structured Clinical Family Interview
SFT	Separated Family Therapy
WAR	Warmth

Introduction

Despite the widely acknowledged clinical portrayals of Eating Disorder families, the number of empirical studies including a structured assessment of the interaction patterns of Anorexia Nervosa (AN) families is still scant. The aim of this chapter is to describe the main findings about Expressed Emotion (EE) in the families of patients with AN, and to describe the impact of such construct on course and outcome of the disorder.

The familial behavioral and emotional environment and the quality of family relationships have raised the interest of clinical researchers because of their relation with expression, development, maintenance and treatment response of psychiatric and physical disorders. To investigate the role of these issues the necessity to develop specific measures of family life emerged. In this context, one specific field of research was identified with the development of the construct of EE, which proved to be a valid and reliable index of family relationships and is now one of the most well-established measures of family affective attitudes.

The concept of EE was developed in the 1950s as a measure of the emotional temperature of the family or, in other words, as a measure of the intensity of the familial emotional response to a stressful situation like having an ill relative. The EE construct was developed by Rutter and Brown (1966) during the course of their studies about the family life-related factors associated to relapse in schizophrenic patients. They observed a significant correlation among schizophrenic patients' outcome and the features of the social group to which patients returned after inpatient or residential treatment. It was found that sometimes it was inadvisable for patients to return to their own families, because of "something" in the emotional environment of the family, i.e. EE, which seemed to play a role in relapse, disease course and outcome. EE refers to the tone, pitch and speed of positive and negative comments, as well as to the content of comments, the affective attitudes, behaviors, emotions, and feelings of a relative (or a significant other as well) directed towards a psychiatric patient.

Broadly speaking, it is a measure of the affective family climate towards an ill family member.

Leff and Vaughn (1985) described high EE as characterized by four attitudes or response styles:

1   high levels of intrusiveness (repeated attempts to establish contact or to offer unsolicited and often critical advice);
2   highly emotional response to patients' illness (angry responses, acute distress reactions which upset the patient);
3   negative attitude towards patients' illness (i.e., doubting that they have control over symptoms; blaming patients or assuming them responsible for their condition);
4   low level of tolerance and high expectations of the patients (i.e., relatives are not really convinced about patients' illness, or are intolerant of their behaviors and social impairments).

The EE affective attitudes and behaviors refer to key aspects of family interaction and typically include five dimensions: criticism, hostility, emotional over-involvement, positive comments and warmth. With more detail, the five dimensions describing EE are the following:

1   Critical Comments (CC): refer to the frequency of critical and derogatory remarks about the ill person;
2   Hostility (HOS): reflects a generalized critical and rejection attitude towards the ill individual;
3   Emotional Over-Involvement (EOI): reflects the emotional investment in the ill person;
4   Warmth (WAR): is a global measure of acceptance of the ill person;
5   Positive Remarks (POS): describe the frequency of praising, appreciating and approving comments towards the ill person.

Of these five scales, CC and EOI are considered the most powerful predictors, according to the existing literature.

Families can be subdivided into two groups, low and high EE. Relatives with low EE are calm, tolerant, flexible in dealing with problems, and more sensitive to patient's needs; on the other hand, relatives with high EE are intrusive, intolerant to patients' needs, showing a negative attitude to the patient's illness, inflexible, with high expectations of the patient, and they tend to repeat negative interaction patterns (Leff and Vaughn, 1985).

However, it should be considered that EE is not a static construct but it changes over time: hence it should be considered as "an aspect of ongoing family interactions" (Kuipers and Bebbington, 1988), the family life's "blood pressure" (Kuipers, Leff and Lam, 1992), or the "emotional temperature" of the family (Vaughn, 1989). Moreover, EE is thought to decrease over the treatment period (Van Furth, Van Strien, Martina, Van Son, Hendrick and Van England, 1996).

Most studies of EE in psychiatric disorders have dealt with schizophrenia and depression (Vaughn and Leff, 1976; Parker and Hadzi-Pavlovic, 1990), and correlations have been reported between high EE scores and poorer treatment outcome and relapse. High EE families are those displaying more CCs, HOS and EOI compared to low EE families. High EE seems to be a stressor for patients, and hence may be associated with relapse. Moreover, also the amount of time that patients and caregivers spend together predicts the relapse rate (Bebbington and Kuipers, 1994).

EE in Eating Disorders (EDs) has been investigated as well, even if less extensively than in schizophrenia (Szmukler, Eisler, Russell and Dare, 1985; Sepulveda, Todd, Whitaker, Grover, Stahl and Treasure, 2009). Although relatively low in prevalence (0.7-1% for Anorexia Nervosa and 1-5% for Bulimia Nervosa) (Fairburn and Harrison, 2003; Hoek and Van Hoeken, 2003; Fairburn, Hay, Welch, 1993; Murray, 2003), EDs are chronic illnesses requiring long-term care and significant involvement of carers including family members, partners or friends. EE scores are usually low in ED families and suggestions have been raised about the need to use different cutoffs from those used in schizophrenic families. Nonetheless, although several studies have found low EE levels in ED families, these seem to play an important role in ED outcome. High EE has been associated with dropout from treatment (including psychotherapy) and poor treatment outcome in patients with AN (Szmukler, Eisler, Russell and Dare, 1985; Sepulveda, Todd, Whitaker, Grover, Stahl and Treasure, 2009), although the relationship between EE and treatment outcome in EDs is still poorly understood.

One last issue: most EE studies in EDs have used objective measures and structured interviews to assess the actual criticism, hostility and over-involvement of caregivers, but over the past years there has also been a focus on patients' perceptions of caregivers' EE. A dual approach including objective measures of caregivers' actual EE and measures of patients' perceptions of their caregivers' emotional stance would likely provide a more thorough and balanced perspective in the assessment of the patient-caregiver dyad (Medina-Pradas, Navarro, Lopez, Grau and Obiols, 2011).

This may also allow the focus to be moved from the "negative" aspects of EE (criticism, hostility, over-involvement), to the "positive" ones (positive comments and warmth), a resource which should be strengthened and valued. For example, warmth may help reduce patients' stress level (Lopez, Hipke, Polo, Jenkins, Karno and Vaughn, 2004) and therefore improve patients' outcome.

Expressed Emotion and Family Dynamics in Eating Disorders

The experience of caregiving is influenced by patient, carer, patient-carer relationship and care-related characteristics, and entails physical and psychological distress (Baronet, 1999). Research about family distress and caregivers' burden in psychiatric disorders has focused mainly on schizo-phrenia and affective disorders, while other diagnoses have been almost neglected (Schulz and Rossler, 2005). Anyway, caregiving for relatives with a psychiatric disorder, independently of diagnosis, is likely to elicit strong emotional reactions in carers, including hopelessness, anger, feelings of guilt and shame. All these emotional reactions may contribute to changes in family affective environment and EE, eventually resulting in critical and/or over-protective attitudes and behaviors (Hooley, 2007).

AN is a serious disorder with an onset which typically occurs during adolescence. Young women with age ranging from 15 to 22 years are the highest risk group; hence many patients are likely to be still living with their family of origin and to rely upon a carer such as a parent for significant assistance with their recovery. Carers may be insecure about how to help best and may fear to cause more harm than benefits. Moreover, they may feel powerless and hopeless and believe that they are not really able to help changing the situation (Highet, Thompson and King, 2005; Perkins, Winn, Murray, Murphy and Schmidt, 2004).

The subjective experience of caring for an individual affected by an ED is to date understudied although preliminary results suggest that caregivers' burden in AN may be similar to that of psychotic patients' relatives (Graap, Bleich, Herbst, Scherzinger, Trostmann and Wancata, 2008; Treasure, Murphy, Szmukler, Todd, Gavan and Joyce, 2001). Distress and burden in caregivers of ED and particularly AN patients may be expected to be high, considering the entanglement of both severe physical and psychological conditions in such disorders and their effects on significant others' distress. People with AN may be highly dependent upon their carers and dominate and control carers' time asking for obsessively precise day-to-day routine especially as far as meals are concerned. Conflict and discussions in the family environment may lead to fractures due to the excessive demands of the ill person and on complex interpersonal interactions (Whitney, Murray, Gavan, Todd, Whitaker and Treasure, 2005; Monteleone, Treasure, Santonastaso, Favaro and Brambilla, 2005; Gilbert, Shaw and Notar, 2000; Hillege, Beale and McMaster, 2006).

While the impact of caring for a person with AN on family environment has not been thoroughly investigated, the role of family dynamics in the development and possibly maintenance of AN has been widely acknowledged since Bruch's (1973) and Selvini Palazzoli's (2006) contributions, and even earlier, dating back to the first descriptions of AN on behalf of Gull (1874) and Lasegue (1873). Gull himself proposed that AN patients would benefit being separated from their families, because some patterns of family interactions might be illness-engendering. Broadly speaking, Bruch (1970), Selvini-Palazzoli (1970, 1974) and Minuchin and coworkers (1975, 1978) described the family of patients with AN as overly close, with problems regarding conflicts, which are either avoided or poorly resolved, and characterized by confusion as regards intergenerational boundaries.

It has been suggested that the families of patients with AN and BN share some specific qualities (Dare, 1983; Selvini-Palazzoli, 1974; Sargent, Liebman and Silver, 1985). These have been well described by Minuchin and coworkers (Minuchin, Baker, Rosman, Liebman,

Milman and Todd, 1975; Minuchin, Rosman and Baker, 1978) who proposed the concept of "psychosomatic family" and "anorexic family". Four transactional characteristics were identified in the anorexic patient's family and supposed to play the role of trigger or maintenance factors: enmeshment, overprotectiveness, rigidity and lack of conflict resolution (Minuchin, Baker, Rosman, Liebman, Milman and Todd, 1975; Minuchin, Rosman and Baker, 1978). Minuchin suggested that the patient is a psychologically vulnerable child whose psychosomatic symptoms play an important role in the family's pattern of conflict avoidance. For example, the specific role of the ill child in conflict avoidance is a positive reinforcement for symptoms, and the child's psychosomatic symptoms may be a homeostatic mechanism regulating family balance and transactions.

As already underscored, an interaction between EE and abnormal eating behaviors has been suggested, regarding a possible role of EE in the development and maintenance of full-syndrome AN and BN (Butzlaff and Hooley, 1998; Bebbington and Kuipers, 1994). Nevertheless, it should be also considered how disruptive the impact of the ED can be on the family and on parents who become the primary caregivers of a severely ill offspring. The causal link between EE and pathology may be at least partially reverted; there is likely to be a bi-directional relationship between illness and EE, since not only high parental EE may reinforce and worsen patients' symptoms, but patients' symptoms and behaviors as well are likely to elicit higher EE in relatives (Szmukler, Eisler, Russell and Dare, 1985; Fairburn and Bohn, 2004). Moreover, caregivers of AN patients seem to be bound to unique demands, stemming from the severity and enduring course of the disorder.

EE may influence caregivers' distress, and high levels of negative EE in carers may lead indeed to higher levels of perceived burden, whereas a reduction of EE levels may be associated with its reduction. The mechanisms underpinning high EE are not clear. Parents' understanding of illness-related issues and perception of their offspring disorders have an impact on their EE, particularly CC and EOI. Parents assuming that the ill offspring have volitional control and choice over their behavior may be more critical, while those assuming that patients are passive and impotent victims of the illness may be more overinvolved (Van Os, Marcelis, Germeys, Graven and Delespaul, 2001). To further complicate this issue, EE may be related to patients' illness duration and to parents' mood disorders.

As stated by a recent review (Zabala, Macdonald and Treasure, 2009) about caregiving burden, psychological distress, and EE in families of ED patients, the majority of studies has found that carers displayed high levels of EE, mostly CCs and EOI.

However, mean CC scores were much lower than those found in schizophrenic families and more likely to reach the cutoff scores established for depression (Zabala, Macdonald and Treasure, 2009; Hodes and Le Grange, 1993; Van Furth, Van Strien, Martina, Van Son, Hendrickx and Van Engeland, 1996). Moreover, Zabala and coworkers (2009) suggested that the levels of CFI and SCFI CCs in families of older patients with longer illness duration are the highest. Given the low number of CCs, it can be raised the hypothesis that parents may find it difficult to express overt criticism towards a severely underweight anorexic kid. Moreover, it has been suggested that in AN families, and broadly speaking ED families, EOI may be a more characteristic response than CC.

Parents (especially mothers) are likely to feel highly anxious because of the severity of their kids' disorder and to show higher level of over-protectiveness; anyway, also regarding EOI, few cases scored above the cutoff point of 3 established for schizophrenia (Zabala, Macdonald and Treasure, 2009).

Researches performed with the FMSS have found high EE families ranging from 21 to 54% of studied samples, and - as already underscored for CFI and SCFI studies - the highest levels of EE were found in families with older and long-standing patients with longer illness duration. However, data about the impact of EE on the course and outcome of AN are still scant and limited by the following:

1   very few centers have focused on this issue;
2   different measures of EE have been used across studies;
3   most studies lack a control group;
4   most studies have a cross-sectional design, despite the time-changing nature of EE.

Hence further research concerning EE in EDs, and particularly AN, may want to investigate the use of time-saving and effective self-report measures of EE (Zabala, Macdonald and Treasure, 2009).

Assessment of Expressed Emotion

The psychometric instruments designed for the assessment of EE include the following:

1. Camberwell Family Interview (CFI; Vaughn and Leff, 1976)

The CFI is a measure of the family's actual EE and is therefore considered the gold standard for the assessment of the family emotional climate. It is a semi-structured interview which requires about 1-2 hours to conduct and 3 hours to code in its complete format. Moreover, it requires an extended period of training to achieve a reliable rating. Because administration is quite time consuming and cumbersome, and because of the extensive training required, the application of the CFI is hard in research settings and even more in everyday clinical practice.

The CFI is rated along five dimensions: criticism or critical comments (CC), hostility (HOS), emotional overinvolvement (EOI), warmth (WAR) and positive remarks (POS). The first and last dimensions are scored as frequency scores, while the others as global scores ranging from 0 to 5, except for hostility which ranges from 0 to 3. The CFI investigates several aspects of family life, including patients' desired and undesired behaviors; it addresses the onset and development of the illness, the impact it has on family life, family members' quarreling and irritability, patients' illness-related symptoms, participation in everyday household tasks, and daily activities. Ratings are made according to the content of the interview as well as on the interviewee's tone of voice.

According to the Anglo-Saxon studies concerning schizophrenia, CFI EE is dichotomized in high and low; specifically, a high EE rating is given when a relative makes 6 or more CCs or expresses any hostility or has an EOI rating of 3 or higher. To adapt the CFI to the ED field, the questions specific for psychotic symptoms have been deleted and instead questions related to ED symptomatology have been added (Van Furth, Van Strien, Martina, Van Son, Hendrickx and Van Engeland, 1996). Moreover, because ED families score lower than schizophrenic ones on EE measures including the CFI, showing a much more muted style of interaction, suggestions have been raised that they may require the use of different and lower cutoffs, especially regarding CCs. Anyway, in ED research a predictive cutoff point for CFI CC has not been clearly established; for example Hoste et al. (2012) used the following to describe high EE: ≥ 1 CC, any HOS, ≥ 3 EOI. An alternative to the traditional division into high or low EE (according to the level of CC and EOI) has been proposed for ED research, treating CFI EE variables as continuous ones (Rein, Perdereau, Curt, Jeammet, Fermanian and Gokart, 2006; Van Furth, Van Strien, Martina, Van Son, Hendrickx and Van Engeland, 1996).

2. Structured Clinical Family Interview (SCFI; Kinston and Loader, 1984)

The SCFI is a measure of family life in which all family members are interviewed together at the same time. The format is that of a semi-structured interview, and it can be used in non-labeled families (families without a referred patient) as well as in families with a referred patient. The SCFI covers several aspects of family life which all family members are encouraged to discuss.

The interview includes questions on family cohesiveness, similarities and differences between family members, roles and responsibilities in the household, conflict, discipline, decision making, and the family's involvement with extended family and the community.

EE ratings are made from the videotaped interview. Ratings are the same as described for the CFI, i.e. CC and POS are measured as frequency counts, HOS is a global measure rated on a 0-3 scale, WAR and EOI are global measures rated 0-5.

Compared to the CFI, the SCFI is much more economical in time, which may help to bridge the gap between everyday clinical practice and research, making it more feasible to assess the construct of EE. Regarding EDs, the use of the SCFI for EE ratings was validated in 16 families against the CFI (Hodes, Dare, Dodge and Eisler, 1999).

3. Five Minute Speech Sample (FMSS; Magaña, Goldstein, Karno, Miklowitz, Jenkins and Falloon, 1986)

The FMSS consists in a 5 minute audio-recorded free speech of a family member who has been asked to talk about the ill relative. Coding of the FMSS requires about 15 minutes, so this measure is much more time-saving than the CFI. The FMSS allows discriminating high and low EE families according to the Critical and Emotional Overinvolvement Dimensions.

Ratings of high or low EE are made possible on the CFI and the FMSS albeit using different subscales, i.e. CC, HOS and EOI for the CFI and Critical EE and high Emotional Overinvolvement EE for the FMSS.

Studies comparing the FMSS and the CFI have been performed and a considerable overlap has been found in families of schizophrenic patients (Magaña, Goldstein, Karno, Miklowitz, Jenkins and Falloon, 1986; Malla, Kazarian, Barnes and Cole, 1991).

4. Level of Expressed Emotion Scale (LEE; Cole and Kazarian, 1988)

The LEE is a 60-item subjective self-report measure based on the conceptual framework developed by Vaughn and Leff (1976).

It measures the EE from a relative (or significant other) perceived from the patient's perspective.

The LEE assesses 4 dimensions, each described by 15 true/false questions: intrusiveness, emotional response, attitude toward the illness, tolerance/ expectations concerning the patient. A high EE is described by a score above the median (Cole and Kazarian, 1993), and anyway, the higher the LEE score, the higher the level of EE. Intrusiveness and tolerance/expectation subscales have been significantly correlated with the CFI CC scale (Cole and Kazarian, 1993).

It should be underscored that perception of EE is not the same as the evaluation of actual family EE, and that such a subjective perception of the family EE by the LEE may reduce the sensitivity of the instrument. As for other kinds of self-assessment, the current psychopathology influences the response to the questionnaire items, and moreover it should be acknowledged that the causal link between EE and pathology may be at least partially reverted. The relationship between illness and EE is likely to be bidirectional, since patients' symptoms and behaviors are likely to elicit higher EE in relatives (Shisslak, Crago and Estes, 1995; Fairburn and Bohn, 2004).

5. Family Questionnaire (FQ; Wiedemann, Rayki, Feinstein and Hahlweig, 2002)

As for the LEE, the FQ was created as a more efficient and research-applicable self-rated alternative to the CFI. It is a 20-item self-report questionnaire based on the CFI (Wiedemann, Rayki, Feinstein and Hahlweig, 2002), with 10 items measuring CC and 10 items measuring EOI. Cutoff scores are suggested for each scale, 23 and 27 respectively; a higher total score indicates higher EE levels. Coomber and King (2011) used only the total scale score and considered scores above 50 as indicating high EE. The FQ is the only self-report measure of EE with a close correspondence to the CC and EOI subscales of the CFI (Wiedemann, Rayki, Feinstein and Hahlweig, 2002), and there are suggestions that the FQ could be an even more sensitive measure of CC than the CFI (Kyriacou, Treasure and Schmidt, 2008; Blair, Freeman and Cull, 1995). Moreover, it seems to be more cost-effective than the FMSS, and has shown better agreement with the CFI on EOI than other short EE questionnaires (Wiedemann, Rayki, Feinstein and Hahlweig, 2002).

Some general considerations can be suggested about the pros and cons of these different approaches. The interest in assessing EE in families led to attempts to develop time-saving measures in terms of interviewing time (for example the FMSS), also considering that less time-consuming measures than the CFI would greatly enhance the applicability of the EE construct. However, it has been suggested that the FMSS may be less likely to elicit high levels of CC and EOI compared to the CFI (Magaña, Goldstein, Karno, Miklowitz, Jenkins and Falloon, 1986; Malla, Kazarian, Barnes and Cole, 1991).

Self-report measures of EE may be preferable to interviews because of easier research applicability. Moreover, the interview methods have been questioned since they may preclude or inhibit the free expression of CC or concern by relatives of patients, and it remains unclear whether speech from individual parents (as in the CFI) would be consistent with their speech style in the presence of their offspring (as in the SCFI) (Cook, Strachan, Goldstein and Miklowitz, 1989). This question is of particular relevance since the system perspective (Minuchin, Baker, Rosman, Liebman, Milman and Todd, 1975; Minuchin, Rosman and Baker, 1978) has suggested assessing EE from interviews involving all family members, in a context which is closer to the one in which patients live. For example, prior to the implementation of the SCFI, Szmukler et al., (1987) assessed EE in ED families during a naturalistic research assessment session including a family meal, and Berkowitz et al. (1987) assessed EE on the basis of their initial therapy sessions. These two attempts shared an important drawback, namely the length of the session and the content of speech were likely to be influenced more by the therapist than by the family, with a consequent impact on ratings. Furthermore, as stated by Berkowitz and coworkers', "initial therapy sessions" included various kinds of family therapy approaches. According to these considerations, a semi-structured or structured interview format was chosen to overcome these limits, with the use of the SCFI (for example, Le Grange, Eisler, Dare and Hodes, 1992). Anyway, some preliminary findings (Valone, Norton, Goldstein and Doane, 1983; Miklowitz, Goldstein, Falloon and Doane, 1984) supported a correspondence between measures of EE by an individual interview and by observation of direct interactions between parents and the ill offspring.

Main Fields of Research about Expressed Emotion and Anorexia Nervosa

Overall, the currently available research about EE in AN has included the following types of studies:

1   studies of EE measures
2   studies comparing EE in AN and other chronic disorders
3   cross-sectional studies
4   longitudinal studies
5   studies of EE as perceived by patients

These areas will be briefly overviewed in the next sections.

1. Studies of EE Measures

Broadly speaking, these studies have assessed the comparability of different EE measures: for example, the CFI and EE measured through a family interview involving all family members at once during a "picnic lunch" (Szmukler, Berkowitz, Eisler, Leff and Dare, 1987), the CFI and the FMSS (Szmukler, Berkowitz, Eisler, Leff and Dare, 1987), the CFI and the SCFI (Hodes, Dare, Dodge and Eisler, 1999). Interestingly, parents tended to be significantly warmer and made more positive comments in the CFI than in the family rating setting in the Szmukler and coworkers study (1987). The proposed explanations about these findings about WAR and POS include: 1) fewer opportunities to express positive feelings and comments in the family interview than in the individual one; 2) the family setting itself may inhibit warmth and positive comments. Similar findings about the possible influence of having all the family members together, which may inhibit POS and WAR and enhance the "negative" facets of EE were described by Hodes and coworkers (1999) in their study comparing CFI and SCFI. Whether this reflects a particular family dynamic is unclear.

It is likely that the complex dynamics characterizing the anorexic family, especially during a meal, enhance the "negative" components of EE (CC, EOI), and on the contrary inhibit the "positive" ones (WAR and POS).

Although CC and EOI are the best defined scales of EE, the other scales including WAR and POS may be useful to elaborate hypotheses about particular patterns of family functioning. This is relevant also as far as treatment is concerned, considering that while on the one hand high EE may worsen patients' distress and symptoms, on the other patients' symptoms may lead to higher EE degrees, in a vicious cycle which needs to be broken.

The comparisons of CFI and FMSS performed by Van Furth et al., (1993) and Rein et al. (2006) yielded different results. Both found lower EE levels than those emerging from schizophrenia studies, but the rate of high final EE measured by the FMSS was higher in Rein's sample than in Van Furth's study.

Moreover, while Van Furth et al. (1993) concluded that there was a limited overlap between FMSS and CFI, Rein et al. (2006) found that the FMSS could be used as a reliable and time-saving substitute for the CFI.

Differences from the findings by Van Furth and coworkers (1993) may be explained considering the samples recruited (ED diagnosis, illness duration) and the timing of assessment.

2. Studies Comparing EE in AN and Other Disorders

A particular line of research on EE in EDs has investigated the EE construct in individuals with AN and with cystic fibrosis (Blair, Cull and Freeman, 1994; Blair, Cull and Freeman, 1995).

This is of interest because cystic fibrosis may be an ideal model to study the impact of a chronic, life-threatening disorder on the family; moreover, it makes up for the lack of studies comparing EE in families of AN patients and of patients with other disorders.

Blair and coworkers (1994) found that CF and AN families were more likely than healthy controls to live in a high EE environment. High EE was due to EOI rather than CCs, and notably overinvolvement was higher in those cases with a more severe illness.

This supports the possibility that high EE in families of severely ill kids whose illness may entail a risk for life is determined more by an overinvolved attitude rather than a critical one.

However, differences were found between CF and AN families, supporting the specificity of some AN family dynamics: for instance, CF families were found to be less critical, not afraid to face difficult issues and showed better problem solving skills, ability to compromise, and clearer communication patterns.

3. Cross-Sectional Studies

Scores on the EE dimensions reported by these studies are usually fairly low (Le Grange, Eisler, Dare and Hodes, 1992; Le Grange, Hoste, Lock and Bryson, 2011). Some of these studies are briefly outlined.

Dare et al. (1994) assessed with the SCFI 26 families with an adolescent kid (under the age of 18; 23 females and 3 males) suffering from an ED (N=18 AN, N=8 BN) and treated on an outpatient basis.

EE scores were quite low, and gender differences emerged in EOI and WAR ratings which were higher in mothers than in fathers. Regarding diagnoses, a significant difference was found between mothers' POS, which were more frequent in mothers of AN patients than in those of BN patients. This study (Dare, Le Grange, Eisler and Rutherford, 1994) found differences between families of AN and BN patients with respect to CC, WAR and POS, but only for POS these were statistically significant. Moreover, AN families' perception of closeness was higher than BN families' one.

It is likely that bulimic behaviors including binging, vomiting and purging are more disturbing for the family and elicit a more explicit disapproval than the self-punitiveness of AN individuals who restrict their food intake. Parents may be inhibited in their expression of disapproval and/or negative emotions towards kids who suffer from a potentially fatal disorder as AN, which is so evident in their severe underweight.

The finding of differences between AN and BN families seems to contradict the hypothesis of a shared pattern in psychosomatic families.

Kyriacou and coworkers (2008) performed an epidemiological study of self-report EE, involving carers of patients with AN and a control sample of parents of female offspring. Both anxiety and depression (measured with the Hospital Anxiety and Depression Scale - HADS) were higher in carers – mostly mothers – than controls; the same result was found for EOI and CC 60% and 47% of carers scored higher on EOI and CC, respectively, compared to 3% and 15% of control parents. 52% of CC variance was explained by anxiety, depression, AN symptomatology, ambivalence in accepting illness, rejection of carer's help, and negative/difficult behaviors, with the last two variables displaying the higher significance. As regards EOI, 63% of variance was explained by AN symptomatology, rejection of carer's help, ambivalence in accepting illness, negative/difficult behaviors, anxiety and depression, with the last three variables showing higher significance.

Higher EOI, as suggested also by Blair (Blair, Freeman and Cull, 1995) may be a more characteristic family reaction than CC in response to a kid's serious illness. Mothers in the carers' group showed higher EOI than fathers, while no gender difference was found in control parents; it can be suggested that this may depend on the caregiving role and on the different impact it has on fathers and mothers' distress. It should be remembered that the burden experienced by carers of an AN offspring is comparable or even heavier than that entailed by other mental illnesses, including schizophrenia (Treasure, Murphy, Szmukler, Todd, Gavan and Joyce, 2001).

The recent study by Hoste and coworkers (2012) aimed to better understand factors directly influencing family interaction and self-expression, including culture and ethnicity. It was focused on cultural variability with respect to meaning and attributions related to the mental illness and on the cultural meaning of family and responsibilities of family members (Jenkins and Karno, 1992). Although no difference was found between white and minority groups on EE, white mothers scored higher on POS and WAR than minority mothers. White and minority fathers were not found to differ significantly. White mothers scored higher than white fathers on POS, WAR and EOI. Minority mothers showed a tendency, albeit not statistically significant, to higher scores on CC and EOI than minority fathers. EE was generally not related to ED psychopathology as measured by the Eating Disorder Examination (EDE); instead, patients from high EE families had longer illness duration, were older and more likely to use diuretics (Hoste, Labuschagne, Lock and Le Grange, 2012).

Coomber and King published two studies (2011, 2012), both reporting data from a larger longitudinal study examining caring for someone with an ED. The 2011 study was about coping strategies and social support and their role as predictors/mediators of caregivers' burden and psychological distress, so it was not primarily focused on EE. Anyway, from this study a role of EE as predictor of caregivers' burden (accounting for 48% of variance), together with carers' total needs emerged. Moreover, the relationship between EE and carers' psychological distress, and between EE and carers' burden were respectively fully and partially mediated by maladaptive coping, suggesting that impact of EE is influenced by maladaptive coping strategies.

4. Longitudinal Studies

Van Furth et al. (1996) performed a study investigating illness course and outcome in the light of EE in a sample of 49 adolescents with an ED diagnosis according to DSM-III-R criteria. The CFI was administered to parents at baseline (first assessment, T1), termination of treatment (T2) and after a 1-year prospective follow-up (T3). Parents' EE was low at intake and further decreased at T1, although the only statistically significant decrease was that of fathers' and mothers' EOI. No difference was found between fathers' and mothers' EE variables. The associations of parental EE with illness-related variables were only scarce, even if a more emotional parental response was found towards patients with an EDNOS diagnosis and using laxatives.

With more detail, differences among diagnostic subgroups (AN, BN+ANBN and EDNOS) were found for the following: mean CC and EOI ratings were higher in EDNOS than in AN patients; fathers' mean HOS ratings were higher for patients using laxatives than for those who did not use laxatives; mothers' POS ratings were higher in the EDNOS patients than in both the other subgroups (AN and BN).

Other notable shortcomings of this study included the identification of a different pattern of coping for fathers and mothers: while mothers who are more critical were also likely to be more overinvolved, fathers are either critical or overinvolved.

Moreover, mothers' CC ratings, EOI and longer treatment duration were the best predictors of outcome.

Eisler et al. (2000) compared Conjoint Family Therapy (CFT) and Separated Family Therapy (SFT) in a randomized controlled trial. 40 patients received either SFT or CFT for 1 year, on an outpatient basis; assessment of all patients, regardless of treatment completion, was performed at baseline, at 3 months, 6 months and 12 months (end-of-treatment).

Briefly, an improved nutritional and psychological state was found in both treatment groups, with similar end-of-treatment results for SFT and CFT. As far as EE is concerned, there were significant reductions of CC from the parents to the ill adolescent and between parents as well, and an increase of WAR between parents at end-of-treatment.

Possible predictors of outcome included the following: previous treatments and illness duration, which were the clearest outcome predictors; degrees of emaciation at baseline; maternal criticism; primary amenorrhoea; non-ED psychiatric history.

Patients in the SFT group fared overall better than those in the CFT one, but this finding was statistically significant only when comparing patients from high EE and low EE families.

The SFT proved to be superior to the CFT for patients from families with high levels of maternal criticism; on the contrary, in low EE families, the outcome was similar in both treatment groups.

In 2007 Eisler et al. reported about the five year follow-up of this 40-patients sample. 38 agreed to be re-assessed and 75% had recovered from the ED. There was little to distinguish the two treatments after 5 years, and again the only significant difference was in families characterized by high levels of maternal criticism, which fared better on SFT than on CFT.

Specifically, patients from families with mother high on criticism showed less improvement in ED symptoms when treated with CFT.

Some hypotheses were suggested for this finding: 1) negative effects of living in a highly critical family environment; 2) persistent influence of parental criticism on sensitive patients; 3) difficulty to develop an effective therapeutic alliance with high EE families.

Predictors of poorer outcome at end-of-treatment included: 1) amount and type of previous treatment; 2) illness duration; 3) degree of weight loss at the beginning of treatment; 4) maternal criticism; 5) history of psychiatric disorder.

At follow-up, only history of having inpatient treatment and maternal criticism predicted outcome; moreover, a significant association was found between maternal criticism at baseline and need for additional treatment.

As supported by both studies conducted by Eisler et al. (2000, 2007), in families with high levels of critical attitudes or overt hostility, conjoint family sessions should be avoided in the initial phase of treatment and rather applied at a later stage, when anxiety around weight and eating is no longer a central issue.

The 2012 study by Coomber and King reported the follow-up data (4 and ½ months, and 9 months) of their previous study (2011) on baseline data. Analyses of variables over the three time points showed that carers of ED patients had on one hand chronic, moderate levels of burden, distress and use of maladaptive coping strategies and on the other hand, a significant decrease of CCs and EOI, of total carers' needs and adaptive coping mechanisms. Analyses of predictors confirmed a significant role for maladaptive coping, EE and total carer needs as long-term predictors of burden for ED carers.

On the contrary, psychological distress could not be predicted longitudinally, suggesting that distress may depend more on the current situation than past events, i.e. a reactive process to current circumstances.

Grover and coworkers (2011) developed an interactive web-based multi-media intervention for caregivers of AN patients, using a formulation-based systemic cognitive-behavioral approach including nine workbooks.

22 complete post-intervention and 18 follow-up assessments were available; measurements were performed at baseline, after the intervention and at 10-12 week follow-up. A significant main effect of time on all outcome measures was found, except for social problem solving.

As regards EE, at baseline there were 37% high FMSS EE carers and 50% high LEE EE carers. Post-intervention scores were high in 19% and 66.7% of carers assessed with the FMSS and LEE, respectively, although no significant change in pre- and post-intervention EE was found with either EE assessment measure.

Finally, significant changes were found on mean EE scores, and overall the Authors found that post-intervention improvements tended to persist during the follow-up period.

In another study, Grover et al. (2011) randomized 64 patients with AN to receive either a highly interactive systemic cognitive-behavioral web-based intervention or ad-hoc usual support (Beat). Assessment was performed at baseline, post-treatment (4 months) and follow-up (6 months). The web-based intervention compared to the control one significantly decreased anxiety, depression and EE (trend) in carers.

To examine baseline EE levels and their predictive value for Family Based Treatment (FBT, a manualized therapy which directly addresses the issue of family criticism) for AN adolescent patients, Le Grange et al. (2011) performed a study involving 86 patients with AN. EE ratings from SCFI were available for 79 carers at baseline; 32.9% families were high in EE, and high EE had no relation with weight or EDE subscales. CC and HOS ratings were similar for mothers and fathers. Mothers showed more EOI than fathers and also more WAR. The latter dimension was found to be related to a good outcome at end of treatment (defined as achievement of weight at or above 95% ideal body weight for age and gender). Patients missing the outcome evaluation were more likely to be from high EE families; anyway the percent of high EE was similar in the good and poor outcome group. Patients with a good outcome were more likely to have fathers and mothers scoring high on WAR.

Goddard and coworkers (2011) assessed the Expert Carers Helping Others (ECHO), a self-help intervention designed to address the interpersonal maintaining factors in carers of ED patients. Carers' unmet needs (Winn, Perkins, Murray, Murphy and Schmidt, 2004; Haigh and Treasure, 2003) and poor coping skills contribute to high levels of EE and consequent possible ineffective or even counterproductive approaches to the ill person's symptoms management. One of the hypotheses to be tested was that ECHO would be more effective on those for whom such intervention is most relevant, for example carers from high EE families and with frequent accommodating and enabling behaviors. Moderators of intervention effect were supposed to include living situation, amount of face-to-face contact and illness duration. Significant moderating effects were found for FQ and AESED for ECHO intervention. In carers with high baseline FQ scores there was a greater decrease in HADS following intervention. Similarly ECHO was most effective in carers with high levels of AESED. The HADS score decrease was greatest for carers with low CSE.

The reduction of FQ post-intervention was greatest for carers who watched a greater proportion of DVDs. Changes in caregiving self-efficacy, EE, and accommodation and enabling behaviors mediated improvements in carer distress and perceived level of functioning of the ED individuals. The impact of ECHO was greatest in carers with highest levels of EE and AESED and lowest self-efficacy.

Pepin and King (2012) tested the Collaborative Skills Training Workshops developed by Treasure and coworkers in a sample of 15 carers (11 mothers and 4 fathers; 80% living with the person affected by the ED) in Australia, to assess whether their effectiveness as tested in the UK (Sepulveda, Lopez, Todd, Whitaker and Treasure, 2008; Goddard, Macdonald and Treasure, 2011) could be replicated in other centers once experienced facilitators had been properly trained.

The Workshops aim at improving carers' wellbeing, coping strategies and problem-solving skills and at modifying ineffective communication patterns (i.e. high EE) and educating carers about the transtheoretical model of change and motivational interviewing.

Assessment of carers was performed with a non-experimental research design at pre-intervention, post-intervention and after an 8-week follow-up. Overall, the workshops proved to be effective in helping carers to interact with their ill relative and improve their coping strategies, reducing their EE (mostly EOI) and perceived burden.

5. Studies of EE as Perceived by Patients

Only recently attention has increasingly been paid to patients' perception of parental EE.

In 2010 Di Paola et al. published a case-control study of perceived EE in ED patients (N=63; 20 AN, 20 BN, 23 BED) and in controls matched for age and education (N=63). They described their own study as the first to explore ED patients' subjective point of view about family communication, atmosphere, and perceived EE. Differently from most studies of EE in EDs, patients were all females; regrettably, but consistently with the existing literature, ED diagnoses were mixed. Patients had higher level of perceived EE on all LEE subscales than controls, but no difference was found in perceived EE among patients' subgroups. Overall, 88.9% of ED patients reported high levels of perceived EE. Correlations were found with ED symptoms measured by the Eating Disorders Examination-Questionnaire (EDE-Q).

Total EDE-Q score correlated with all LEE subscales and with LEE total EE, and total LEE score correlated with weight, eating and shape concerns.

Perceived EE was found to be independent of age, type of significant other, amount of weekly contact (cutoff = 35 hours), and treatment duration. A relationship was found between the caregiver's emotional response and tolerance on one hand and dysfunctional attitudes and behaviors toward food, weight and body shape on the other, and EE also seemed correlated with guilt.

A recent study (Medina-Pradas, Navarro, López, Grau and Obiols, 2011) performed in 77 inpatients (93.5% women) from an ED specialist center in Barcelona involved patients with different ED diagnoses (46.7% AN, 31.2% BN, 22.1% EDNOS) with a long illness history (average illness history since first contact with mental health services: 8.8 years). AN patients perceived less EOI and more WAR (BDSEE) than EDNOS ones, and scored lower on impulse regulation than EDNOS patients. Taken together, these findings showed that the most stressful emotion perceived on behalf of their caregivers was criticism, followed by EOI and last by WAR. Moreover, patients' stress levels were related positively to CCs and EOI but negatively to WAR, and patients' perceived criticism-related stress was associated with ED behaviors and attitudes (all subscales of the EDI-2 except for perfectionism and maturity fears). On the contrary, no correlation was found between stress due to EOI and WAR and any ED symptom.

EE-related stress was not influenced by depression, self-esteem, anxiety, BMI and amount of contact with the caregiver.

Positive correlations were found between perceived CCs and EOI and several EDI-2 items. On the other hand, a negative correlation was found between perceived WAR and the following EDI-2 items: body dissatisfaction, ineffectiveness, perfectionism, and social insecurity. No correlation was found between CFI scales and ED symptoms.

This study underscores the importance to address both "negative" and "positive" facets of EE: while CC and EOI should be decreased, it is important to emphasize the importance of enhancing WAR.

Limits of the Currently Available Research

The currently available research about EE in AN is characterized by several limitations; small sample size and self-referred samples, to name a few. Many studies lack a control group including either healthy controls or families coping with other illnesses; a clinical assessment of patients is often missing and information about ED symptoms, diagnosis and history are often gathered from parents; most samples are mixed, both as regards diagnosis and gender. Studies are performed in samples which are highly heterogeneous regarding mean age and mean illness duration. Sampling characteristics, including age distribution, diagnosis, socioeconomic factors, have an impact on the EE levels described by different studies; for instance, higher levels of EE may be found in older patients, using laxatives or meeting criteria for a full BN diagnosis, or in patients with comorbidities.

Timing of evaluation is highly variable and this is relevant since the longer is illness duration, the higher may be critical EE scores as measured with the CFI (Szmukler, Eisler, Russell and Dare, 1985; Van Furth, Van Strien, Martina, Van Son, Hendrickx and Van Engeland, 1996). EE levels are lower when patients improve (for example, as in the study by Rein and coworkers, when the CFI is administered to parents at the end of patient's hospitalization) and when they are not living with their families. This suggests that EE levels of outpatients' families are likely to be higher than those of families whose ill relative is hospitalized, hence limiting the possibility to compare results of studies performed in different settings and at different time-points of EE assessment.

The available tools to measure EE can widely vary and are not consistently structured; for example, perception of EE as with the LEE is not the same as the evaluation of actual family EE. Moreover, it is not clear whether EE scales should be treated as categorical or continuous variables, and in the first case, there is a lack of agreement concerning the cutoff score. Last, it should be considered that the link between EE and pathology may be at least partially reverted, and the relationship between illness and EE is likely to be bidirectional, since patients' symptoms and behaviors are likely to elicit higher EE in relatives (Shisslak, Crago and Estes, 1995; Fairburn and Bohn, 2004).

Conclusion

1 Low scores on EE in ED families are usually reported in the literature, although the reason for this is not totally clear. A link has been suggested (Dare, Le Grange, Eisler and Rutherford, 1994) between the clinical appearance of problems in conflict resolution and the low scores on CC, EOI, HOS and WAR in parents of ED patients. ED family members seem to have limited skills in facing and tolerating strong affective communication. This pattern of communication may be particularly evident during adolescence, since conflicts between parents and kids in this period cannot be

faced without the willingness to show strong feelings. A low-key pattern of affective expression and a muted response style may be typical of ED families (Le Grange, Hoste, Lock and Bryson, 2011).

2   An essential consideration is that families should not be blamed or considered responsible for the ED, but instead cherished as a resource in patients' treatment, to promote their recovery (LeGrange, Lock, Loeb and Nicholls, 2010). Families have often been blamed and considered responsible of causing or exacerbating mental illness, and EE has long had a negative connotation. A change of focus on EE and a shift of attention from what families are doing wrong to families as a resource, may help increasing familial WAR and refocus attention on family strengths rather than weaknesses (Hoste, Labuschagne, Lock and Le Grange, 2012; López, Hipke, Polo, Jenkins, Karno and Vaughn, 2004).

3   An important shortcoming of previous EE research, was the largely negative connotation of EE emerging from studies ignoring WAR and POS. Recently, there have been suggestions that parental WAR and POS (but especially WAR) may be more important than CC and HOS in determining the emotional temperature of the family (Le Grange, Hoste, Lock and Bryson, 2011; Hoste, Labuschagne, Lock and Le Grange, 2012). Therefore reasons behind WAR differences may be important to determine. These may partly depend on parents' attributions of their offspring's ED: for instance, relatives are likely to be warmer and less critical if they do not consider the patients responsible for his/her illness, or if they do not believe that the ill person can control illness-related behaviors. From this point of view, interventions lowering parental blame and enhancing problem solving strategies within the families may be helpful, as well as therapy supporting parents to show more WAR and make more POS towards their kid.

4   Some parents showing high EE may feel particularly challenged by their kids' AN and display a self-blaming attitude. A special care is needed to avoid family members feeling that a family treatment approach means that there is something wrong with the family, and that the family is the cause of the problem. On the contrary, interventions are warranted to help carers gain confidence in their abilities to challenge the illness and to decrease their sense of burden.

5   An approach focused on improving carers' mood and quality of life as well is warranted. Moreover, given the correlation between both EOI and CC and negative/difficult behaviors (Kyriacou, Treasure and Schmidt, 2008), it would be useful also to provide carers with interventions aimed at improving their management and coping skills with ED behaviors. Treatment approaches should stress that the family is not to be seen as the cause of the disorder, but instead cheered as a resource to help the patient overcome the disorder. Detailed information should be provided about the ED and the psychological consequences of starvation, including the compulsive quality of some anorexic behaviors. A non-critical and non-blaming attitude should be encouraged.

6   The efficacy of family therapy for adolescent AN (NICE 2004) is supported by follow-up studies of adolescents suffering from AN (Minuchin, Rosman and Baker, 1978; Russell, Szmukler, Dare, and Eisler, 1987; Eisler and Dare, 2000; Lock, Agras, Bryson and Kraemer, 2005). There is considerable evidence to support the importance of family therapy and broadly speaking of family interventions as

treatment of choice for children and adolescents with AN. Moreover, there is a growing evidence about the effectiveness of family-based interventions in adults with AN as well. The role of family dynamics as far as EDs are concerned, and the impact that the ED has on the family itself underscore and support the importance of family involvement in therapy, and of addressing possible family-related trigger and/or maintenance stimuli.

References

Baronet, A. Factors associated with caregiver burden in mental illness: A critical review of the research literature. *Clinical Psychology Review* 1999; 19:819–841.

Bebbington, P., Kuiper, L. The predictive utility of expressed emotion in schizophrenia: an aggregate analysis. *Psychological Medicine* 1994; 24: 707-718.

Berkowitz, R. Rating expressed emotion from initial family therapy sessions (a pilot study). *Journal of Family Therapy* 1987; 9:27-37.

Blair, C., Cull, A., Freeman, C. Psychosocial functioning of young adults with cystic fibrosis and their families. *Thorax* 1994; 49:798-802.

Blair, C., Freeman, C., Cull, A. The families of anorexia nervosa and cystic fibrosis patients. *Psychological Medicine* 1995; 25:985–993.

Brown, G. W., Birely, J. L. T., Wing, J. K. Influence of family life on the course of schizophrenic disorders: a replication. *British Journal of Psychiatry* 1972; 121:241-258.

Bruch, H. *Eating Disorders: Obesity, Anorexia Nervosa, and the Person Within.* New York: Basic Books 1973.

Bruch, H. Psychotherapy in Primary Anorexia Nervosa. *Journal of Nervous and Mental Diseases* 1970; 105:51-67.

Butzlaff, R. L., Hooley, J. M. Expressed emotion and psychiatric relapse: a meta-analysis. *Archives of General Psychiatry* 1998; 55:547-552.

Cole, J. D., Kazarian, S. S. Predictive validity of the Level of Expressed Emotion (LEE) Scale: readmission follow-up data for 1, 2, and 5-year periods. *Journal of Clinical Psychology* 1993; 49:216-8.

Cole, J. D., Kazarian, S. S. The Level of Expressed Emotion Scale: a new measure of expressed emotion. *Journal of Clinical Psychology* 1988; 44: 392-397.

Coomber, K., King, R. M. A longitudinal examination of burden and psychological distress in carers of people with an eating disorder. *Social Psychiatry and Psychiatric Epidemiology* 2011.

Coomber, K., King, R. M. Coping strategies and social support as predictors and mediators of eating disorder carer burden and psychological distress. *Social Psychiatry and Psychiatric Epidemiology* 2012; 47:789–796.

Cook, W. L., Strachan, A. M., Goldstein, M. G., Miklowitz, D. J. Expressed emotion and reciprocal affective relationships in families of disturbed adolescents. *Family Process* 1989; 28:337.

Dare, C., Le Grange, D., Eisler, I., Rutherford, J. Redefining the psycho-somatic family: family processed of 26 eating disorder families. *International Journal of Eating Disorder* 1994; 16:211-226.

Dare, C. Understanding anorexia nervosa and bulimia. Columbus: Ross Laboratories 1983. *Family therapy for families containing an anorectic youngster;* 28–37.

Di Paola, F., Faravelli, C., Ricca, V. Perceived expressed emotion in anorexia nervosa, bulimia nervosa, and binge-eating disorder. *Comprehensive Psychiatry* 2010; 51:401–405.

Eisler, I., Dare, C. Family therapy for adolescents anorexia nervosa: the results of a controlled comparison of two family interventions. *Journal of Child Psychology and Psychiatry* 2000; 41(6):727-736.

Eisler, I., Simic, M., Russell, G. F. M., Dare, C. A randomised controlled treatment trial of two forms of family therapy in adolescent anorexia nervosa: a five-year follow-up. *Journal of Child Psychology and Psychiatry* 2007; 48(6):552–560.

Fairburn, C. G., Hay, P. J., Welch, S. L. Binge eating and bulimia nervosa: distribution and determinants. In: Fairburn, C. G., Wilson, G. T. (eds) *Binge eating: nature assessment and treatment.* The Guilford Press, New York 1993; 123–143.

Fairburn, C. G., Harrison, P. J. Eating disorders. *Lancet* 2003; 361:407–416.

Fairburn, C. G., Bohn, K. Eating disorder NOS (EDNOS): an example of the troublesome "not otherwise specified" (NOS) category in DSM-IV. *Behaviour Research and Therapy* 2004; 43:691-701.

Gilbert, A. A., Shaw, S. M., Notar, M. K. The impact of eating disorders on family relationships. *Eating Disorders* 2000; 8:331–345.

Goddard, E., Macdonald, P., Treasure, J. An examination of the impact of the Maudsley Collaborative Care Skills Training workshops on patients with anorexia nervosa: a qualitative study. *European Eating Disorders Review* 2011; 19:150–161.

Graap, H., Bleich, S., Herbst, F., Scherzinger, C., Trostmann, Y., Wancata, J. The needs of carers: a comparison between eating disorders and schizo-phrenia. *Social Psychiatry and Psychiatric Epidemiology* 2008; 43: 800–807.

Grover, M., Williams, C., Eisler, I., Fairbairn, P., McCloskey, C., Smith, G., Treasure, J., Schmidt, U. An Off-Line Pilot Evaluation of a Web-Based Systemic Cognitive-Behavioral Intervention for Carers of People with Anorexia Nervosa. *International Journal of Eating Disorders* 2011; 44: 708–715.

Gull, W. Anorexia nervosa (apepsia hysterica, anorexia hysterica). *Transaction Clinical Society of London* 1874; 7:22.

Haigh, R., Treasure, J. Investigating the needs of carers in the area of eating disorders: development of the Carer's Needs Assessment Measure (Ca-NAM). *European Eating Disorders Review* 2003; 11:125–41.

Highet, N., Thompson, M., King, R. Experiences of living with a person with an eating disorder: the impact on the carers. *Eating Disorders* 2005; 13: 327–344.

Hillege, S., Beale, B., McMaster, R. Impact of eating disorders on family life: individual parents' stories. *Journal of Clinical Nursing* 2006; 15(8):1016-22.

Hodes, M., Dare, C., Dodge, E., Eisler, I. The assessment of expressed emotion in a standardised family interview. *Journal of Child Psychology and Psychiatry* 1999; 40:617–625.

Hodes, M., Le Grange, D. Expressed emotion in the investigation of eating disorders: A review. *International Journal of Eating Disorders* 1993; 13: 279–288.

Hoek, H. W., van Hoeken, D. Review of the prevalence and incidence of eating disorders. *International Journal of Eating Disorders* 2003; 34:383–396.

Hooley, J. M. Expressed emotion and relapse of psychopathology. *Annual review of Clinical Psychology* 2007; 3:329-352.

Hoste, R. R., Labuschagne, Z., Lock, J., Le Grange, D. Cultural Variability in Expressed Emotion among Families of Adolescents with Anorexia Nervosa. *International Journal of Eating Disorders* 2012; 45(1):142–145.

Jenkins, J. H., Karno, M. The meaning of expressed emotion: Theoretical issues raised by crosscultural research. *American Journal of Psychiatry* 1992; 149:9–21.

Kinston, W., Loader, P. Eliciting whole-family interaction with a standardized clinical interview. *Journal of Family Therapy* 1984; 6:347-363.

Kyriacou, O., Treasure, J., Schmidt, U. Expressed emotion in eating disorders assessed via self-report: An examination of factors associated with expressed emotion in carers of people with anorexia nervosa in comparison to control families. *International Journal of Eating Disorders* 2008; 41:37–46.

Kuipers, L., Bebbington, P. Expressed emotion research in schizophrenia: theoretical and clinical implications. *Psychological Medicine* 1988; 18: 893-909.

Kuipers, L., Leff, J., Lam, D. *Family work for schizophrenia, a practical guide.* Gaskell, Royal College of Psychiatrists 1992.

Lasegue, C. On hysterical anorexia. *Medical Times and Gazette* 1873; 2:265-266.

Leff, J. P., Vaughn, C. *Expressed emotion in families.* London: Guilford 1985.

Le Grange, D., Eisler, I., Dare, C., Hodes, M. Family criticism and self-starvation: A study of expressed emotion. *Journal of Family Therapy* 1992; 14:177-192.

Le Grange, D., Hoste, R. R., Lock, J., Bryson, S. Parental expressed emotion of adolescents with anorexia nervosa: Outcome in family-based treatment. *International Journal of Eating Disorders* 2011; 44(8):731-734.

Le Grange, D., Lock, J., Loeb, K., Nicholls, D. Academy for eating disorders position paper: the role of family in eating disorders. *International Journal of Eating Disorders* 2010; 43:1-5.

Le Grange, D., Hoste, R. R., Lock, J., Bryson, S. W. Parental expressed emotion of adolescents with anorexia nervosa: Outcome in family-based treatment. *International Journal of Eating Disorders* 2011; 44: 731–734.

Lock, J., Agras, W. S., Bryson, S., Kraemer, H. C. A comparison of short- and long-term family therapy for adolescent anorexia nervosa. *Journal of the American Academy of Child and Adolescent Psychiatry* 2005; 44(7):632-9.

López, S. R., Hipke, K. N., Polo, A. J., Jenkins, J. H., Karno, M., Vaughn, C. Ethnicity, expressed emotion, attributions, and course of schizophrenia: Family warmth matters. *Journal of Abnormal Psychology* 2004; 3:428–439.

Magaña, A. B., Goldstein, J. M., Karno, M., Miklowitz, D. J., Jenkins, J., Falloon, I. R. A brief method for assessing expressed emotion in relatives of psychiatric patients. *Psychiatry Research* 1986; 17(3):203-12.

Malla, A. K., Kazarian, S. S., Barnes, S., Cole, J. D. Validation of the Five-Minute Speech Sample in measuring expressed emotion. *Canadian Journal of Psychiatry* 1991; 36:297–299.

Medina-Pradas, C., Navarro, J. B., López, S. R., Grau, A., Obiols, J. E. Dyadic view of expressed emotion, stress, and eating disorder psychopathology. *Appetite* 2011; 57:743-748.

Miklowitz, D. J., Goldstein, M. J., Falloon, I. R. H., Doane, J. E. Interactional correlates of expressed emotion in the families of schizophrenics. *British Journal of Psychiatry* 1984; 144:482-487.

Minuchin, S., Baker, B. L., Rosman, B. L., Liebman, R., Milman, L., Todd, T. C. A conceptual model of psychosomatic illness in children: family organization and family therapy. *Archives of General Psychiatry* 1975; 32: 1031-1038.

Minuchin, S., Rosman, B. L., Baker, B. L. *Psychosomatic families: anorexia nervosa in context.* Cambridge, MA: Harvard University Press 1978.

Monteleone, P., Treasure, J., Santonastaso, P., Favaro, A., Brambilla, F. Families of people with eating disorders. In: Sartorius, N., Leff, J., Lopez-Ibor, J. J., Maj, M., Okasha, A. (eds) *Families and mental disorder: from burden to empowerment*, Wiley, New York 2005; 113–125.

Murray, T. Wait not, want not: factors contributing to the development of anorexia nervosa and bulimia nervosa. *The Family Journal: Counseling and Therapy for Couples Families* 2003; 11:276–280.

National Institute for Clinical Excellence. Eating disorders: Core interventions in the treatment and management of anorexia nervosa, bulimia nervosa and related eating disorders. London: NICE 2004.

Parker, G., Hadzi-Pavlovic, D. Expressed emotion as a predictor of schizophrenic relapse: An analysis of aggregated data. *Psychological Medicine* 1990; 20:961-965.

Pepin, G., King, R., Collaborative Care Skills Training workshops: helping carers cope with eating disorders from the UK to Australia. *Social Psychiatry and Psychiatric Epidemiology* 2012.

Perkins, S., Winn, S., Murray, J., Murphy, R., Schmidt, U. A qualitative study of the experience of caring for a person with bulimia nervosa. Part 1: the emotional impact of caring. *International Journal of Eating Disorders* 2004; 36:256–268.

Rein, Z., Perdereau, F., Curt, F., Jeammet, P., Fermanian, J., Gokart, N. Expressed Emotion and Anorexia Nervosa: The Validation of the Five-Minute Speech Sample in Reference to the Camberwell Family Interview. *International Journal of Eating Disorders* 2006; 39:217–223.

Russell, G. F. M., Szmukler, G. I., Dare, C., Eisler, I. An evaluation of family therapy in anorexia nervosa and bulimia nervosa. *Archives of General Psychiatry* 1987; 44:1047–1056.

Rutter, M. L., Brown, G. W. The reliability and validity of measures of family life and relationships in families containing a psychiatric patient. *Social Psychiatry* 1966; 1:38.

Sargent, J., Liebman, R., Silver, M. Family therapy for anorexia. *Handbook of Psychotherapy for Anorexia Nervosa and Bulimia* (Garner, D., Garfinkel, P., eds). The Guilford Press, New York, 1985.

Schulz, B., Rossler, W. Caregiver burden in mental illness: Review of measurement, findings and interventions in 2004-05. *Current Opinion in Psychiatry* 2005; 18:684-691.

Selvini Palazzoli, M. Contesto e metacontesto nella terapia della famiglia. *Archivio di Psicologia, Neurologia e Psichiatria* 1970; 31.

Selvini Palazzoli, M. L'anoressia mentale. *Dalla terapia individuale alla terapia familiare.* Raffaello Cortina Editore 2006.

Selvini Palazzoli, M. 1974. Self-starvation. *From individual to family therapy in the treatment of anorexia nervosa.* Trad.it. 1981, nuova edizione Cortina, Milano 2006.

Sepulveda, A. R., Lopez, C., Todd, G., Whitaker, W., Treasure, J. An examination of the impact of "the Maudsley eating disorder collaborative care skills workshops" on the well being of carers: a pilot study. *Social Psychiatry and Psychiatric Epidemiology* 2008; 43:584–591.

Sepulveda, A. R., Todd, G., Whitaker, W., Grover, M., Stahl, D., Treasure, J. Expressed emotion in relatives of patients with eating disorders following skills training program. *International Journal of Eating Disorders* 2009.

Shisslak, C. M., Crago, M., Estes, L. S. The spectrum of eating disturbances. *International Journal of Eating Disorders* 1995; 18:209-19.

Szmukler, G. I., Berkowitz, R., Eisler, I., Leff, J., Dare, C. Expressed emotion in individual and family settings: a comparative study. *British Journal of Psychiatry* 1987; 151:174-178.

Szmukler, G. I., Eisler, I., Russell, G. F. M., Dare, C. Anorexia nervosa, parental expressed emotion, and dropping out of treatment. *British Journal of Psychiatry* 1985; 147:265-271.

Treasure, J., Murphy, T., Szmukler, G., Todd, G., Gavan, K., Joyce, J. The experience of caregiving for severe mental illness: A comparison between anorexia nervosa and psychosis. *Social Psychiatry and Psychiatric Epidemiology* 2001; 36:343–347.

Valone, K., Norton, J. P., Gowsmmt, M. J., Doane, J. Parental expressed emotion and affective style in an adolescent sample at risk for schizo-phrenia spectrum disorders. *Journal of Abnormal Psychology* 1983; 92: 399-407.

Van Furth, E. F., Van Strien, D. C., Martina, L. M. L., Van Son, M. J. N., Hendrickx, J. J., Van Engeland, H. Expressed emotion and the prediction of outcome in adolescent eating disorders. *International Journal of Eating Disorders* 1996; 20:19-31.

Van Furth, E. F., Van Strien, D. C., Van Son, M. J., Van Engeland, H. The validity of the Five-Minute Speech Sample as an index of Expressed Emotion in parents of eating disorder patients. *Journal of Child Psycho-logy and Psychiatry* 1993; 34(7):1253-60.

Van Os, J., Marcelis, M., Germeys, I., Graven, S., Delespaul, P. High expressed emotion: Marker for a caring family? *Comprehensive Psychiatry* 2001; 42:504–507.

Vaughn, C. Annotation: Expressed emotion in family relationships. *Journal of Child Psychological and Psychiatry* 1989; 30:13-22.

Vaughn, C. E., Leff, J. P. The measurement of expressed emotion in the families of psychiatric patients. *British Journal of Social and Clinical Psychology* 1976; 15:157-165.

Vaughn, C. E., Leff, J. P. The influence of family and social factors on the course of psychiatric illness: a comparison of schizophrenic and depressed neurotic patients. *British Journal of Psychiatry* 1976; 129:125-137.

Wiedemann, G., Rayki, O., Feinstein, E., Hahlweig, K. The family questionnaire: development and validation of a new self-report scale for assessing expressed emotion. *Psychiatry Research* 2002; 109:265-279.

Whitney, J., Murray, J., Gavan, K., Todd, G., Whitaker, W., Treasure, J. Experience of caring for someone with anorexia nervosa: qualitative study. *British Journal of Psychiatry* 2005; 187:444-459.

Winn, S., Perkins, S. J., Murray, J., Murphy, R., Schmidt, U. A qualitative study of the experience of caring for a person with bulimia nervosa. Part 2: Carers' needs and experiences of services and other support. *International Journal of Eating Disorders* 2004; 36:269–79.

Zabala, M. J., Macdonald, P., Treasure, J. Appraisal of caregiving burden, expressed emotion and psychological distress in families of people with eating disorders: a systematic review. *European Eating Disorders Review* 2009; 17:338-349.

In: New Developments in Anorexia Nervosa Research ISBN: 978-1-63117-551-0
Editors: Carla Gramaglia and Patrizia Zeppegno © 2014 Nova Science Publishers, Inc.

Chapter 5

Neuropsychology of Anorexia Nervosa

*Riccardo Pignatti**

Neurocentro della Svizzera Italiana, Ente Ospedaliero Cantonale, Lugano, Switzerland;
European School of Hypnotic Psychotherapy, AMISI,
Milan, Italy

Abstract

In the past, some Authors used to consider Anorexia Nervosa (AN) a body-schema perceptive deficit. In fact, the misjudgements of size in AN were found to be specifically linked to body measurements and not to objects. However, the lack of controlled studies (e. g. correlations with body weight or with the duration of illness, comparisons between judgement about oneself and others, explicit vs. implicit answers) led to reject the hypothesis of AN as a mere perceptual deficit. So, AN could not be reduced to a "bottom-up" informational bias leading to sedimentation of symptoms.

Nevertheless, there is growing evidence of neuropsychological defects in AN patients, but these issues are now being investigated in relation to their psycho-biological state. In fact, the manifestations of neuropsychological impairment can range from superficial and transient states (psychomotor slowness due to acute physical deterioration) to endophenotypic characteristics (issues of cognitive rigidity involving both AN patients and their non-affected parents and relatives). Contemporary research is particularly focused on the latter issues as they are the most relevant to understand cognition in AN.

The onset of AN in adolescence can interrupt the "pruning" process of the frontal lobes, the main neurological event taking place during adolescence. This alteration in frontal networks can account for executive and reasoning defects in accordance with "central" hypotheses explaining cognitive biases in AN. Recent acquisitions from neurobiological studies led the researchers to formulate new theories about the disadvantage AN patients show on the prevision of long-term consequences of their behaviour and on gestaltic thought. "Weak central coherence", neurotransmitters alterations, theory of mind, stable traits of personality, and inherited markers are all

---

* Corresponding author: Email: riccardopignatti@gmail.com.

possible, and, maybe, coexistent theoretical frames which can explain and drive the research on AN cognition.

It is recommended that neuropsychology of AN should be not considered an attempt to reduce such a complex manifestation to a neurological disease. Nevertheless, neurobehavioral studies can shed some light on the link between cognition and behaviour, and provide clinicians with new instruments to improve their work with patients and families.

1. Introduction

The etiology of Anorexia Nervosa (AN) is still debated. Given the lifespan nature of the disease, it is difficult to differentiate premorbid pathogenic factors from changes resulting from the acute or chronic phases of the illness. It is also difficult to establish direct correlations between physiological disturbances and their clinical consequences, or conversely to assume that the restoration of physiological parameters equals the disappearance of the underlying mental disorder (Gicquel, 2013). Alongside these considerations, therapies for AN are still very complicated and no pharmacological, dietetic/ nutritional or psychotherapeutic approach is to date reaching a stand-alone scientific evidence of effectiveness. In 2011, the World Federation of Societies of Biological Psychiatry conducted a survey on Pharmacotherapy in Eating Disorders (EDs). After examining 20 randomized controlled trials on AN and more than 60 on Bulimia Nervosa (BN) and Binge-Eating Disorders (BED), the authors concluded that additional research is needed for the improvement of the treatment of EDs, and especially AN (Aigner, Treasure, Kaye, & Kasper, 2011). A further issue is that AN has manifold characteristics, ranging from Restricter (AN-RE) to Binge-purging type (AN-BP), with the latter having fuzzy borders with the diagnosis of BN or Eating Disorder Not-Otherwise Specified.

Social explanations are predominant and the history of development of AN symptoms reflects a strong influence of familiar and cultural environment. Besides, research-based evidence showed an increasing role of the brain in the pathogenesis and maintenance of AN. Yet, the different phenotypes, the comorbidities (e.g. anxiety and depression), and the environmental causes make it difficult to identify a 1-to-1 relation between endophenotypical-genetical markers and psychiatric disease. Taken together, these observations support an approach to AN that is both developmental and integrative, reflecting both the complexity of the pathways involved and the developmental timescales of these pathways (Gicquel, 2013). Thus, a global vision on etiology and physiopathology is substituting the mere description of symptoms as the basis for diagnoses and therapies. For these and many other reasons, a simplistic point of view should be discouraged. Nevertheless, the scientific application of neuroscience to AN can offer new insights on brain-behavior interface and give some suggestions to AN therapists. So, this chapter aims at providing an overview of the neuropsychology of AN, without forgetting mandatory points of view for a non-reductionist approach. Performing a neuropsychological investigation on psychiatric diseases is like taking a photograph out of the window. Suppose we can shoot a quite complex landscape, with moving cars, pedestrians, buildings, mountains, and a particular sunlight or artificial lights underlining some details rather than others. We are looking at the photograph as a single frame, but the objects inside it tell very different stories. Cars are in the photo but they are captured while running on the road, and soon after they will be gone, while buildings are a stable part of the landscape, reflecting some features of their inhabitants. The mountains and countryside have been there for thousands of years and strongly influenced where the buildings could be built and where people live. Out of such metaphor, one can obtain precise values from neuropsychological testing, yet the examiner must relate them to the clinical history of the patient in order not to mix state and trait effects. No clarification on the history of Earth can be provided by an alien visitor who is watching our photo, because he cannot distinguish the meaning of mountains from that of buildings, though he can be able to describe them in the deepest detail. So, the observer must know the meaning of what he is talking about before providing conclusions, even if those conclusions might come from plain data. A similar approach is recommended in the study of AN, because strong influences on cognitive functioning are coming from both state and trait clinical features. Such issues are well known from clinical psychologists, who usually perform tests aimed at relating eating behaviors with personality, familiar background, as well as with state anxiety. Very different psychological and neurobehavioral aspects may be found in AN. For example, when people suffering from AN are experiencing periods of extreme starvation, a hospitalization aimed at coercing food intake can be required. Such intervention might only be a medical intervention, taking place during a dramatic "state" moment in which an emergency procedure needs to be applied. By contrast, long-term therapies should be applied after stabilization; so, the therapist should investigate embedded family characteristics rather than obsessive-compulsive personality traits. The same disease might be treated in different ways, each requiring to be applied at a proper time. Research should pursue the same goal when trying to focus on neuropsychological features characterizing such a fluctuating and complex syndrome.

In fact, most neuropsychological tests are deeply influenced from both state and trait situations, but disentangling them can be hard, being such tests not thought and standardized for this aim. For example, a speed task might be deeply influenced by state or trait values, personality structured cognitions, drug intake, or by daily mood and anxiety fluctuations. So, the researcher must pay particular attention to the psychological background of subjects. Matching neuropsychological results with brain imaging techniques, co-occurring physical and psychological measurements, and the use of matched control groups can reduce the risk of inaccurate conclusions.

2. Approach to Neuropsychology of AN

The first studies on the neuropsychology of AN (Bruch, 1962) underlined a peculiar neurobehavioral style, with concrete thinking and impaired abstraction. In contrast to common beliefs, AN patients did not show better intellectual performances than the general population, either in acute state of starvation or during recovering. Indeed, a study (Gillberg, Gillberg, Rastam, & Johansson, 1996) showed that mean IQ as obtained by means of the WAIS-R did not differ between AN and controls (102.9 and 106.5, respectively). The Performance IQ was lower in AN than in controls. In particular, people suffering from AN showed low profiles in subtests such as Visual Puzzles: such result is in accordance with renowned difficulties in global and gestaltic perception and in synthesis of information. On the other hand, people with AN outperformed controls in the Block Design subtest, requiring concrete problem-solving thinking and attention to details.

The recent theoretical approach accounts for AN behaviors as a pathological search for challenges which partly compensates a feeling of helplessness and thereby restores self-esteem, and this may help understanding why this behavior is so resistant to change (Rotenberg, 2000). High-order cognition activities are surely more adequate to explain such a complex and persistent behavior, with a model of top-down influences. Social cognition, decision-making, mental flexibility are examples of the new theoretical frames explaining thinking and reasoning activities. These high-order cognitive predispositions are perhaps unconscious to subjects, who can deny or minimize their failure to adaptation. In other words, patients should not be considered "guilty" for their condition; perhaps, they are willing to change, nonetheless their internal predispositions prove to be stronger than their will. The "secondary benefits" of their psychopathology can even fulfill the subjects' need of receiving attention from relatives or friends. In fact, the process of starvation is often used as a distorted way to get attention from relatives. If directly asked, people with AN usually deny their thinness and show fear to become fat and heavy. Neuropsychological investigations can effectively detect the underlying cognitions and perseverations which can explain or, at least, be related to this behavior, without soliciting the subjects' defenses. The neuropsychologist can provide "aseptic" tests, developed for other purposes, which can help to identify some basic flaws in AN awareness, even though the subjects might obtain average scores at psychometrical tests assessing their behavior towards food. One obvious advantage of neuropsychological screening over tests focused on pathological eating behavior is the lack of any direct relationship with eating and the food domain. Thus, tests originally addressed to social cognition or mental flexibility could bypass patients' resistance which is likely to be elicited by questions concerning nutrition and/or eating-related behaviors; in fact, questionnaires on eating behavior itself inevitably stimulate such resistance. Such method can be extended to other psychopathology and eating behaviors, such as in morbid obese people (Pignatti et al., 2006).

Furthermore, research on neurological underpinnings of cognitive functions gained great attention in the scientific community, together with the development of finer methods of brain imaging and brain mapping.

For example, during past years, some scholars used to consider AN a pure deficit of body-schema perception. This condition has been related to overestimation of the subject's body weight or shape, accompanied by negative body image and intense fear of becoming fat (Molinari, 1995; Probst, Vandereycken, Van Coppenolle, & Pieters, 1995). Due to the misperception of body size, patients tend to deny the severity of weight loss. Yet, it is unclear whether the body image bias is etiologic or a consequence of AN. The possible association between self-esteem and body satisfaction and the relationship of the latter to actual size estimation supports the hypothesis that size perception may be closely tied to satisfaction with non-physical aspects of self (Garner, 1981).

In fact, the misjudgment of size in AN is specifically linked to body measurement and not to objects (Majewski, 1997). The suggestion that people with AN are motivated to distort perception of their body size is consistent with the proposal that the differences in body size distortion between eating disordered subjects and controls are exclusively due to affective factors (Gardner & Bokenkamp, 1996).

However, the lack of controlled studies dealing with correlations with body weight or with illness duration, comparisons between judgment on oneself and on others, the influence of a probably distorted desire of thinness on explicit answers, led to reject the hypothesis of AN as a perceptual deficit. So, AN could not be reduced to a "bottom-up" informational bias leading to sedimentation of symptoms. Data to define AN a neuropsychological deficit are still lacking; however, there is evidence of neuropsychological bias, misperception included, in AN. In fact, recent research is combining neuroimaging, neuropsychological and psychological models to provide a more elaborated theory on the emotional perception of self, which is moving from the pure perceptual deficit. For example, research indicates the fusiform gyrus as the structure responsible for processing the visual appearance of the human body. In patients with AN, fMRI investigations showed a selectively reduced activation in the fusiform gyrus when patients were shown their own body (Sachdev, Mondraty, Wen, & Gulliford, 2008). AN showed a lower activation than controls in the medial prefrontal cortex and right fusiform gyrus in response to body checking vs. neutral images showing another healthy female's body in action. Body shape concern scores, obtained after self-evaluation on anxiety caused by images, were also negatively related to the medial prefrontal cortex activation in the AN group (Suda et al., 2013). On the other hand, an important activation of the insula occurred when controls viewed their own body image; such activation did not occur in patients. Being the insula a key to the representation of the body scheme, such difference in activity might once again explain why patients with AN distort their own image. Moreover, a lack of the integration process between visual and somatosensory cortex was also found in acute, but not in recovered, AN individuals, with relation to altered visuo-spatial performances in copy tasks (Favaro et al., 2012). Taken together, these investigations are therefore suggesting that the alterations in activities of specific brain structures can suppress the cognitive, perceptual and emotional processing of personal body image in AN (for a review on neuroimaging studies on AN and ED, see Tejado Lde, Ruiz, Trebbau, Diaz-Marsa, & Perera, 2010).

In a life-span perspective, it should be noticed that the onset of AN during adolescence can interrupt the "pruning" process of the frontal lobes, the main neurological event taking place in adolescence, so the infantile perfectionism can lead to cognitive rigidity in adults because of both social and neurobehavioral reasons. Long-standing malnutrition during adolescence and young adulthood can indeed produce "biological scars" that maintain and accelerate the disorder and likely result in chronic psychopathology during adulthood (Herpertz-Dahlmann, Seitz, & Konrad, 2011). Neuroendocrino-logical changes, such as elevated cortisol levels, contributing to alterations in cognitive performance, can occur in young individuals with AN. In contrast to the findings in adult patients, adolescent patients with AN did not display a marked deficit in set-shifting abilities. Instead, they demonstrated a perfectionistic cognitive style that was characterized by an increased Reaction Time (RT) in shift trials but improved accuracy. Illness at its onset and the incomplete maturation of the prefrontal cortices can moderate the impact of cognitive rigidity (Buhren et al., 2012).

Therefore, theories on cognition are now being structured to provide new insights on relations among cognition, neurotransmitters, cortical thickness and mind-body interaction. Researchers have also the goal to unveil stable traits of cognition and personality which are difficult to modify, and to distinguish them from fluid and dynamic features.

3. Neuropsychological Tests for AN

Some of the most commonly used and quoted neuropsychological tests for people with AN are described in Table 1. Many of them are not provided with a specific clinical standardization, yet they are useful for scientific investigation on cognition issues such as flexibility, decision-making, set-shifting, and so on. In some cases, AN patients did not perform worse than controls, but their scores were more influenced by personality and clinical issues. Consequently, it is more cautious to talk about *bias* rather than *deficits* when people with AN show low performances but test standardization is not available. In any case, it is always recommended to administer a broad screening battery, in accordance with the observation that a single test cannot identify a single cognitive ability; moreover, it should be considered that all tests can be influenced by manifold features, such as working memory size and insight abilities, bearing in mind the role of state and trait psychopathologies (see also Tchanturia and colleagues, 2004, for further details).

**Table 1. Synthetic explanation of neuropsychological tests
quoted in the chapter**

Brixton Test (Burgess & Shallice, 1997)
The examinee is asked to foretell the movement of a blue circle that changes position after each answer. The movement pattern occasionally changes and the subject has to abandon the old answer criterion to infer a new one.
Picture Set or Set Flexibility Test (Surguladze, 1995)
The examinee is shown some sets of four figures, globally 18 tests, with the task of pointing out which objects have something in common. The subject has to modify his/her strategy of response three times throughout the test. In fact, the tests are divided into three groups; the first can be divided based according to the objective category, the second according to the material composing the objects and the third according to their functions.
Cat Bat Task (Eliava, 1964; Tchanturia, Morris, Surguladze, & Treasure, 2002)
The examinee is asked to complete the words of a short story with the missing letter, as quickly and accurately as possible. In the first part of the story the subject should insert the letter *c* in order to form the word *cat*, whereas in the second part this word is no longer appropriate and the letter to be inserted is *b* so as to form the word *bat*, so that in the last part the examinee has to modify his/her cognitive strategy based on the context.
Haptic Illusion Task (Tchanturia, Serpell, Troop, & Treasure, 2001; Uznadze, 1966)
This is a tactile perceptive set-shifting test using three wooden balls with a 5 cm diameter and one 8 cm diameter ball. The examinee, blindfolded, has to estimate the size of the two balls which, in turn, are set in his/her hands. In the first phase the biggest ball and one of the small ones are positioned for 15 times in each of the subject's hands, always maintaining the same position. In the second phase the subject has to hold one of the smallest balls in each hand for 30 times and is asked whether he/she perceives any difference in their size. Many examinees have the illusion that the ball they are keeping in the hand previously holding the biggest ball is smaller than the other one.
Hayling Sentence Completion Test (Burgess & Shallice, 1997)
This test consists of 20 sentences in which the final word is missing. The sentences are divided into two sections (A and B) each containing 10 sentences. The missing words are matched by frequency and age of acquisition.

In Section A (response initiation), participants are required to respond to half of the incomplete sentences with a word accurately completing the sentence (e.g., when you go to bed, you have to turn out… "lights"). In Section B (response inhibition), participants are presented with the remaining 10 incomplete sentences; now participants are asked to pronounce a word completely unrelated to the sentence (e.g., take rackets and balls, let us go and play… "apple"). Two practice items are read before each section. Participants are also encouraged to respond as fast as they can.

Iowa Gambling Task (Bechara et al., 1994)

In the computerized version of the Iowa Gambling Task (IGT), participants are given a loan of $2000 play money and are told to make choices in order to maximize their gains, with minimal instructions regarding the rules of the task. Over 100 trials, they choose between four decks of cards (A, B, C, D) two of which yield high immediate gain ($100) but larger future losses ("disadvantageous decks": A and B) and two yielding lower immediate gain ($50) but smaller future losses ("advantageous decks": C and D). Each of the 10 cards from decks A and B are worth $1000, but deck A includes five unpredictable punishments ranging from $150 to $350, with a total loss of $1250, while deck B includes one large punishment of $1250. Each of the 10 cards from deck C or D are only worth $500, but the punishment is also smaller, ranging from $25 to $75 in deck C with a total loss of $250, and a single loss of $250 in deck D. Decks A and B are disadvantageous because they cost more in the long run, while decks C and D are advantageous because they result in an overall gain. Subjects that don't provide far-seeing answers at the IGT belong to a category of patients like the alcohol addicted and the pathologic gamblers. All these categories of patients share a "myopia" towards the future consequences of their actions and their decisions seem strictly connected to an immediate reward, which cannot be postponed (the pleasure of the substance, the thrill of the bet). The uncertainty created by the task, together with the possibility of rearranging choices after initial feedbacks, led researchers to discriminate between choices under ambiguity (first 50 cards) and choices under risk (last 50 cards) (Brand, Labudda, & Markowitsch, 2006).

Wisconsin Card Sorting Test (Heaton, Chelune, Talley, Kay, & Curtiss, 1993).

The test includes four stimulus cards and two identical decks of 64 fixed-sequence response cards. The examinee is asked to pair each card with the four stimulus cards, following a criterion he/she has to determine after the feedback (yes/no) received by the examiner. Three possible criteria (color, shape and number of items) are applied, but the right association is changing over time; subjects are required to adjust their choices only relying on the received feedback.

Trail-Making Test (Lezak, Hovieson, & Loring, 2004)

The test consists of two parts, Part A and Part B. In Part A, the examinee is asked to connect with a pen trail the numbered dots presented on a sheet, in growing order. In Part B, the examinee should complete a similar task, now stressing their working memory by continuously switching from numbers to letters (set-shifting).

Matching Familiar Figure Test (utilized in Southgate et al., 2008)

The test requires to identify an object among others that are very similar to it. This test is devoted to distinguish impulsive and thoughtful strategy by means of speed and precision of answers.

4. Starvation Effects: Reversibility on Cognition?

For a more in-depth comprehension, Table 2 provides a generic schematization about lower and upper levels of neurobehavioral issues related to AN.

Table 2. A synthesis of AN neuropsychological deficits with relation to various levels of state-trait neurobiological features. Symptoms range from more global and undifferentiated deficits (bottom line) to specific and heritable characteristics (top line). Research is still focusing on defining the level and pervasiveness of each characteristic

Biological State	Characteristics	AN manifestation
Hereditary genetic marker (Endophenotype)	Affecting also siblings and parents; resistant to treatment	Perceptive and set-shifting rigidity. Debate on the possible inclusion of decision-making and excessive attention to details
Personality stable marker	Trait or personality features resisting after recovering from acute states	Autistic Spectrum Disorder symptoms: alexithymia and personal distress. Attention to details to the detriment of gestaltic perception, decision-making defects
Acute state of both physical deterioration and psychopathology; starvation effects of restriction	Global and undifferentiated downfall. All subjects in this condition (not only AN) may present these characteristics	Slowdown of the motor-sensory reflexes, learning abilities, and abstract thinking deficit

At the lowest level, we can find the most unspecific aspects which are thought to affect both AN subjects and all individuals experiencing starvation. Though it is objectively hard to disentangle the role of generic defects due to starvation from that of cognition bias in AN, the nutritional status has an impact on cognitive abilities and spatial memory indeed (Benton & Sargent, 1992); mild cognitive impairment on focused attention, memory and visuo-spatial processing were also found specifically in the acute state of AN (Jones, Duncan, Brouwers, & Mirsky, 1991). Feeding can improve the low performance on tests assessing attentional, perceptual, and motor functions which is typical of the acute phase of starvation (Szmukler et al., 1992). The plasma cortisol levels are significantly elevated in patient with EDs such as AN: this imbalance might provide a direct impact on vigilance. Some researches indicate that the continued glucose deprivation or restriction may induce an impairment in retrieving memories (Benton & Sargent, 1992). In an attentional task, a significant negative correlation of cortisol levels with hit-rate and a significant positive correlation with reaction time to hits were found, while other clinical characteristics were not related to cognitive performance (Laessle, Fischer, Fichter, Pirke, & Krieg, 1992). Yet, this observation was afterwards criticized and conclusions were not confirmed by other studies (Seed, McCue, Wesnes, Dahabra, & Young, 2002).

The weight gain alone cannot yet be considered the only factor needing to be restored in order to obtain a remission of AN symptoms, and the use of different criteria to compose "acute" and "recovered" groups can act as confounding factors among different studies. As no association was found between cognitive and clinical improvement, a significant role for mediating factors, such as changes in metabolic brain turnover and in steroid hormones was supposed. The impairment in speed-demanding tasks may however be peripheral, and secondary to slowed motor functioning, rather than slowed mental processing speed, given that a large percentage of patients with AN were found to be impaired on specific test measures of psychomotor speed. This interpretation seems plausible in keeping with the observation that, as task demands became more complex (i.e. from motor speed, to manual dexterity speed, to processing speed) smaller effect sizes were found between patients with AN and healthy controls (Roberts, Tchanturia, & Treasure, 2010). In fact, speed or reaction time (RT) cannot be considered distinct, independent, measures of cognitive functioning. The different complexity of speed tasks, from simple RT (e.g. the time needed to press a button after the stimulus perception) to complex visuo-spatial tests, should require the involvement of different high-order cognitive functions indeed. Furthermore, resilience abilities (Keifer et al., 2010) and, on the other side, a reduction in cognitive flexibility can be either a good or bad prognostic factor, thus being able to either moderate or worsen performances in complex speed tasks.

5. High-Order Cognition

In the previous paragraph, transient-state characteristics were described. Now, following the suggestions of literature (Martinez, Cook-Darzens, Chaste, Mouren, & Doyen, 2013; Southgate, Tchanturia, & Treasure, 2009), we can identify the most characterizing dimensions related to cognitive-affective biases in AN. Such biases involve attention, cognitive flexibility, decision-making, and emotion processing: all of them can be considered as neuropsychological constructs mirroring AN typical features, such as perfectionism, obsessive-compulsive rituals, impairments in social functioning, and alexithymia, respectively. These dimensions range from trait features persisting after the dramatic symptom manifestations (periods of intense restriction and starvation) to endophenotypical traits, which may even be observed in healthy relatives. Though this distinction cannot be easily carried on and different factors might overlap and sum to other psychopathologies, we follow this order for clarity purposes.

5.1. Personality Stable Markers: From Attention to Details to Alexithymia

Recent acquisitions about attention in AN are described in the "Weak Central Coherence" (WCC) theory. Subjects with WCC are expected to pay excessive attention to details, thus losing the meaning of the whole verbal or visuo-spatial item (Lopez, Tchanturia, Stahl, Booth, et al., 2008). In fact, some studies demonstrated that subjects with EDs, particularly AN, may show good set-shifting performances (Galimberti, Martoni, Cavallini, Erzegovesi, & Bellodi, 2011), especially in verbal domains (Roberts, Tchanturia, Stahl, Southgate, & Treasure, 2007), high school performances and even outperform healthy controls in tasks requiring attention to details (Lopez, Tchanturia, Stahl, Booth, et al., 2008). For example, the "Perfectionism" trait seems to facilitate fast psychomotor response in drawing or copying written patterns, both in an acute and in a non-acute phase (Pieters et al., 2005; Pieters et al., 2003). Moreover, subjects with AN outperform controls in precision and speed at the Matching Familiar Figure test, once more demonstrating a strong preference for a detail-based information processing (Southgate, Tchanturia, & Treasure, 2008).

In contrast, AN subjects can easily fail in applying a good organizational strategy on figure copies, despite a good accuracy (Lindner, Fichter, & Quadflieg, 2013; Lopez, Tchanturia, Stahl, Booth, et al., 2008), or in global interpretation of the stimuli (Gillberg,

Rastam, Wentz, & Gillberg, 2007). This tendency cannot be attributed to the clinical stage, as no relation to psychopathology scales and no speed impairment has been found. Later on, these results were confirmed and explained with the WCC hypothesis (Lopez, Tchanturia, Stahl, Booth, et al., 2008; Lopez, Tchanturia, Stahl, & Treasure, 2008), and similarities between EDs and Autism Spectrum Disorders (ASD) were therefore supposed (Oldershaw, Treasure, Hambrook, Tchanturia, & Schmidt, 2011). These data can also explain some apparently incongruent observations in literature: an excessive cognitive control on details can either improve or damage speed and decision-making procedures.

Literature suggests some interesting connection between AN and a category of subjects suffering from genetic disorder called Prader-Willi Syndrome (PWS). PWS subjects' behavioral phenotype includes dramatic hyperphagia, obsessive-compulsive symptoms, repetitive behavior and social deficits similar to those of ASD (Dimitropoulos & Schultz, 2007). Interestingly, some individuals with PWS, despite of a mild-moderate intellectual impairment, show abilities in solving achromatic jigsaw puzzles by means of shape-based strategies (Verdine, Troseth, Hodapp, & Dykens, 2008). Such observation approaches the WCC observed in AN subjects. Moreover, Frank and colleagues (2004) described how neuroimaging demonstrated that challenges such as food distortions may activate cingulate, frontal, temporal, and parietal regions in AN. So, a correspondence between opposite extremes of eating behaviors in different pathologies, such as AN and PWS, is not so unlikely, given that PWS patients also show an aberrant serotonergic functioning which, in turn, is strongly implicated in hyperphagia (Dykens, Roof, Bittel, & Butler, 2011). These shared characteristics (particular eating attitudes, hyper-attention to details, serotonin disruption) between people with AN and subjects with Autism Spectrum Disorders (ASD) are opening new debates on the possible inscription of (some) anorexic patients in the category of high-functioning autism. Rastam and colleagues stated that 20% of their AN group met criteria for ASD comorbidity due to social and empathy restrictions (Rastam, Gillberg, Gillberg, & Johansson, 1997). Furthermore, recent acquisitions on cognition and socio-communicative deficits are reinforcing the likelihood of the inclusion of AN in the ASD category (Anckarsater et al., 2012). In fact, it currently appears plausible to consider ASD the result of defects on many cognitive processes (Happe, 2003), with relation to the disruption of emotional communications, such as in alexithymia. Neuroimaging studies (Wagner et al., 2007; Zastrow et al., 2009) supported the hypothesis that cognitive rigidity may be a stable trait persisting after the acute phase of symptoms; its association with a low level of somatic awareness can also explain the shared difficulties on emotional recognition both in AN and ASD. Alexithymia, which can be defined a difficulty in identifying and describing emotional states (Taylor, 1984) is a well-researched construct in literature dealing with EDs, as it is well known that emotions detection and expression can be reduced or impaired in subjects with AN (Zonnevylle-Bender, van Goozen, Cohen-Kettenis, van Elburg, & van Engeland, 2004). Alexithymia is related to a weakness in executing Theory-of-Mind (ToM) tasks, as the reduced understanding of others' mental states can include both cognitive and emotive issues. The difficulty in regulating personal emotions and impairments in ToM tasks are trait characteristics in AN (Harrison, Sullivan, Tchanturia, & Treasure, 2009) as they do not resolve after weight restoration. Such symptoms can be both causes and consequences of chronic personal distress in AN (Beadle, Paradiso, Salerno, & McCormick, 2013).

Moreover, it seems plausible that the abovementioned focus on details (WCC) may also interfere with a previously abnormal social functioning in AN and ASD. For example, features processing might disrupt recognition of facial emotions, and reduce context-sensitive interpretation of social behavior or verbal expressions (Happe & Frith, 2006). People with AN and those with ASD can also show similar needs for sameness and difficulties understanding their own emotions and putting themselves into another's perspective, with comparable performances in ad-hoc self-reports questionnaires measure-ing autistic traits (Autism-Spectrum Quotient), empathy (Empathy Quotient-short and Interpersonal Reactivity Index), systemizing (Systemizing Quotient-short) and alexithymia (Bermond-Vorst Alexithymia Questionnaire-B) as reported by Courty and colleagues (2013). Yet, the partial preservation of verbal abilities might be helpful to explain why AN patients cannot be assigned tout-court to ASD, which can instead show verbal impairments both on a lexical and pragmatic level. Whilst both groups can show WCC and the over mentioned social impairment, AN presents a mixed profile of verbal proficiency and visuo-spatial weakness, together with a normal IQ, similar to the cognitive processing style shown by people with high functioning autism or Aspergers (Lopez, Tchanturia, Stahl, Booth, et al., 2008).

An indirect proof confirming the researchers' hypotheses on alexithymia comes from the IGT (Bechara, Damasio, Damasio, & Anderson, 1994), a test assessing skills such as decision-making, delaying reinforce, and preventing negative future consequences of choices. Besides the cognitive issues, the IGT can evaluate the ability to use emotional signals under uncertainty conditions: AN acute patients show decreased anticipatory Skin Conductance Response (SCR) prior to choosing cards and reduced SCR after losses when compared to controls (Tchanturia et al., 2007). The association between impaired decision making ability and a decreased autonomic response is consistent with the Somatic Marker Hypothesis (Damasio, 1996) and with the inability to pay attention to internal emotions in addition to alexithymia. Despite the reduction of SCR was typical of AN, and was also observed in a BN sample (Liao et al., 2009), people with either BN or AN scored significantly worse than a control group on IGT on both overall task performance and across the task learning (Brogan, Hevey, & Pignatti, 2010). The two clinical groups did not differ significantly from each other (or compared to obese patients), indicating that IGT performance may be a common neuropsychological correlate of the patients' disturbed eating behavior. Another study showed women with BN scored worse than controls in the second set of 50 choices of the IGT (choices under risk), and showed some correlations with BN symptoms (Boeka & Lokkenz, 2006). Evidences of a relation between decision-making failures and clinical characteristics were supported by means of a correspondence between IGT performance and obsessive-compulsive traits in BN, but not in AN (Liao et al., 2009). Nevertheless, since both AN and BN clinical groups did not perform within the negative range on the IGT (as is for instance the case of Ventromedial Prefrontal Cortex damaged patients), this may indicate that they were somehow sensitive to punishment; therefore, their performance deficit may be due to a damaged reward processing or vulnerability to distraction (Alvarez-Moya et al., 2009). Another study (Guillaume et al., 2010) found normal decision-making abilities from IGT in euthymic and non-medicated patients with ED, and researchers suggest that a cognitive bias on executive function may be related to depression and to its pharmacological treatment, which can affect serotonin circuits. Whether decision-making itself can be disrupted in women recovered from AN or not is still unclear and literature provides contrasting findings (Danner et al., 2012; Lindner, Fichter, & Quadflieg, 2012). Furthermore, results from some recent works comparing both AN and BN on Hayling Task, WCST, Trail-Making Test (TMT), and IGT indicate that both groups showed some specific impairments during tasks requiring the discovery and maintenance of a strategy (Pignatti & Bernasconi, 2013). The difficulties giving the correct answer on WCST, as well as developing a long-term winning strategy in the IGT (Brogan et al., 2010) or organizing an efficient, structured strategy of copy (Lopez, Tchanturia, Stahl, Booth, et al., 2008) can account for the hypothesis that stable personality traits such as perfectionism and novelty-seeking can limit the adoption of both global and flexible strategies. It should also be noticed that task instructions may influence performances in high-attention demanding tasks. In fact, the instructions of tests assessing executive functions are peculiar, being the subject provided with explicit instructions on TMT Part B and Hayling Task. Even though set-shifting and inhibition tasks are difficult to perform, the expected way to resolve these tasks is clearly stated before starting the test, and run-in situations are developed specifically to ensure comprehension. In contrast, WCST and IGT instructions generate ambiguous situations which the subject is asked to solve by means of a strategy he/she has to develop, together with a "theory of the task". This cognitive operation could be very close to that required by ToM, in which subjects must put themselves in someone else's shoes and try to formulate hypothesis about external behaviors.

To sum up, recent research highlights that cognitive style, personality fixed traits, and socio-emotional difficulties are all involved in the maintenance of EDs and particularly AN, so as observed in ASD patients (Harrison, Sullivan, Tchanturia, & Treasure, 2010; Harrison, Tchanturia, Naumann, & Treasure, 2012; Russell, Schmidt, Doherty, Young, & Tchanturia, 2009). Moreover, these results particularly fit with a theory on maintenance of restriction in AN (Schmidt & Treasure, 2006), which identifies the integration of four factors (perfectionism/cognitive rigidity, experiential avoidance, pro-anorectic beliefs, response of close others) as responsible for chronic food refusal. This model is particularly suitable to integrate with evidences from neuropsychology because, as in many of the quoted works, it is not based on the role of weight and shape-related factors but it gives a long-term vision on stable, culture-free factors acting as a vicious circle.

5.2. Exploring the Endophenotype: Cognitive Rigidity

Gould & Gottesman (2006) described the "endophenotype" as "the quantifiable component in the genes-to-behaviors pathways, distinct form psychiatric symptoms, which make genetic and biological studies manageable". In neuropsychology, it deals with the heritable, state-independent cognitive features characterizing both patients and unaffected relatives.

Set-shifting tasks ask the examinee to move across different contexts by shifting reference points. Failures in these tasks can account for perseveration of thinking and inflexible behavior; in other words, incapability to adapt to changing contexts.

Set-shifting difficulties are well-known in literature about AN and EDs (Roberts et al., 2007), but it is important to distinguish between performance on visual or perceptual set-shifting tasks (e.g. Trail Making Task part B; Wisconsin Card Sorting Test (WCST)) and verbal set-shifting tasks (e.g. Phonemic Fluency, Controlled Oral Word Association Task), as a poor performance on the former suggests a more severe impairment than a poor performance on the latter.

Research aimed at searching a possible endophenotype of set-shifting difficulties and the same tests have often been administered to patients' relatives, too (usually, the healthy sisters). Results did not show significant differences between patients with AN and their sisters in set-shifting tasks. Yet, healthy sisters performed worse than controls recruited in the general population, revealing rigidity especially in perceptual tasks (see Haptic Illusion). Researchers underlined that results from these tasks were state-independent, as AN patients' difficulties were consistent, independent of acute state of illness, weight gain, and complete remission (Holliday, Tchanturia, Landau, Collier, & Treasure, 2005). Since a set-shifting deficit also occurs in other pathologies (e.g. obsessive-compulsive spectrum disorders, schizophrenia), it is better to consider it a possible familiar predisposition for AN (Roberts et al., 2010), rather than a distinctive cognitive bias.

In a task of haptic exploration, the mean exploration time was similar in AN patients and controls. The quality of reproduction of the haptic stimuli and the EEG pattern (theta-power changes) indicate a cortical dysfunction and deficits in somatosensory integration processing of the right parietal cortex in AN patients even after weight gain (Grunwald, Ettrich, Assmann, et al., 2001; Grunwald, Ettrich, Krause, et al., 2001; Grunwald, Weiss, Assmann, & Ettrich, 2004). A rigidity of perception might add up to a rigidity of thinking: when both are expressed they can be associated to the acute state of AN, while perceptive rigidity alone might predispose to the development of AN or to a shifting to BN, probably in consequence of an increased compulsivity (Roberts et al., 2007; Roberts et al., 2010; Tchanturia et al., 2004). The rigidity observed in sisters of AN patients can instead be compensated by a good functioning in real life, for example by conducting strong self-control-demanding jobs.

The inclusion of some cognitive issues among personality markers rather than endophenotypes is still matter of debate. Recent research is, in fact, aimed at evaluating whether an approach based on endophenotypical investigation may clarify the literature on most critical points. Some recent evidences are in fact leading to the inclusion of decision-making defects on IGT among inheritable biases (Galimberti et al., 2013). The same attention has been recently paid to the possible inclusion of WCC and set-shifting deficit among candidate endophenotypes of AN (Roberts, Tchanturia, & Treasure, 2013). In fact, families may have a strong impact, from genetic to communicational levels, in such patients and future research should aim at providing more refined distinctions on cognitive-affective patterns, which can help to disentangle some psychological issues that are to date still believed undifferentiated. Besides that, the knowledge about fluid and modifiable features allowed clinicians to adapt the Cognitive Remediation Therapy (CRT), initially developed for psychotic patients, to cognitive characteristics of AN. Preliminary results from early controlled studies show good compliance and some improvements on both set-shifting abilities and flexibility of thinking (Tchanturia, Lloyd, & Lang, 2013).

References

Aigner, M., Treasure, J., Kaye, W. & Kasper, S. (2011). World Federation of Societies of Biological Psychiatry (WFSBP) guidelines for the pharmacological treatment of eating disorders. *World Journal of Biological Psychiatry*, *12*(6), 400-443. doi: 10.3109/15622975.2011. 602720

Alvarez-Moya, E. M., Jimenez-Murcia, S., Moragas, L., Gomez-Pena, M., Aymami, M. N., Ochoa, C., . . . Fernandez-Aranda, F. (2009). Executive functioning among female pathological gambling and bulimia nervosa patients: preliminary findings. *Journal of the International Neuropsychological Society, 15*(2), 302-306. doi: S1355617709090377 [pii] 10.1017/S1355617709090377

Anckarsater, H., Hofvander, B., Billstedt, E., Gillberg, I. C., Gillberg, C., Wentz, E. & Rastam, M. (2012). The sociocommunicative deficit subgroup in anorexia nervosa: autism spectrum disorders and neurocognition in a community-based, longitudinal study. *Psychological Medicine, 42*(9), 1957-1967. doi: 10.1017/s0033291711002881

Beadle, J. N., Paradiso, S., Salerno, A. & McCormick, L. M. (2013). Alexithymia, emotional empathy, and self-regulation in anorexia nervosa. *Annals of Clinical Psychiatry, 25*(2), 107-120.

Bechara, A., Damasio, A. R., Damasio, H. & Anderson, S. W. (1994). Insensitivity to future consequences following damage to human prefrontal cortex. *Cognition, 50*(1-3), 7-15.

Benton, D. & Sargent, J. (1992). Breakfast, blood glucose and memory. *Biological Psychology, 33*(2-3), 207-210.

Boeka, A. G. & Lokkenz, K. L. (2006). The Iowa gambling task as a measure of decision making in women with bulimia nervosa. *Journal of the International Neuropsychological Society, 12*(5), 741-745. doi: Doi 10.1017/S1355617706060887

Brand, M., Labudda, K. & Markowitsch, H. J. (2006). Neuropsychological correlates of decision-making in ambiguous and risky situations. *Neural Networks, 19*(8), 1266-1276. doi: 10.1016/j.neunet.2006.03.001

Brogan, A., Hevey, D. & Pignatti, R. (2010). Anorexia, bulimia, and obesity: Shared decision making deficits on the Iowa Gambling Task (IGT). *Journal of the International Neuropsychological Society, 16*(4), 711-715. doi: Doi 10.1017/S1355617710000354

Bruch, H. (1962). Perceptual and conceptual disturbances in anorexia nervosa. *Psychosomatic Medicine, 24*, 187-194.

Buhren, K., Mainz, V., Herpertz-Dahlmann, B., Schafer, K., Kahraman-Lanzerath, B., Lente, C. & Konrad, K. (2012). Cognitive flexibility in juvenile anorexia nervosa patients before and after weight recovery. *Journal of Neural Transmission, 119*(9), 1047-1057. doi: 10.1007/s00702-012-0821-z

Burgess, P. W. & Shallice, T. (1997). *The Hayling and Brixton Tests*. Bury St. Edmonds, UK: Thames Valley Test Company Ltd.

Courty, A., Maria, A. S., Lalanne, C., Ringuenet, D., Vindreau, C., Chevallier, C., . . . Berthoz, S. (2013). Levels of autistic traits in anorexia nervosa: a comparative psychometric study. *BMC Psychiatry, 13*(1), 222. doi: 10.1186/1471-244x-13-222

Damasio, A. R. (1996). The somatic marker hypothesis and the possible functions of the prefrontal cortex. *Philosophical Transactions of the Royal Society B: Biological Sciences, 351*(1346), 1413-1420. doi: 10.1098/rstb.1996.0125

Danner, U. N., Sanders, N., Smeets, P. A., van Meer, F., Adan, R. A., Hoek, H. W. & van Elburg, A. A. (2012). Neuropsychological weaknesses in anorexia nervosa: set-shifting, central coherence, and decision making in currently ill and recovered women. *International Journal of Eating Disorders, 45*(5), 685-694. doi: 10.1002/eat.22007

Dimitropoulos, A. & Schultz, R. T. (2007). Autistic-like symptomatology in Prader-Willi syndrome: a review of recent findings. *Current Psychiatry Reports, 9*(2), 159-164.

Dykens, E. M., Roof, E., Bittel, D. & Butler, M. G. (2011). TPH2 G/T polymorphism is associated with hyperphagia, IQ, and internalizing problems in Prader-Willi syndrome.

Journal of Child Psychology and Psychiatry, 52(5), 580-587. doi: 10.1111/j.1469-7610.2011.02365.x

Eliava, N. (1964). *A problem of set in cognitive psychology*. Tblisi, Georgia: Academic Press.

Favaro, A., Santonastaso, P., Manara, R., Bosello, R., Bommarito, G., Tenconi, E. & Di Salle, F. (2012). Disruption of visuospatial and somatosensory functional connectivity in anorexia nervosa. *Biological Psychiatry*, 72(10), 864-870. doi: 10.1016/j.biopsych.2012. 04.025

Frank, G. K., Bailer, U. F., Henry, S., Wagner, A. & Kaye, W. H. (2004). Neuroimaging studies in eating disorders. *CNS Spectrums*, 9(7), 539-548.

Galimberti, E., Fadda, E., Cavallini, M. C., Martoni, R. M., Erzegovesi, S. & Bellodi, L. (2013). Executive functioning in anorexia nervosa patients and their unaffected relatives. *Psychiatry Research*, 208(3), 238-244. doi: 10.1016/j.psychres.2012.10.001

Galimberti, E., Martoni, R. M., Cavallini, M. C., Erzegovesi, S. & Bellodi, L. (2011). Motor inhibition and cognitive flexibility in eating disorder subtypes. *Progress in Neuro-Psychopharmacology and Biological Psychiatry*. doi: S0278-5846(11)00314-9 [pii] 10.1016/j.pnpbp.2011.10. 017

Gardner, R. M. & Bokenkamp, E. D. (1996). The role of sensory and nonsensory factors in body size estimations of eating disorder subjects. *Journal of Clinical Psychology*, 52(1), 3-15. doi: 10.1002/(SICI)1097-4679(199601)52:1<3::AID-JCLP1>3.0.CO;2-X

Garner, D. M. (1981). Body image in anorexia nervosa. *Canadian Journal of Psychiatry*, 26(4), 224-231.

Gicquel, L. (2013). Anorexia nervosa during adolescence and young adulthood: Towards a developmental and integrative approach sensitive to time course. *Journal of Physiology - Paris*. doi: S0928-4257(13)00012-0 [pii] 10.1016/j.jphysparis.2013.03.010

Gillberg, I. C., Gillberg, C., Rastam, M. & Johansson, M. (1996). The cognitive profile of anorexia nervosa: a comparative study including a community-based sample. *Comprehensive Psychiatry*, 37(1), 23-30.

Gillberg, I. C., Rastam, M., Wentz, E. & Gillberg, C. (2007). Cognitive and executive functions in anorexia nervosa ten years after onset of eating disorder. *Journal of Clinical and Experimental Neuropsychology*, 29(2), 170-178. doi: 770386515 [pii] 10.1080/13803390600584632

Gould, T. D. & Gottesman, II. (2006). Psychiatric endophenotypes and the development of valid animal models. *Genes, Brain and Behavior*, 5(2), 113-119. doi: 10.1111/j.1601-183X.2005.00186.x

Grunwald, M., Ettrich, C., Assmann, B., Dahne, A., Krause, W., Busse, F. & Gertz, H. J. (2001). Deficits in haptic perception and right parietal theta power changes in patients with anorexia nervosa before and after weight gain. *International Journal of Eating Disorders*, 29(4), 417-428.

Grunwald, M., Ettrich, C., Krause, W., Assmann, B., Dahne, A., Weiss, T. & Gertz, H. J. (2001). Haptic perception in anorexia nervosa before and after weight gain. *Journal of Clinical and Experimental Neuropsychology*, 23(4), 520-529. doi: 10.1076/jcen. 23.4.520.1229

Grunwald, M., Weiss, T., Assmann, B. & Ettrich, C. (2004). Stable asymmetric interhemispheric theta power in patients with anorexia nervosa during haptic perception even after weight gain: a longitudinal study. *Journal of Clinical and Experimental Neuropsychology*, 26(5), 608-620. doi: 10.1080/13803390409609785

Guillaume, S., Sang, C. N. T., Jaussent, I., Raingeard, I., Bringer, J., Jollant, F. & Courtet, P. (2010). Is Decision Making Really Impaired in Eating Disorders? *Neuropsychology*, *24*(6), 808-812. doi: Doi 10.1037/A0019806

Happe, F. (2003). Cognition in autism: one deficit or many? *Novartis Foundation Symposium*, *251*, 198-207; discussion 207-112, 281-197.

Happe, F. & Frith, U. (2006). The weak coherence account: detail-focused cognitive style in autism spectrum disorders. *Journal of Autism and Developmental Disorders*, *36*(1), 5-25. doi: 10.1007/s10803-005-0039-0

Harrison, A., Sullivan, S., Tchanturia, K. & Treasure, J. (2009). Emotion recognition and regulation in anorexia nervosa. *Clinical Psychology & Psychotherapy*, *16*(4), 348-356. doi: 10.1002/cpp.628

Harrison, A., Sullivan, S., Tchanturia, K. & Treasure, J. (2010). Emotional functioning in eating disorders: attentional bias, emotion recognition and emotion regulation. *Psychological Medicine*, *40*(11), 1887-1897. doi: 10.1017/s0033291710000036

Harrison, A., Tchanturia, K., Naumann, U. & Treasure, J. (2012). Social emotional functioning and cognitive styles in eating disorders. *British Journal of Clinical Psychology*, *51*(3), 261-279. doi: 10.1111/j.2044-8260.2011.02026.x

Heaton, R. K., Chelune, G. J., Talley, J. L., Kay, G. G. & Curtiss, G. (1993). *Wisconsin card sorting test manual* Odessa, FL: Psychological Assessment Resources, Inc.

Herpertz-Dahlmann, B., Seitz, J. & Konrad, K. (2011). Aetiology of anorexia nervosa: from a "psychosomatic family model" to a neuropsychiatric disorder? *European Archives of Psychiatry and Clinical Neurosciences*, *261 Suppl 2*, S177-181. doi: 10.1007/s00406-011-0246-y

Holliday, J., Tchanturia, K., Landau, S., Collier, D. & Treasure, J. (2005). Is impaired set-shifting an endophenotype of anorexia nervosa? *American Journal of Psychiatry*, *162*(12), 2269-2275. doi: 10.1176/appi.ajp.162. 12.2269

Jones, B. P., Duncan, C. C., Brouwers, P. & Mirsky, A. F. (1991). Cognition in eating disorders. *Journal of Clinical and Experimental Neuropsychology*, *13*(5), 711-728. doi: 10.1080/01688639108401085

Keifer, E., Duff, K., Beglinger, L. J., Barstow, E., Andersen, A. & Moser, D. J. (2010). Predictors of neuropsychological recovery in treatment for anorexia nervosa. *Eating Disorders: The Journal of Treatment & Prevention*, *18*(4), 302-317. doi: 10.1080/10640266.2010.490120

Laessle, R. G., Fischer, M., Fichter, M. M., Pirke, K. M. & Krieg, J. C. (1992). Cortisol levels and vigilance in eating disorder patients. *Psychoneuroendocrinology*, *17*(5), 475-484.

Lezak, M. D., Hovieson, D. B. & Loring, D. W. (2004). *Neuropsychological Assessment*, New York: Oxford University Press.

Liao, P. C., Uher, R., Lawrence, N., Treasure, J., Schmidt, U., Campbell, I. C., . . . Tchanturia, K. (2009). An examination of decision making in bulimia nervosa. *Journal of Clinical and Experimental Neuropsychology*, *31*(4), 455-461. doi: Pii 901493254 Doi 10.1080/13803390802251378

Lindner, S. E., Fichter, M. M. & Quadflieg, N. (2012). Decision-making and planning in full recovery of anorexia nervosa. *International Journal of Eating Disorders*, *45*(7), 866-875. doi: 10.1002/eat.22025

Lindner, S. E., Fichter, M. M. & Quadflieg, N. (2013). Central coherence in full recovery of anorexia nervosa. *European Eating Disorders Review*, *21*(2), 115-120. doi: 10.1002/erv.2213

Lopez, C., Tchanturia, K., Stahl, D., Booth, R., Holliday, J. & Treasure, J. (2008). An examination of the concept of central coherence in women with anorexia nervosa. *International Journal of Eating Disorders*, *41*(2), 143-152. doi: 10.1002/eat.20478

Lopez, C., Tchanturia, K., Stahl, D. & Treasure, J. (2008). Central coherence in women with bulimia nervosa. *International Journal of Eating Disorders*, *41*(4), 340-347. doi: 10.1002/eat.20511

Majewski, M. L. (1997). *Children and adolescents with eating disorders: How do they estimate their body size?* Paper presented at the 14th World Congress on Psychosomatic Medicine, Cairns, Australia.

Martinez, G., Cook-Darzens, S., Chaste, P., Mouren, M. C. & Doyen, C. (2013). [Anorexia nervosa in the light of neurocognitive functioning: New theoretical and therapeutic perspectives.]. *Encephale*. doi: 10.1016/j. encep.2012.06.004

Molinari, E. (1995). Body-size estimation in anorexia nervosa. *Perceptual & Motor Skills*, *81*(1), 23-31.

Oldershaw, A., Treasure, J., Hambrook, D., Tchanturia, K. & Schmidt, U. (2011). Is anorexia nervosa a version of autism spectrum disorders? *European Eating Disorders Review*, *19*(6), 462-474. doi: 10.1002/ erv.1069

Pieters, G., Hulstijn, W., Vandereycken, W., Maas, Y., Probst, M., Peuskens, J. & Sabbe, B. (2005). Fast psychomotor functioning in anorexia nervosa: effect of weight restoration. *Journal of Clinical and Experimental Neuropsychology*, *27*(8), 931-942. doi: U3160705780Q7074 [pii] 10.1080/13803390490918093

Pieters, G., Sabbe, B., Hulstijn, W., Probst, M., Vandereycken, W. & Peuskens, J. (2003). Fast psychomotor functioning in underweight anorexia nervosa patients. *Journal of Psychiatric Research*, *37*(6), 501-508. doi: S0022395603000670 [pii]

Pignatti, R. & Bernasconi, V. (2013). Personality, clinical features, and test instructions can affect executive functions in Eating Disorders. *Eating Behaviors*, *14*(2), 233-236. doi: S1471-0153(12)00131-6 [pii] 10.1016/j. eatbeh.2012.12.003

Pignatti, R., Bertella, L., Albani, G., Mauro, A., Molinari, E. & Semenza, C. (2006). Decision-making in obesity: a study using the Gambling Task. *Eating and Weight Disorders*, *11*(3), 126-132.

Probst, M., Vandereycken, W., Van Coppenolle, H. & Pieters, G. (1995). Body size estimation in eating disorder patients: testing the video distortion method on a life-size screen. *Behaviour Research and Therapy*, *33*(8), 985-990.

Rastam, M., Gillberg, C., Gillberg, I. C. & Johansson, M. (1997). Alexithymia in anorexia nervosa: a controlled study using the 20-item Toronto Alexithymia Scale. *Acta Psychiatrica Scandinavica*, *95*(5), 385-388.

Roberts, M. E., Tchanturia, K., Stahl, D., Southgate, L. & Treasure, J. (2007). A systematic review and meta-analysis of set-shifting ability in eating disorders. *Psychological Medicine*, *37*(8), 1075-1084. doi: S0033291707009877 [pii] 10.1017/S0033291707009877

Roberts, M. E., Tchanturia, K. & Treasure, J. L. (2010). Exploring the neurocognitive signature of poor set-shifting in anorexia and bulimia nervosa. *Journal of Psychiatric*

Research, 44(14), 964-970. doi: S0022-3956(10)00070-1 [pii] 10.1016/j.jpsychires.2010.03.001

Roberts, M. E., Tchanturia, K. & Treasure, J. L. (2013). Is attention to detail a similarly strong candidate endophenotype for anorexia nervosa and bulimia nervosa? *The World Journal of Biological Psychiatry Psychiatry, 14*(6), 452-463. doi: 10.3109/15622975.2011.639804

Rotenberg, V. S. (2000). Guest editorial. *International Journal of Psychiatry in Clinical Practice, 4*(2), 89-92.

Russell, T. A., Schmidt, U., Doherty, L., Young, V. & Tchanturia, K. (2009). Aspects of social cognition in anorexia nervosa: affective and cognitive theory of mind. *Psychiatry Research, 168*(3), 181-185. doi: 10.1016/ j.psychres.2008.10.028

Sachdev, P., Mondraty, N., Wen, W. & Gulliford, K. (2008). Brains of anorexia nervosa patients process self-images differently from non-self-images: an fMRI study. *Neuropsychologia, 46*(8), 2161-2168. doi: 10.1016/j.neuropsychologia.2008.02.031

Schmidt, U. & Treasure, J. (2006). Anorexia nervosa: valued and visible. A cognitive-interpersonal maintenance model and its implications for research and practice. *British Journal of Clinical Psychology, 45*(Pt 3), 343-366.

Seed, J. A., McCue, P. M., Wesnes, K. A., Dahabra, S. & Young, A. H. (2002). Basal activity of the HPA axis and cognitive function in anorexia nervosa. *The International Journal of Neuropsychopharmacology, 5*(1), 17-25.

Southgate, L., Tchanturia, K. & Treasure, J. (2008). Information processing bias in anorexia nervosa. *Psychiatry Research, 160*(2), 221-227. doi: S0165-1781(07)00256-9 [pii] 10.1016/j.psychres.2007.07.017

Southgate, L., Tchanturia, K. & Treasure, J. (2009). Neuropsychology in eating disorders. In S. J. Wood, A. N. B. & P. C. (Eds.), *The Neuropsychology of mental Illness* (316-325). Cambridge: Cambridge University Press.

Suda, M., Brooks, S. J., Giampietro, V., Friederich, H. C., Uher, R., Brammer, M. J., . . . Treasure, J. (2013). Functional neuroanatomy of body checking in people with anorexia nervosa. *International Journal of Eating Disorders*. doi: 10.1002/eat.22150

Surguladze, S. (1995). Insight and characteristics of fixed set in patients with schizophrenia. *Journal of Georgian Medicine,* (2), 58-60.

Szmukler, G. I., Andrewes, D., Kingston, K., Chen, L., Stargatt, R. & Stanley, R. (1992). Neuropsychological impairment in anorexia nervosa: before and after refeeding. *Journal of Clinical and Experimental Neuropsychology, 14*(2), 347-352. doi: 10.1080/01688639208402834

Taylor, G. J. (1984). Alexithymia: concept, measurement, and implications for treatment. *American Journal of Psychiatry, 141*(6), 725-732.

Tchanturia, K., Anderluh, M. B., Morris, R. G., Rabe-Hesketh, S., Collier, D. A., Sanchez, P. & Treasure, J. L. (2004). Cognitive flexibility in anorexia nervosa and bulimia nervosa. *Journal of the International Neuropsychological Society, 10*(4), 513-520. doi: 10.1017/ s1355617704104086

Tchanturia, K., Liao, P. C., Uher, R., Lawrence, N., Treasure, J. & Campbell, I. C. (2007). An investigation of decision making in anorexia nervosa using the Iowa Gambling Task and skin conductance measurements. *Journal of the International Neuropsychological Society, 13*(4), 635-641. doi: 10.1017/s1355617707070798

Tchanturia, K., Lloyd, S. & Lang, K. (2013). Cognitive remediation therapy for anorexia nervosa: current evidence and future research directions. *International Journal of Eating Disorders*, *46*(5), 492-495. doi: 10.1002/eat.22106

Tchanturia, K., Morris, R. G., Surguladze, S. & Treasure, J. (2002). An examination of perceptual and cognitive set shifting tasks in acute anorexia nervosa and following recovery. *Eating and Weight Disorders*, *7*(4), 312-315.

Tchanturia, K., Serpell, L., Troop, N. & Treasure, J. (2001). Perceptual illusions in eating disorders: rigid and fluctuating styles. *Journal of Behavior Therapy and Experimental Psychiatry*, *32*(3), 107-115.

Tejado Lde, A., Ruiz, R. M., Trebbau, H., Diaz-Marsa, M. & Perera, J. L. (2010). Functional magnetic resonance studies in eating behavior disorders. *Actas espanolas de psiquiatria*, *38*(3), 183-188.

Uznadze, D. N. (1966). *The psychology of set*. New York: Consultants' Bureau.

Verdine, B. N., Troseth, G. L., Hodapp, R. M. & Dykens, E. M. (2008). Strategies and correlates of jigsaw puzzle and visuospatial performance by persons with Prader-Willi syndrome. *American Journal on Mental Retardation*, *113*(5), 343-355. doi: 10.1352/2008.113:342-355

Wagner, A., Aizenstein, H., Venkatraman, V. K., Fudge, J., May, J. C., Mazurkewicz, L., . . . Kaye, W. H. (2007). Altered reward processing in women recovered from anorexia nervosa. *American Journal of Psychiatry*, *164*(12), 1842-1849. doi: 164/12/1842 [pii] 10.1176/appi.ajp.2007. 07040575

Zastrow, A., Kaiser, S., Stippich, C., Walther, S., Herzog, W., Tchanturia, K., . . . Friederich, H. C. (2009). Neural correlates of impaired cognitive-behavioral flexibility in anorexia nervosa. *American Journal of Psychiatry*, *166*(5), 608-616. doi: appi.ajp.2008.08050775 [pii] 10.1176/ appi.ajp.2008.08050775

Zonnevylle-Bender, M. J., van Goozen, S. H., Cohen-Kettenis, P. T., van Elburg, T. A. & van Engeland, H. (2004). Emotional functioning in adolescent anorexia nervosa patients--a controlled study. *European Child & Adolescent Psychiatry*, *13*(1), 28-34. doi: 10.1007/s00787-004-0351-9

In: New Developments in Anorexia Nervosa Research ISBN: 978-1-63117-551-0
Editors: Carla Gramaglia and Patrizia Zeppegno © 2014 Nova Science Publishers, Inc.

Chapter 6

Male Eating Disorder Pathology: A Brief Report Based on Two Outpatients with Anorexia Nervosa

Anna Brytek-Matera[1],*, Bernard Blanchard[2]
and Małgorzata Starzomska[3]

[1]University of Social Sciences and Humanities, Campus in Katowice, Poland
[2]Centre d'Accueil pour la Santé des Adolescents, Metz, France
[3]Cardinal Stephan Wyszynski University, Institute of Psychology, Warsaw, Poland

Abstract

Background: The purpose of the present report was to evaluate body image, self-esteem, clinical features of eating disorders and symptoms of mood and anxiety disorders in male adolescents with anorexia nervosa.

Methods: Two adolescent male outpatients (aged 16 and 17) who fulfill the Diagnostic and Statistical Manual of Mental Disorders-IV criteria for anorexia nervosa participated in this study. We used the Contour Drawing Rating Scale, the Body Attitude Test, the Body Image Avoidance Questionnaire, the Self-Esteem Inventory, the Eating Disorder Inventory and the Hospital Anxiety and Depression Scale.

Results: The results of this report show that both the actual-ideal and the actual-ought self-discrepancy (in both cases), grooming and weighing (in both cases), mood and anxiety disorders (in both cases), drive for thinness (in one case) as well as eating restraint (in one case) play a major role in the male eating disorder pathology.

Conclusions: The results of the current report could be useful to open new paths for future research in the area of male anorexia nervosa.

Keywords: Male adolescents – anorexia nervosa – body image – self-esteem

---

* Corresponding author: Anna Brytek-Matera. University of Social Sciences and Humanities, Campus in Katowice, Techników 9, 40-326 Katowice, Poland. E-mail: abrytek-matera @swps.edu.pl.

Introduction

Anorexia nervosa in men still causes a lot of controversy despite the fact that among people suffering from anorexia nervosa men seem to be similar to women in terms of the clinical characteristic and coexisting mental diseases (Lindblad et al., 2006; Woodside et al., 2001).

Although in many respects such an analogy is justified (i.e. psycho-pathological order, comorbidity, course and consequences), there are still some reports on significant differences in this area. Linblad et al. (2006) claim that anorexia nervosa is diagnosed in men later than in women, which results from later looking for help in comparison with women. This might be caused by men's fear of being suspected of suffering from a "feminine disease" or by men's more successful masking the disease with physical activity. What is more, the researchers stress the prevalence of asexuality or homosexuality in men with the diagnosed anorexia nervosa or lack of heterosexual contacts (Linblad et al., 2006). It is also worth emphasising that "male" anorexia, in comparison with the "female" anorexia, is more frequently accompanied by disorders in a sense of gender identity (Crisp et al., 2006), for example, fear of homosexuality strongly connected with the perception of one's own body shape and weight.

Furthermore, anorexia nervosa in men in comparison with women is characterised by more intense physical activity, better care of body shape and lesser of the body weight (Linblad et al., 2006). The research conducted by Oybode et al. (1988) revealed that this disease in men has a worse (only slightly though) prognosis than in women. In addition, in comparison with women, it is more frequently accompanied by other psychiatric disorders (Crisp et al., 2006), and suicide attempts are more frequent (Krasnow, 1996).

A serious problem posed by anorexia in men is the lack of tools correctly diagnosing this disease and resulting from it the lack of reliable diagnostics and insufficient research into this area (Scott, 1986).

All the differences between anorexia nervosa in women and men can constitute an artefact since the number of the examined men was low in comparison with the women (Linblad et al., 2006).

One of the reasons for neglecting research into anorexia nervosa in men is a small number of cases, focusing on psychodynamic concepts clearly feminising the issue of anorexia, overestimation of the amenorrhoea criterion, emphasising that the disease in men is secondary to other psychiatric diseases (Scott, 1986).

In this context, each study of men with anorexia nervosa can be of great value and will contribute to broadening the knowledge of the men's counterpart of anorexia nervosa in women.

Anorexia nervosa occurs (during a lifetime) in approximately 1 in 200 girls and women and 1 in 2,000 boys and men (APA, 2000; Keel and McCormick, 2010).

Current research indicates that the percentage of men suffering from anorexia nervosa compared with women is approximately one to nine or ten (Keel and McCormick, 2010; Williamson et al., 2004).

Other studies show that 1 in 8 adolescents with anorexia nervosa, having less than 14 years old, is male (Katzman and Golden, 2008). The prevalence of anorexia nervosa is from 0.16% to 0.3% in men (Hudson et al., 2007; Ricciardelli and McCabe 2004) and from 0.3% to

2.2% in women (Hoek and van Hoeken, 2003; Favaro et al., 2004; Keski-Rahkonen et al., 2007). Since the literature on the subject related to the research into eating disorders focuses mostly on female population (which is caused, among others, by the fact that men account for "only" 10% of all clinical cases; Weltzin et al., 2005), the authors made an attempt to evaluate variables which, in their opinion, play a significant role in the pathology of anorexia nervosa. The purpose of the present study was to identify the psychological factors associated with body image, cognitive-behavioural aspects of eating disorders, self-esteem and symptoms of mood and anxiety disorders in male adolescents with anorexia nervosa, through the description of two cases.

Methods

Participants

Two adolescents fulfilling diagnostic criteria of anorexia nervosa according to the DSM-IV-TR (APA, 2000) classification participated in the research. Due to the fact that it was the male population D criterion (amenorrhea) was a priori excluded. The men were treated on an outpatient basis in *Maison des Adolescents de la Moselle* in Metz (Lotharingia, France) and were under the constant psychological and psychiatric supervision. The study was approved by the ethics committee. The detailed characteristics of the examined patients are shown in Table 1.

Materials

Two male adolescents with anorexia nervosa were assessed with the Contour Drawing Rating Scale (CDRS), the Body Attitude Test (BAT), the Body Image Avoidance Questionnaire (BIAQ), the Eating Disorders Inventory (EDI), the Self-Esteem Inventory (SEI) and the Hospital Depression and Anxiety Scale (HADS).

For the evaluation of the body image the Contour Drawing Rating Scale (Thompson and Gray, 1995) was used. The CDRS shows nine men contour drawings varied in terms of body mass, ranging from very slim (1) to obese (9). The examined men were requested to choose: their current body contour ("Please circle the silhouette that presents your current body size"), the contour they would like to have ("Please circle the silhouette that presents your ideal body size") and the one they should have in other people's opinions ("Please circle the silhouette that presents the figure men should have"). Application of this method helps establish: the actual body size (which include the figure that people believes they actually possesses), the ideal body size (which contains the figure that people would like to possess) and the ought body size (which includes the figure that people believe they should possess). Current versus ideal body size perception (actual–ideal self-discrepancy) and current versus ought body size perception (actual-ought self-discrepancy) were also calculated in our study. The CDRS has good test-retest reliability over a one-week time span ($r = .78$, $p < 0.0005$) (Thompson and Gray, 1995). Test-retest administration of the CDRS was carried out for a subsample of 32 subjects (Thompson and Gray, 1995), however in a large sample of adolescent girls (n =

1056), Wertheim et al. (2004) reported 14-week test-retest reliabilities ranging from .71 to .90 (test-retest reliability for current size, ideal size and current-ideal discrepancy mostly exceeded 0.70) and provided evidence of satisfactory construct and discriminant validity (Frederick et al., 2008).

Table 1. Characteristics of adolescent male with anorexia nervosa

Variable	Case 1	Case 2
Age	17 years	16 years
Height	177 cm	175 cm
Actual weight	56 kg	49 kg
Ideal weight	59 kg	65 kg
Body Mass Index	17,87 kg/m²	16,00 kg/m²
Education	Secondary school	Secondary school
Family situation	Parents lived together	Parents were divorced
Weigh themselves every day	Yes	No
Frequency weigh themselves	Twice a day	-
Body satisfaction	Yes	No
Duration of eating problems	7 months	11 years
Type of anorexia nervosa	Restricting type	Binge eating/purging type
Psychological/psychiatric care	Yes	Yes
Hospitalisation	No	No

The Body Attitude Test (Probst et al. 1995) is a self-report questionnaire used to evaluate the subjective body experience and the attitude towards one's body. The questionnaire has been developed for female patients suffering from eating disorders. The BAT consists of three factors: negative appreciation of body size (e.g., "I feel my body as a burden"), lack of familiarity with one's own body (e.g., "My body appears as if it's not mine") and general body dissatisfaction (e.g., "When I compare myself with my peers' bodies, I'm dissatisfied with my own"). The questionnaire consists of 20 items to be scored on a six-point scale (ranging from "always" to "never"). Items are scored from 5 ("always") to 0 ("never"), with two reverse-scored items (4 and 9). Total scores range from 0 to 100, with higher scores indicating more deviated body experience. The BAT shows good reliability (internal consistency and test-retest) and validity (convergent and discriminant) as well as has good convergent validity with existing body experience related questionnaires (Probst et al., 1995). This method underwent a translation/back-translation standard procedure.

The Body Image Avoidance Questionnaire (Rosen et al., 1991; Maïano et al., 2009) was used for the evaluation of behaviours accompanying the distorted body image. The questionnaire consists of 19 items constituting subscales referring to: (1) a tendency for concealing or masking their appearance by means of their outfit, e.g. wearing loose clothing (subscale clothing; 36.4% of the variance); (2) avoidance of social situations where food, body mass or appearance are involved (subscale social activities; 9.7% of variance); (3) eating restraint (7.3% of variance) and (4) taking care of appearance and body mass can be in the centre of attention (subscale grooming and weighing; 6.9% of variance). Each of the items is evaluated according to a six-point scale (from "never" to "always"). The BIAQ has good internal consistency (the Cronbach's alpha = .89) (Maïano et al., 2009).

Attitudes and behaviours related to eating and cognitive-behavioural aspects of anorexia nervosa and bulimia nervosa were evaluated with the Eating Disorder Inventory (Archinard et al., 2002; Garner et al., 1983). This method consists of 64 items (evaluated according to a six-point scale ranging from "always" to "never"). The EDI is an internationally widely used questionnaire with good reliability. Internal consistency coefficients ranging from .83 to .93 (for eating disorder samples) and test-retest reliability coefficients ranging from .85 to .95 have been reported for the eight scales. The Drive for Thinness scale includes information about preoccupation with weight, restrictive tendencies and the individual's entrenchment in an extreme pursuit of thinness. The Bulimia scale indicates the tendency towards episodes of uncontrollable overeating and may be followed by the impulse to engage in self-induced vomiting. The Body Dissatisfaction scale assesses dissatisfaction with overall shape and size, evaluating different parts of body (e.g. buttocks, hips). The Ineffectiveness scale includes statements about worthlessness, inadequacy and lack of control over life. The Perfectionism scale involves the need for superiority of personal achievements. The Interpersonal Distrust scale measures feelings of distrust and alienation concerning close relationship. The Interoceptive Awareness scale relates to one's ability to recognize, identify and respond to emotions and sensations of hunger or satiety. Maturity Fears scale indicates concerns about growing older and the desire to remain in the security of childhood. Higher scores indicate greater levels of eating pathology (Garner et al., 1983).

The Self-Esteem Inventory (Coopersmith, 1984) was used for evaluation attitudes and behaviours related to the evaluation of one's own self-esteem in the four areas of human functioning: general (aspect of self-esteem related to the general sense of self-esteem), social (aspect of self-esteem related to a person's functioning among people), family (aspect of self-esteem related to functioning and mutual relationships in the family) and school/work (aspect of self-esteem related to achievements, ambitions, and involvement in school/ work activity). Additionally, Coopersmith (1984) created a lie subscale that is to be regarded as an indicator of defensive attitudes in replies to questions included in the questionnaire. Respondents have an option of choosing answers: "it's like me" or "it's not like me". 26 points is the highest result on the general scale whereas for the remaining scales it is 8. The total result for the questionnaire is 50. Achieving the score 33 and less indicates a very low sense of one's own self-esteem. The SEI possesses a satisfying internal consistency (with Cronbach's a ranging from .77 to .90), and a good test-retest reliability (r = .90 to .96; over a one-month interval) (Coopersmith, 1984).

The evaluation of the mood and anxiety disorders level (excluding somatic symptoms) was made with the Hospital Anxiety and Depression Scale (Razavi et al., 1989; Zigmond and Snaith, 1983). The HADS is a brief self-assessment questionnaire constructed in order to evaluate the levels of anxiety and depression among medical outpatients. The HADS consists in 14 items (7 for each subscale). Each item has to be answered by the patient on a four point (0-3) response category; thus the possible scores range from 0 to 21 for anxiety and 0 to 21 for depression. An analysis of scores, in relationship with severity of symptoms, showed that a score of 0 to 7 for either subscale could be regarded as being in the normal range, a score of 8 to 10 being just suggestive of the presence of the respective morbid state and a score of 11 or higher indicating probable presence ("caseness") of the psychopathology (Snaith, 2003). The items do not include physical indicators of psychological distress such as headache or weight loss, which could result in false positive responses. In the HADS, severity ratings correlated highly with psychiatric assessments ($r = .74$ for anxiety and $r = .70$ for depression) (Zigmond and Snaith, 1983).

Results

Body image, body attitudes, behaviours accompanying the disturbed body image, cognitive-behavioural aspects of eating disorders, evaluation attitudes and behaviours related to self-esteem in the four areas of human functioning (related to social life, family, school and general) and the level of anxiety and depression symptoms (excluding somatic symptoms) were assessed in two young male patients with anorexia nervosa. Results are shown in Table 2.

Table 2. The results of the psychological variables tested in two young men with anorexia

Variables (sub-scales of the used methods)	Case 1	Case 2	General score (from minimum to maximum) for each of the used method
CDRS - Actual self	3	4	1-9
CDRS - Ideal self	5	5	1-9
CDRS - Ought self	6	5	1-9
CDRS - Actual-ideal self-discrepancy	-2	-1	-
CDRS - Actual-ought self-discrepancy	-3	-1	-
BAT - Negative appreciation of body size	6	1	0-35
BAT - Lack of familiarity with one's own body	10	10	0-35
BAT - General dissatisfaction	7	2	0-20
BIAQ - Clothing	12	6	0-45
BIAQ - Social activities	0	0	0-20
BIAQ - Eating restraint	10	5	0-15
BIAQ - Grooming and weighing	13	13	0-15
EDI - Drive for thinness	15	0	0-21
EDI - Bulimia	3	2	0-21
EDI - Body dissatisfaction	2	9	0-27
EDI - Ineffectiveness	1	4	0-30
EDI - Perfectionism	5	5	0-18
EDI - Interpersonal distrust	3	0	0-21
EDI - Interoceptive awareness	3	1	0-30
EDI - Maturity fears	4	1	0-24
SEI - General self-esteem	19	19	0-26
SEI- Social self-esteem	6	7	0-8
SEI - Familial self-esteem	7	8	0-8
SEI - Professional self-esteem	8	8	0-8
SEI - Lie scale	5	4	0-8
HADS - Depression	4	13	0-21
HADS - Anxiety	8	11	0-21

Note: CDRS – Contour Drawing Rating Scale, BAT – Body Attitude Test, BIAQ – Body Image Avoidance Questionnaire, EDI – Eating Disorders Inventory, SEI – Self-esteem Inventory, HADS – Hospital Depression and Anxiety Scale.

In the area of body image, for the first male adolescent there was actual–ideal self-discrepancy (of very low intensity) and a moderate actual–ought self-discrepancy. Weaker discrepancies (in both actual-ideal and actual-ought self-discrepancy) were observed in the second male adolescent.

As for the attitudes towards one's own body, the assessed men achieved low scores in terms of negative evaluation of the body size, lack of intimacy with their own body and general dissatisfaction with their own bodies. However, what should be stressed here is a relatively high score for the first boy, which was connected with general dissatisfaction with his own body.

With regard to the behaviours frequently accompanying the disturbed body image, the adolescents achieved low scores in terms of a tendency to conceal or mask their appearance by means of clothing and avoidance of social situations where food, body mass or appearance are the focus of attention. However, the first patient, unlike the other one, achieved a very high score in terms of restrained eating. Both patients scored high in the aspect of taking care of their appearance and body mass.

In the area of general, social, family and professional sense of self-esteem, both adolescents scored very high. However, it should be noted that both patients scored moderately high on the lie scale, which might indicate an intense defensive attitude to the questionnaire.

However, on all the eight scales of the EDI, the male adolescents' scores were low, with the only exception of the drive for thinness subscale, where the first adolescent scored 15 points (out of a maximum score of 21) as opposed to the latter who scored no points on this subscale. No score on the drive for thinness subscale may suggest denial or minimization of problems.

As regards mood and anxiety disorders are concerned it can be observed a slight (the first patient) and moderate intensity of anxiety symptoms (the second patient) as well as higher intensity of depression symptoms in the second patient.

Discussion

The present results showed that the body image self-discrepancy was presented in two male cases, disturbed body attitudes did not appear in two adolescent outpatients and probable presence of the mood disorder was found in two male cases.

It should be emphasized that the two male adolescent patients achieved low scores on almost all the subscales used.

The only exceptions are the following scores of one patient: drive for thinness (subscale of the EDI) and eating restraint (subscale of the BIAQ). According to Bruch (1971) two groups of anorexia nervosa in the male need to be distinguished: (a) an atypical group wherein refusal to eat is incidental to another psychiatric condition (without common features except non-eating and cachexia) and (b) a genuine or primary form with many common features: body-image disturbances, relentless pursuit of thinness achieved by reducing food intake, *inaccurate body* weight *perception,* and an all-pervasive sense of ineffectiveness. Disturbed eating behaviors and the pursuit of thinness in these cases represent a desperate effort to establish a sense of control and identity (Bruch, 1971).

Body image is an important topic of empirical and clinical interest for men (Pope et al., 2000). Current knowledge suggests that men with anorexia nervosa display a lower tendency to be slim and lower dissatisfaction with their bodies compared to women with anorexia (Woodside et al., 2001). However, in comparison with healthy men, they show bigger dissatisfaction with their own body (Gila et al., 2005).

The research indicates that a smaller proportion of body dissatisfied men desire to lose weight and reduce overall body mass (O'Dea and Abraham, 2002; Murray et al., 2013; Olivardia et al., 2004), while a larger proportion of men show a stronger preference for an idealized muscular physique (Murray et al., 2013).

Murray et al. (2010) believe that drive for thinness in anorexia nervosa and drive for muscularity in muscle dysmorphia share similar attention to diet and compensatory excessive exercising.

Our results confirmed body image self-discrepancy in both the anorexic male outpatients. Consistently with the literature, the actual-ought self-discrepancy seems to be especially important in the prediction of dieting and anorexic symptoms, while the actual-ideal self-discrepancy seems to be especially important in the prediction of bulimic symptoms (Weishuhn, 2006).

Moreover, both outpatients scored high in taking care of their appearance and body mass and achieved moderately high results in terms of prevalence of anxiety symptoms (in the case of depression, only one boy scored high).

It is interesting to note that both patients scored high on the lie scale (of the SEI). This score may be a result of an intense defensive attitude to the questionnaire, which is related to a tendency to minimize or deny the entity of problems. As a rule, denial of disease is typical of patients with anorexia nervosa (Vitousek et al., 1991) and is may be considered as "symptomatic" (Vandereycken, 2006), therefore the obtained results should not be surprising.

One of the reasons intensifying such attitudes in men might be the fear of suffering from the "feminine disease" (and the fear of stigmatisation resulting from it) because anorexia nervosa is regarded as a women's disease.

The characteristics of male adolescents with anorexia nervosa are unclear to many professionals. This preliminary report of two cases of male anorexia supports the role of psychological factors connected with body image, cognitive-behavioural aspects of eating disorders and symptoms of mood and anxiety disorders.

The results of the current report could be useful in suggesting new paths for future research in the area of male anorexia nervosa, which should involve larger samples.

Future research may contribute to a better understanding of male eating disorders as far as functioning in social life, family, and emotional areas are concerned.

Reviewed by Dr. Carla Gramaglia and Prof. Patrizia Zeppegno, Institute of Psychiatry, Università del Piemonte Orientale "Amedeo Avogadro", Novara, Italy

References

American Psychiatric Association (2000). *Diagnostic and Statistical: Manual of Mental Disorders DSM-IV-TR (Text Revision)*. Washington, DC: American Psychiatric Press.

Archinard, M., Rouget, P., Painot, D., and Liengme, C. (2002). Inventaire des troubles alimentaires 2. In: M. Bouvard and J. Cottraux (Eds.), *Protocoles et échelles d'évaluation en psychiatrie et psychologie* (pp. 249-251). Paris: Masson.

Bruch, H. (1971). Anorexia nervosa in the male. *Psychosomatic Medicine*, 33 (1), 31-48.

Coopersmith, S (1984). *Manuel d'Inventaire d'Estime de Soi*. Paris: CPA.

Crisp, A., Gowers S., Joughin, N., McClelland, L., Rooney, B., Nielsen, S., Bowyer, C., Halek, C., and Hartman. D. (2006). Anorexia nervosa in males: similarities and differences to anorexia nervosa in females. *European Eating Disorders Review*, 14(3), 163-167.

Favaro, A., Ferrara, S. and Santonastaso, P. (2004). The spectrum of eating disorders in young women: a prevalence study in a general population sample. *Psychosomatic Medicine*, 65(4), 701-708.

Frederick, D. A., Forbes, G. B. and Berezovskaya, A. (2008). Female body dissatisfaction and perceptions of the attractive female body in Ghana, the Ukraine, and the United States. *Psychological Topics*, 17(2), 203-219.

Garner, D. M., Olmsted, M. P. and Polivy, J. (1983). The eating disorder inventory: a measure of cognitive-behavioral dimensions of anorexia nervosa and bulimia. In: P. L. Darby, P. E. Garfinkel, D. M. Garner, and D. V. Coscina (Eds.), *Anorexia nervosa: recent developments in research* (pp. 173-184). New York: Alan R. Liss.

Gila, A., Castro, J., Cesena, J., and Toro, J. (2005). Anorexia nervosa in male adolescents: body image, eating attitudes and psychological traits. *Journal of Adolescent Health*, 36(3), 221-226.

Hudson, J. I., Hiripi, E., Pope, H. G. Jr and Kessler, R. C. (2007). The prevalence and correlates of eating disorders in the National Comorbidity Survey Replication. *Biological Psychiatry*, 61(3), 348-358.

Hoek, H. W. and van Hoeken, D. (2003). Review of the prevalence and incidence of eating disorders. *International Journal of Eating Disorders*, 34 (4), 383-396.

Katzman, D. K. and Golden, N. H. (2008). Anorexia nervosa and bulimia nervosa. In: L. S. Neinstein, C. M. Gordon, D. K. Katzman, D. S. Rosen, and E. R. Woods (Eds.), *Adolescent health care: a practical guide* (pp. 447-496). Fifth edition. Philadelphia: Lippincott Williams and Wilkins.

Keel, P. K. and McCormick, L. (2010). Diagnosis, assessment, and treatment planning for anorexia nervosa. In: C. M. Grilo and J. E. Mitchell (Eds.), *The treatment of eating disorders: a clinical handbook* (pp. 3-27). New York: The Guildford Press.

Keski-Rahkonen, A., Hoek, H. W., Susser, E. S., Linna, M. S., Sihvola, E., Raevuori, A., Bulik, C. M., Kaprio, J., and Rissanen, A. (2007). Epidemiology and course of anorexia nervosa in the community. *American Journal of Psychiatry*, 164(8), 1259-1265.

Krasnow, M. (1996). *My life as a male anorexic*. London: Routledge.

Lindblad, F., Lindberg, L. and Hjern, A. (2006). Anorexia nervosa in young men: a cohort study. *International Journal of Eating Disorders*, 39(8), 662-666.

Maïano, C., Morin, A. J., Monthuy-Blanc, J., and Garbarino, J. M. (2009). The Body Image Avoidance Questionnaire: assessment of its construct validity in a community sample of French adolescents. *International Journal of Behavioral Medicine*, 16(2), 125-135.

Murray, S. B., Rieger, E., Karlov, L., and Touyz, S. W. (2013). Masculinity and femininity in the divergence of male body image concerns. *Journal of Eating Disorders*, 1, 11.

Murray, S. B., Rieger, E., Touyz, S. W., and De la Garza García, Y. (2010). Muscle dysmorphia and the DSM-V conundrum: Where does it belong? A review paper. *International Journal of Eating Disorders*, 43(6), 483-491.

Olivardia, R., Pope, H. G., Borowiecki, J. J., and Cohane, G. H. (2004). Biceps and body image: The relationship between muscularity and self-esteem, depression, and eating disorder symptoms. *Psychology of Men and Masculinity*, 5(2), 112-120.

Oyebode, F., Boodhoo, J. A. and Schapira, K. (1988). Anorexia nervosa in males: clinical features and outcome. *International Journal of Eating Disorders*, 7(1), 121-124.

O'Dea, J. and Abraham, S. (2002). Eating and exercise disorders in young college men. *Journal of American College Health*, 50(6): 273-278.

Pope, H. G., Phillips, K. A. and Olivardia, R. (2000). *The Adonis complex: how to identify, treat, and prevent body obsession in men and boys*. New York: Touchstone.

Probst, M., Vandereycken, W., Van Coppenolle, H., and Vanderlinden, J. (1995). The Body Attitude Test for patients with an eating disorder: psychometric characteristics of a new questionnaire. *Eating Disorders: The Journal of Treatment and Prevention*, 3(2), 133-145.

Razavi, D., Delvaux, N., Farvacques, C., and Robaye, E. (1989). Validation de la version francaise du HADS dans une population de patients cancéreux hospitalisés. *Revue de Psychologie Appliquée*, 39(4), 295-308.

Ricciardelli, L. and McCabe, M. (2004). A biopsychosocial model of disordered eating and the pursuit of muscularity in adolescent boys. *Psychological Bulletin*, 130(2), 179-205.

Rosen, J. C., Srebnik, D., Saltzberg, E., and Wendt, S. (1991). Development of a Body Image Avoidance Questionnaire. *Journal of Consulting and Clinical Psychology*, 3(1), 32-37.

Scott, D. W. (1986). Anorexia nervosa in the male: a review of clinical, epidemiological and biological findings. *International Journal of Eating Disorders*, 5(5), 799-719.

Snaith, R. P. (2003). The Hospital Anxiety And Depression Scale. *Health and Quality of Life Outcomes*, 1, 29.

Thompson, J. K. and Gray, J. J. (1995). Development and validation of a new body image assessment scale. *Journal of Personality Assessment*, 64(2), 258-269.

Vandereycken, W. (2006). Denial of illness in anorexia nervosa - a conceptual review: Part 1 diagnostic significance and assessment. *European Eating Disorders Review*, 14(5), 341-351.

Vitousek, K. B., Daly, J. and Heiser, C. (1991). Reconstructing the internal world of the eating-disordered individual: overcoming denial and distortion. *International Journal of Eating Disorders*, 10(6), 647-666.

Weishuhn, A. S. (2006). *Perfectionism, self-discrepancy, and disordered eating in black and white women*. Master of art thesis. University of Missouri-Columbia.

Weltzin, T. E., Weisensel, N., Franczyk, D., Burnett, K., Klitz, C., and Bean, P. (2005). Eating disorders in men: update. *Journal of Men's Health and Gender*, 2(2), 186-193.

Wertheim, E. H., Paxton, S. J. and Tilgner, L. (2004). Test-retest reliability and construct validity of the Contour Drawing Rating Scale in a sample of early adolescent girls. *Body Image*, 1(2), 199-205.

Williamson, D. A., Martin, C. K. and Stewart, T. (2004). Psychological aspects of eating disorders. *Best Practice and Research Clinical Gastroenterology*, 18(6), 1073-1088.

Woodside, D. B., Garfinkel, P. E., Lin, E., Goering, P., Kaplan, A. S., Goldbloom, D. S., and Kennedy, S. H. (2001). Comparisons of men with full or partial eating disorders, men without eating disorders, and women with eating disorders in the community. *American Journal of Psychiatry*, 158 (4), 570-574.

Zigmond, A. and Snaith, R. P. (1983). The Hospital Anxiety and Depression Scale. *Acta Psychiatrica Scandinavica*, 67(6), 361-370.

In: New Developments in Anorexia Nervosa Research   ISBN: 978-1-63117-551-0
Editors: Carla Gramaglia and Patrizia Zeppegno   © 2014 Nova Science Publishers, Inc.

Chapter 7

The Relation between Risk Factors and Recovery in Eating Disorders

Dr. Greta Noordenbos[*]

Clinical Psychology, Leiden University, The Netherlands

Abstract

Recovery from eating disorders such as anorexia and bulimia nervosa is a difficult process which often takes a long time. Which factors are important in the process of recovery? Are patients recovered when symptoms have been reduced, or is it also necessary to tackle the underlying risk factors?

In research, risk factors for eating disorders and recovery are often seen as two different topics. This chapter, however, is intended to discuss what research about recovery can learn from research about risk factors. As long as the main risk factors for eating disorders - including negative body evaluation, low self-esteem, lack of emotion regulation, and coping strategies - are not reduced, there is a high risk that eating disorder patients will have a relapse, especially if treatment was only directed at the reduction of eating disorder symptoms.

First, an overview of research into risk factors for and recovery from eating disorders is presented, followed by the results of interviews with fifty-seven fully recovered patients. From these it becomes clear that it is important for patients not only to eat in a healthy way and to recover from all the negative physical consequences of their eating disorder, but also to develop more self-esteem and a positive body attitude, to learn to express their emotions, needs and feelings, and to develop better social coping strategies and relationships. Only when the underlying risk factors for their eating disorder were reduced did participants no longer feel the need to diet and evaluated themselves as fully recovered. Finally, some implications for the treatment of eating disorders are mentioned, based on information from the research review and the interviews.

Keywords: Eating Disorders, Risk Factors, Criteria for Recovery

[*] Correspondence: Dr. Greta Noordenbos: Clinical Psychology, Leiden University. Wassenaarseweg 52, 2333 AK, Leiden, The Netherlands. E-mail: Noordenbos@FSW.Leidenuniv.nl.

1. Introduction

To understand why recovery from an eating disorder is so difficult and takes so much time it is important to understand why the eating disorder was developed in the first place. Eating disorders never come "out of the blue", but are preceded by many problems and risk factors (Abbate-Daga et al, 2007; Fairburn et al,1997; Jacobi et al, 2004; Stice, 2002; Striegel-Moore & Bulik, 2007).

In this section a review is presented of the most important risk factors for the development of an eating disorder, followed by a discussion about patients' first experiences with dieting, the psychological, social, and physical consequences of the eating disorders, and finally the factors which are important for recovery.

The risk factors for eating disorders can be divided into genetic and biological, psychological, and socio-cultural factors (Keel, 2005).These factors make persons vulnerable to a pattern of dieting and developing a disturbed attitude towards eating, which can result in an eating disorder.

Many eating disorder patients have family members who have or have had an affective disorder such as depression, alcohol problems, a drugs addiction, or an eating disorder (Keel, 2005). Although these genetic factors never predict the development of an eating disorder, they do make the person more vulnerable than people without these risk factors. The psychological risk factors mentioned most often by eating disorder patients are low self-esteem and negative self-and-body-evaluation (Cervera et al, 2003; Noordenbos, 2013). Perfectionism and fear of failing in the eyes of others are also important risk factors for developing an eating disorder (Jacobi et al, 2004). These patients set themselves very high standards, and feel that they fail when they do not realize their own benchmark. If they fail they are very critical about themselves. This inner criticism is described by several therapists, for instance Bruch (1978), who writes about an 'inner dictator', while Claude-Pierre (1997) mentions an 'inner negativist' and Kortink (2008) describes an 'inner saboteur'.

An important risk factor is a negative body attitude, and the fear of becoming overweight or fat. Negative comments about the body, or being teased about one's weight and appearance are important factors in the development of a negative body attitude. Social and cultural factors also play an important role in the development of an eating disorder, such as the slimming ideal and dieting behavior of mothers, sisters and friends, strict weight standards in ballet schools, or sports in which weight plays an important role, such as skating and athletics (Levine & Smolak, 1998; Pinhas et al, 1999).

Risk factors, however, are never predictors for eating disorders, and no single risk factor in itself is enough to develop such a disorder. Moreover, several of the risk factors which precede eating disorders are part of a 'normal' growth and development process. This makes it difficult to determine whether these risk factors are 'normal', or 'pathological'. Protective factors are also important, such as positive and supportive relations with parents and peers.

It has been suggested that the more risk factors there are, the greater the possibility that young women start to diet in a culture where being slim is the ideal for the female body and being overweight is frowned upon (Noordenbos, 2013). Most eating disorder patients start a diet because they feel fat or are afraid of becoming fat. Feeling fat is closely connected with several negative stereotypes, such as not being attractive and sexy, being dim-witted, lazy, ugly, etcetera. The worse patients' self- and body evaluation, the greater their fear of becoming fat and being criticized or teased because of it (Pinhas et al, 1999).

Although all eating disorder patients start to diet in order to lose weight, not all people who diet develop an eating disorder. Many people try to avoid becoming overweight or obese and follow a diet in order to lose weight, but most of them stop when they have reached their target weight. This, however, is not the case with anorectic patients, who continue their slimming behavior and start to diet in an extreme way which is a high risk factor for developing an eating disorder (Noordenbos, 2013; Stice, 2002). One of the most striking characteristics of anorexia nervosa is patients' continuation of extreme dieting even after considerable weight loss (DSM-IV; APA, 2000: DSM-5, APA, 2013). Their eating behavior and weight is very important for patients' self-evaluation. This connection between food regulation and self-evaluation is one of the core criteria for anorexia and bulimia nervosa in the DSM-5: "self-evaluation is unduly influenced by body shape and weight".

According to Bruch (1978), anorexia nervosa is a consequence of an impaired development of identity and individualisation. Before the development of anorexia nervosa there is a strong tendency to conform to the expectations of others, and to hide one's own feelings, needs and emotions. Because of their impaired self-esteem and low sense of identity anorectic patients feel very dependent on others. When they reach puberty and adolescence they feel the need to develop more autonomy and become independent from their parents, but they feel hampered by their impaired identity. When they start to diet, anorectic patients feel they are developing their own identity, and are proud to have control over their food intake and weight. This gives them very positive feelings about themselves and motivates them to continue their disordered eating behavior (Noordenbos, 2013).

A consequence of extreme dieting and weight loss is that negative emotions are no longer felt. Some eating disorder patients feel completely dissociated from their body and its needs. According to Bruch (1978) some anorectic patients experience their body and mind as two separate entities, with the mind having to control the despised body. Some anorectic patients force themselves to live according to extreme ascetic rules, which enable them to neglect all bodily needs and feelings such as hunger, cold, and pain.

It is striking that anorectic patients are unable to see how emaciated their body has become. The prouder they are of their extreme slimming behavior, the less they see how skeletally thin they have become. According to Bruch (1978),their self-deceit protects them from a fundamental feeling of desperation, with their slimming behavior as the only foothold that gives them a feeling of identity and control. Bruch (1978) described this as brainwashing: "To prevent their weight from increasing they brainwash themselves: their feelings of hunger are felt as positive and safe. They are proud of being able to resist their hunger; that gives them a feeling of control and self-esteem. Some of them even develop feelings of superiority when they compare themselves with others who are not able to continue their diet".

During the first stage the eating disorder is often considered a "friend", who gives a safe feeling of control and hold, but when patients are confronted with its negative consequences they realize that the eating disorder is not bringing what they hoped for. The "friend" has become a foe (Serpell et al, 1999; Serpell et al., 2002; Tierney and Fox, 2010). Extreme emaciation and starvation severely disturb patients' mental and emotional state. Bruch (1978) reported that some patients have hallucinatory experiences. At the stage of severe starvation all personal characteristics disappear, and eating disorder patients become more and more alike in appearance, emotions, thoughts and behavior. At this stage patients are no longer able to experience emotions, and lose every contact with reality. Some anorectic patients become dissociated from their body; they become depersonalised and feel completely numb (Bruch, 1978).Starvation also has consequences for the neurological and hormonal systems, and can even lead to reduced brain volume (Amianto et al, 2013; Keel, 2005).

When their body urgently needs food many anorectic patients become very restless and hyperactive (van Elburg, 2007). Because of the lack of food and extreme emaciation the production of hormones decreases in both women and men (Keel, 2005). Female anorectics have irregular periods, or none at all. Many patients develop osteoporosis (Tenwolde, 2000); some have cardiac problems, especially arrhythmias, because of potassium loss as a consequence of vomiting and the frequent use of laxatives. Only when their physical condition deteriorates severely do patients actually start to worry about their health (Noordenbos, 2013).

Although most eating disorder patients are very sensitive to others' emotions, they have poor skills in acknowledging their own feelings. In the period before the development of the eating disorder, patients often find it difficult to express their emotions, especially negative feelings such as disappointment, irritation, anger, or fury (Beales & Dolton, 2000). They may try to avoid or suppress these negative emotions, and hide them from others, and often use their eating disorder as a strategy to achieve this (Jantz & Murray, 2002). Anorectic and bulimic patients find it difficult to get in touch with their feelings, and to differentiate and describe them. They often suffer from alexithymia, which means that they are not able to 'read' and describe their emotions adequately (Jimerson, Wolfe, Franko, Covino & Sifneos, 1994). In treatment it is important that the therapist should be able to explore and accept patients' negative emotions, and to help patients do the same. However, when patients stop dieting, these negative feelings return. For that reason emotion regulation is crucial in combating an eating disorder (van Elburg, 2007; Zonnevijlle-Bender et al., 2004).

To recover from an eating disorder not only physical and psychological improvement is important, but also improved social relations (Rorty et al, 1993). For eating disorder patients, improving self-esteem and self-respect is one of the most important aspects in their process of recovery (Fodor, 1997). Without this the risk of relapse is very high (Fennig et al, 2002; Strober, et al, 1997).

Besides the eating disorder, many patients suffer from comorbid disorders such as mood disorders, obsessive compulsive disorder, post-traumatic stress disorder, and self-harming behaviors (Agras & Apple, 1997; Steinhausen, 2002). An important question is whether improvement in comorbid disorders is important for the recovery from eating disorders. When comorbidity -- such as a mood disorder or an obsessive-compulsive disorder -- is a consequence of the eating disorders this might improve after recovery from the eating disorder. However, when the comorbidity -- such as a traumatic stress disorder-- precedes the eating disorder, the eating disorder can be a strategy to cope with the comorbidity. In the latter case the comorbidity needs to be addressed in treatment. Also if the eating disorder is accompanied by a clinically relevant comorbidity, this additional disorder should be carefully addressed and treated, regardless of whether it preceded the eating disorder or is a consequence of it.

2. Experiences of Eating Disorder Patients

The aim of this study was to uncover the main risk factors preceding the eating disorder, and find out whether the reduction of the underlying risk factors was important for the recovery from an eating disorder. The following research questions were developed and used as a basis for interviews with patients who had developed an eating disorder and were recovered from it:

1. What were the main risk factors in the period before their eating disorder?
2. What motivated them to diet and to continue their diet in an extreme way?
3. What were the stages in the development of their eating disorder?
4. When did they become motivated for treatment and recovery?
5. Which factors were important in their process of recovery?
6. Was the reduction of underlying risk factors important to realize full recovery?

The participants were 57 fully recovered patients, 52 women and 5 men, with ages ranging from 18 to 52 years, mean age 28 years. Criterion for inclusion was that recovery from an eating disorder such as anorexia nervosa or bulimia nervosa had to have lasted for at least two years. The mean age of onset of their eating disorder was 16 years (range 12- 24). All participants had started with extreme dieting, and 74% had a period of restrictive anorexia nervosa, but sooner or later 63% of them started binging and purging behavior. This can be seen as a transdiagnostic crossover to bulimia nervosa, as described by Fairburn et al. (2003). In total, 26% of the participants started with bulimia nervosa without having had a period of anorexia nervosa. The mean duration of the eating disorders was 7 years, in a range of 1-38 years.

All participants had filled in an informed consent form. All interviews were anonymized.

The topics for the interviews were drawn from research about risk factors and recovery in eating disorders, but participants were free to introduce other factors and recovery criteria.

The risk factors and criteria for recovery mentioned by the participants were counted and percentages calculated. If risk factors and criteria for recovery were mentioned by more than 50% of the participants, they were evaluated as relevant and summarized in this chapter. Percentages were counted for the whole group of female and male participants. If a risk factor or recovery criterion was mentioned by only female or only male participants this will be mentioned.

3. Results

In this section the following topics will be described: main risk factors, first period of dieting, maintenance factors, consequences, turning point and ambivalent motivation, and important factors in the process of recovery.

3.1. Risk Factors for Developing an Eating Disorder

The risk factors for the development of an eating disorder that emerged from the interviews can be roughly grouped as follows:

1) individual-related
2) relationship-related
3) culture-related

1) Individual-Related Risk Factors

Lack of Self-Esteem and Negative Self-Evaluation

The psychological problems mentioned most often by eating disorder patients were lack of self-esteem and negative self-evaluation (99%). Because of their low self-esteem they felt insecure about themselves (97%), and tended to seek support from others (95%). In order to receive approval and support they did their best to comply with others' expectations (89%). However, they were very insecure about their own opinions and found it difficult to express their thoughts and feelings (92%): they wanted to avoid any criticism (85%), because they saw censure as rejection (86%).

Perfectionism, Fear of Failure and Inner Critic

In the period before the eating disorder anorectic patients were often extreme perfectionists (97%). They had very high standards for themselves and were never satisfied with their performances (96%). They never felt good enough and always thought they needed to be better (95%). At school they tried to please their teachers by doing their best in order to get the highest grades (92%), but even if they had high grades they often felt that this was not good enough (97%). Eating disorder patients were often very critical about themselves (89%). This self-critical attitude was there even before they started to diet, but increased after the development of the eating disorder (79%). They blamed themselves for every mistake (75%).

Impaired Identity Development

Because the participants were very insecure about themselves they found it difficult to develop their own identity (84%). They often tried to please their parents and to conform to their expectations, but this made it difficult to detach themselves from their parents and develop their own identity. They preferred to avoid conflicts and to hide their own opinions and feelings from others, because they were afraid of being criticised and rejected (92%).

Negative Body Attitude

The negative self-evaluation in the period before the eating disorder was strongly related to a negative body evaluation (95%). Especially during puberty, when girls develop more fat tissue around their hips, their breasts grow, and they start to have their periods, the female participants became insecure about their body (79%). For most anorectic girls menstruation was not a pleasant experience, because it was often combined with painful sensations, a bloated feeling, and tension in the breasts (79%). Moreover, every comment about their physical development was felt as negative (94%). This triggered their wish to change their body in order to reduce their negative body image (99%). An important trigger was the experience of being teased with being overweight (54%). When patients were teased they felt powerless and completely rejected by others. Their body evaluation became highly negative and they started to hate their body (54%).

Other experiences with a negative impact on body attitude include negative sexual experiences, mentioned by 56% of the participants, with up to 15.7% of the interviewees reporting experiences of sexual abuse.

2) Relationship-Related

Compliant and Pleasing Behavior

In the period before the development of an eating disorder many patients were kind and obedient children who did their best at school and at home (85%). However, at the root of this compliant behavior was the fear of not being able to cope with the expectations of their parents and teachers (82%). They often felt they were not allowed to be who they really were (74%), and hence tried to conform to the image they thought others had of them (74%).

Hiding Thoughts and Opinions from Others

Patients were often afraid to express their real feelings and opinions, and hid them from others if they felt that these views might be different from what others felt or thought (74%). They adjusted to others as much as possible, and felt valued for their pleasing behavior (72%). Already long before the development of their eating disorder they had learned that outward behavior and appearance was important to gain approval from others (86%).

Sensitivity to the Needs of Others

Many patients said that in the period before the development of their eating disorder they were very sensitive to the needs and feelings of others (89%). They were able to register subtle signals from their parents, especially signs of sorrow, disappointment, anger, depression, fear, or stress (84%). The consequence of this sensitivity to others' expectations and needs was that patients instead showed a tendency to neglect their own needs and feelings (89%). They became experts in caring about others, but did not learn to express their own needs, and hid their own problems from their parents (74%). However, behind this complaint and pleasing behavior they felt there was a deep lack of self-esteem (98%).

3) Culture-Related

The Cultural Ideal of the Slim Body

It was not only the development of their body during puberty and negative sexual experiences that made participants insecure about their body, but also the pictures of "ideal" models of thinness (74%). Patients became sensitive to pictures of slim models, and negatively evaluated the discrepancy between their own body and the ideal one (73%). If they had friends, sisters or parents who went on a diet, the pressure to slim down became even stronger (53%).

3.2. First Period of Dieting

The Start of a Diet

All eating disorder patients started dieting in order to lose weight (100%). At the beginning, dieting and weight loss gave them feelings of self-esteem and control (96%), which motivated them to continue their slimming behavior, even after severe weight loss (95%).They had unrealistically high expectations about losing weight (98%), and saw their slimming behavior as a "solution" to their psychological problems (92%). Although the first dieting period in eating disorder patients does not differ from the dieting behavior of healthy dieters, there are significant differences in expectations regarding losing weight. Individuals who developed an eating disorder expected that after weight loss they would have more self-esteem and more self-respect (98%). They expected more acceptation from others (92%); that they would no longer being teased (56%); and would feel more in control over their body (97%). The initial weight loss was experienced as very positive, and self-esteem increased substantially (98%).

From Light to Extreme Dieting

Because of their first positive experiences with dieting, patients started to diet in an extreme way, and drastically reduced the intake of sweets, snacks, fat, and sugar (100%). They started to eat smaller portions, less or no potatoes, pasta, or meat, or only fruit and vegetables (92%). Sooner or later they skipped meals and snacks (89%). Moreover, they started an extremely rigorous exercising regime (74%). Their target weight was much lower than the expected Body Mass Index for their age and gender (89%). Even after considerable weight loss they continued their extreme dieting, because slimming behavior gave them positive feelings of self-esteem and being in control of their life (98%). This positive self-evaluation was very important for them, and stimulated them to neglect their feelings of hunger (84%). They absolutely clung to their feeling of control about food and weight (94%).

Suppression of Feelings of Hunger and Satiety

In the first period of extreme dieting patients struggled to refrain from eating when they felt hungry, but when they succeeded they were rewarded by strong feelings of control and self-respect (100%). The longer they were able to withstand their feelings of hunger, the stronger and more successful they felt (98%). Eating disorder patients trained themselves to ignore their feelings of hunger, fatigue, and cold (86%). They felt strong when they were able to ignore all the negative consequences of extreme dieting and starvation (82%). They managed not to listen to the sensations of their body, and to disconnect body and mind (64%).

Dieting Became a Core Identity

Many eating disorder patients said that the first stage of dieting gave them a sense of self and identity (98%). This positive view of extreme dieting made it very difficult for them to stop their regime, because they were afraid to lose control over their food and weight again, and to lose their positive self-image and feeling of identity (98%).

Control over Food and Body

Being able to control their body gave patients a feeling of power over their physical needs (89%). By dieting and reducing weight the participants were able to stop their body developing further (54%). It is especially girls who had had negative or abusive sexual experiences who used extreme slimming as a way to desexualize their body.

3.3. Maintenance Factors

Denial of Problems

During the first stage of the eating disorder patients denied having any problems (100%). On the contrary, their eating behavior was not a problem for them, but a 'solution' to many problems they had before they started to diet. Their motivation to start dieting was not only to lose weight, but also to gain more self-esteem and feel better about themselves and their body (96%). When they started to diet they felt in control over their food and were very proud of their slimming behavior (96%). At this stage they did not experience any problems – rather the reverse (94%). So why give up this 'solution'?

No Motivation for Treatment

Extreme dieting gave patients so many positive experiences that they were not motivated to change their eating behavior (99%). On the contrary, the only thing they wanted was to continue their dieting regime in order to keep control over their body (98%). They were proud of their successful strategy of food reduction and weight loss (98%). It was not until much later, when they were confronted with unexpected negative physical, psychological and social consequences, that they realized their eating behavior not only offered positive experiences, but also had many negative consequences (98%).

3.4. Consequences of Eating Disorders

The participants mentioned several negative psychological, social, and physical consequences.

Rigid Rules and Obsessive-Compulsive Behavior

Quite soon after starting to diet, anorectic patients developed obsessive thoughts and set themselves rigid rules (98%). They became obsessed by the amount of calories they thought they were allowed to eat (98%), carefully counted the number of calories in all the food they ate, and counted how many calories they were allowed during their next meal (85%).

The patients were convinced that 'eating less is better and eating more is bad' and 'losing weight is positive and gaining weight is negative' (98%). They became completely obsessed by these dogmas. Many patients visited pro-Ana websites, where anorectic patients stimulate each other to become as thin as possible (54%). Pro-Ana websites advocate a destructive way of thinking in which anorectic behavior is promoted as a 'lifestyle'. Beliefs about slimming behavior are presented as unquestionable, and comments on people who are not able to bring down their weight are extremely negative and denigrating.

Inner Critic

Although at first the dieting successes gave patients positive feelings, these feelings sooner or later disappeared, whereas the negative and critical thoughts increased (99%). This is likely to happen when patients are scared to death by the idea of losing the "identity" they gained through the eating disorder. Moreover, severe starvation may lead to the development of depressive symptoms. Negative thoughts dominated eating disorder patients' whole life (98%). Anorectic patients developed a very strict, obsessive and controlling attitude, leading to the suppression or denial of their biological needs and desires (95%). They came to be completely dominated by this inner controlling instance (98%), which was often heard as an inner critical 'voice' governing their lives and forbidding them to feel any pleasure or satisfaction (65%).

Depressed Moods

Although patients often started dieting because they wished to increase their self-esteem, they eventually became very negative about themselves and all positive feelings evaporated (99%). Instead of feeling better they became extremely sad and were no longer able to experience any positive emotion (86%). Some of them developed suicidal thoughts at this stage (24%).

Social Consequences

During the first stage of an eating disorder the social consequences are often not yet clearly apparent, because patients hide their distorted attitude towards eating as much as possible (95%). They started to avoid contacts with others, because they were afraid that others might discover how disturbed their eating behavior was (95%). However, in the long run the social consequences of their eating disorder became more severe (95%). They started to distrust others and lost friends (85%). Many participants were unable to continue their education or job (51%). The longer the duration of the eating disorder, the more these patients become isolated and locked within themselves, also as a consequence of their severe physical condition.

Physical Consequences

Sooner or later extreme dieting led to several negative physical consequences, such as tiredness (98%), lack of energy (95%), low temperature (65%), brittle nails (52%), damage to teeth (53%), constipation (65%), problems with stomach and bowels (54%), and disturbed sleep (88%). In case of severe emaciation the body felt exhausted, and very painful (78%): when all fat tissue had disappeared patients sat directly on their bones (64%). They could not sleep because they felt hungry and constantly thought about food, or because lying in bed was very painful after they had become extremely emaciated (88%). Many anorectic patients became very restless and sometimes hyperactive (53%). The female anorectics had irregular periods, or none at all (97%). Some patients developed osteoporosis (52%).

3.5. Turning Point and Ambivalent Motivation

What started as a strategy intended to increase self-esteem sooner or later turned out to be a trap (99%). Patients' feeling of control was only about eating and weight, whereas their psycho-social development stagnated (98%). Confronted with negative consequences the participants slowly realized that their 'solution' had become a serious problem, and they started to actively worry about their health (98%). When the negative consequences became very severe and dominated their lives, the patients realized that this was not what they had hoped for (74%). When they felt they had hit the bottom of the pit, they were desperate and became more motivated to recover (82%). They finally realized that their disorder had many damaging consequences, and eventually acknowledged that it was not a friend but an enemy who destroyed their life (82%). The eating disorder had become a prison from which they could not escape.

When the negative consequences became very serious, most eating disorder patients realized that they could not go on living this way (75%). Some of them realized that by continuing their eating disorder they risked death (54%). Interestingly, this rate is quite low, just half of the interviewees. However this may be, at this stage many eating disorder patients experienced a "turning point" and felt the need to change (76%). Some patients realized that their quality of life had become very poor and that they had to choose between life and death (52%). After this turning point they slowly became motivated to change and to seek help (89%).

Ambivalent Motivation for Change

When the negative consequences dominated their lives, most patients did realize they could not continue their eating behavior (75%). But even if they were aware that the eating disorder had life-threatening consequences, their motivation to change was still ambivalent, because they feared losing their self-esteem and control over their life (87%).

Even when the participants suffered from severe physical, psychiatric, and psychological consequences it was not easy for them to break through their eating disorder (99%). They were scared of eating more and gaining weight (98%), and were still extremely critical of themselves when they tried to eat more (97%). Some eating disorder patients were afraid to lose their identity, which was deeply connected with their eating disorder (89%). Moreover, having lived with an eating disorder for a long time had impaired their interoceptive awareness, including the ability to discriminate between hunger and satiety (95%). Their body had become accustomed to their way of eating (99%). They feared the return of all the problems they had before they developed the eating disorder, such as extremely low self-esteem, a negative body image, and the inability to express emotions and needs (89%). All these fears and doubts made their motivation to change highly ambivalent. Most of them had several "turning points" at which they decided to change (76%) – every time they were really convinced that they wanted to get rid of their eating disorder, but they were also afraid to ask for help and treatment (94%).

Fear of Asking for Help

Usually patients waited very long before they dared to ask for help (96%). They felt too ashamed, and were too afraid to lose control over their life (95%). The fear of change was often greater than the motivation to recover. It was especially the five male participants with an eating disorder who found it very difficult to ask for help (100% of the male participants). They were afraid to become stigmatized with having a "women's disease" (89% of the male participants).

3.6. Important Factors in the Process of Recovery

Overcoming the Fear of Increasing Food Intake

For those participants in this study who had anorexia nervosa, one of the most difficult problems was to reduce their *fear* of increasing their food intake and weight (100%). After months or even years of anorectic eating behavior they had lost all conception of what constitutes a healthy amount of food.

During the first period of increased food intake and weight gain they had many emotional problems and felt scared and guilty (98%). Their self-evaluation was poor, and they felt as if they were losing control not only over their food and weight, but over their whole life (97%).

For patients who had developed bulimia nervosa it was important to stop their binges and purging behaviors. They had to learn to eat normal amounts of food without vomiting, using laxatives, or extreme exercising.

Changing Cognitions about Food

Anorectic patients were obsessed by the idea that 'calories are fat and fat is bad". Having repeated this dogma for many years they found it very difficult to change their beliefs about food and calories (99%). Patients often reported that they had to learn all over again that calories are necessary to give energy to their body and brain (95%), and that eating enough calories is necessary for physical and psychological wellbeing (95%).

In order to improve their eating behavior patients had to learn to eat three meals a day at a regular time (86%). Participants with bulimia realized they had to reduce their binges and purging behaviors, as well as the intake of laxatives, diuretics, and slimming pills (92%). Those participants who used extreme exercising as a strategy to compensate for their caloric intake had to learn to reduce their physical activities. Recovered patients told us that they were no longer obsessed by food and weight (97%) and were able to eat without counting calories (96%).

Developing a Positive Body Evaluation

An important factor in the process of recovery was the development of a more positive body attitude (99%). Patients learned to accept their body and to focus on its positive aspects, instead of only seeing the negative sides (92%). They learned that dieting is not the solution to their negative body evaluation (95%).

Being Able to Listen to Physical Sensations

To recover from their eating disorder it was important that patients learned to listen to physical sensations: feelings of hunger or satiety, being tired, or being cold (98%). Becoming sensitive to these feelings was a process that took much time and training. Patients reported that a useful approach to becoming more connected with their bodily sensations was body-focused therapy, in which they had to explore their physical sensations (56%). This therapy helped them to become more in touch with their body and to express what they felt: tiredness, stress, cold or warmth, and hunger.

Physical Recovery

Regarding the physical recovery from eating disorders the focus was on regaining a normal weight. However, for anorectic patients a low weight was often not their most important problem. They suffered more from lack of energy and tiredness, insufficient sleep, damage to their teeth, dry skin, brittle nails, and hair loss (85%). The motivation to reduce these physical consequences of their eating disorder was often higher than the motivation to gain weight (85%), but in order to improve the physical problems it was necessary for anorectic patients to eat more and gain weight.

The most important aspects of physical recovery mentioned by the participants were: no longer feeling tired and having enough energy (98%), a healthy and stable weight (83%), a normal body temperature (71%), overcoming constipation and bowel problems (67%), improved sleep quality (81%), and having healthy teeth, nails, and hair (76%).

Many negative physical consequences of eating disorders disappeared after patients' food intake had improved, and their weight had become stable and within the normal range for age and height (89%). Their body temperature became normal, and the production of hormones was enough for women to have regular periods (87%). Problems with low blood pressure and a slow heartbeat, as well as disturbances of heart rhythm, diminished (62%). Constipation and bowel problems improved after the intake of laxatives was reduced (84%). Most sleep disturbances disappeared (81%). Skin became less dry and pale, and hair and nails became stronger (76%). However, not all physical consequences of an eating disorder disappeared completely after weight and food intake were restored. For the rebuilding of damaged teeth it was necessary to consult a dentist (57%), and osteoporosis could not be reverted (53%).

Increased Self-Evaluation

As described above, low self-esteem and a negative self-evaluation were major problems in the period leading up to the development of an eating disorder. All recovered patients told us that they had developed more self-esteem and a better self-evaluation (100%). They became less eager to please others (89%), less dependent on the approval of others, and less afraid of rejection (79%). They also learned better to listen to their own feelings and emotions (95%). It was very helpful for them to have become more assertive (89%) and to dare to express their own opinions (89%). They were able to reduce their fear of being criticized or rejected when expressing their own thoughts and opinions (79%), and had learned that having a conflict does not mean that other people reject you, and that a conflict can be discussed without serious consequences (57%).

Reduced Perfectionism and Fear of Failure

Moreover, patients' perfectionism and fear of failure diminished (94%), as well as their self-criticism (99%) Their sense of self was empowered, and their self-respect substantially improved (100%). They developed a more healthy and realistic way of thinking about themselves (89%). Their feeling of 'self' and self-respect had become much stronger (99%). As a method to change their opinions about themselves they had found cognitive behavior therapy (CBT) very useful (74%).

3.9. Improved Strategies to Regulate Emotions

To recover from an eating disorder it is important to develop healthy strategies to cope with negative emotions. The participants learned to accept their negative emotions (86%) and also to express them, rather than avoiding or hiding them (86%). After the first step of recognizing and exploring their emotions they learned to accept even negative emotions as part of their personality (78%).

Mindfulness proved a useful strategy to help patients focusing on what they feel (55%). This strategy helped them to become more sensitive to the physical sensations of being tired and cold, or hungry or satisfied (55%). Mindfulness also helped them to pay more attention to emotions, and explore instead of avoid them (54%).

Accepting Negative Emotions

An important aim underlying anorectic patients' extreme dieting is to feel less sad and depressed and more upbeat. Although the first effect of dieting is a general improvement in mood, these positive feelings sooner or later fade away. After some time, patients felt even more sad and depressed. Unfortunately, when they learned to eat more and their weight increased they again felt all the negative emotions which they had tried to avoid (98%). Their first reaction was often to suppress these negative feelings again by extreme dieting, but during the process of recovery they learned to accept and to express their negative emotions (87%).

Psycho-education about the relationship between food and emotions was a very useful part of the treatment (76%), and cognitive behavior therapy had proved very important in correcting patients' disturbed cognitions about food and weight (79%).

Improving Social Relations

A consequence of their eating disorders was that the participants had become more and more isolated because they wanted to hide their eating problems from others (99%). Moreover, they described how, at the most critical stage of their disorder, they were no longer able to go to school or work (51%) Their social world became very small and they had only few contacts left.

During the process of recovery the patients learned to make more contact with peers (89%), they were taught better social coping strategies, and had to become more assertive (85%). During therapy patients learned to take initiatives and to be less afraid of revealing their personal thoughts and emotions.

Developing Intimate Relations

Many recovered patients stated that in the period before their eating disorder their contacts with others were quite superficial, because they did not feel secure enough to talk about their deeper emotions and opinions (72%). When their self-esteem increased they learned to talk about their inner thoughts and emotions, which most patients viewed as an important condition for developing more intimate contacts (75%).

Becoming involved in an intimate relationship was often very helpful in the process of recovery (52%). However, participants often found it difficult to enter into physical intimacy because they felt very insecure about their body and were afraid of being criticized. Negative sexual experiences were also an obstacle to developing more intimate relations.

Continuation of Education and Career

Participants reported that during the process of recovery they succeeded in going to school again (53%), continuing their job, or doing volunteer work (47%). This increased their contacts with peers and colleagues. Reintegration in the labor market not only helped to increase their social contacts, but also gave them more self-esteem (89%) and improved their financial position (47%).

4. Limitations of the Study

This research was based on interviews with a selected group of patients who evaluated themselves as fully recovered from their eating disorder for a period of two years or longer. Non-recovered, or not yet recovered patients were not included in this study. Unfortunately, not all eating disorder patients recover.

Another limitation of this study is that all interviews were retrospective: they covered the period before participants developed their eating disorder, the first period of dieting, the development into extreme dieting and its consequences, and their process of recovery. Participants' memories might have been influenced by the treatment and their experiences with recovery. The patients in this study had different treatments and therapies. Although they often mentioned which treatment had helped them to recover, the project was not intended as an effect or outcome study of therapies for eating disorders.

This qualitative study, in which participants were interviewed, has yielded much information about their experiences. Because these experiences were reported in their own words the patient perspective has become as clear as possible. A limitation of qualitative research, however, is that no statistical analyses are possible on interviews. More quantitative research, using a prospective design, is needed to confirm the results.

The assessment involved a mixed sample regarding gender and diagnoses. The impact of recovery on family dynamics, although interesting, has not been explored.

Conclusion

The participants interviewed for this study mentioned many risk factors that may be relevant in the period before the development of an eating disorder. In the recovery process it was important not only to improve food intake, but also to work on the underlying risk factors which had motivated patients to start dieting

One encouraging outcome of this study was that in the interviews the recovered patients proved actually able to tell their story from the beginning to the end of their eating disorder, and to identify what they felt as critical issues in the process of developing an eating disorder and recovering from it.

What Can We Learn from the Literature Review and the Interviews?

1. First of all, an eating disorder does not just start when patients decide to diet. Before this period they have already had many psychosocial problems, such as low self-esteem, wanting to please others, fear of rejection, negative body image, etcetera. The development of extreme dieting cannot be understood without acknowledging the earlier problems for which patients try to find a solution. For them, dieting is not the problem – it is the solution to earlier troubles. For that reason it is very important that any treatment should address these underlying problems. Without that, only the symptoms of extreme dieting are reduced, but if patients are still suffering from all the underlying factors the risk of relapse is very high (Strober et al, 1997; Fennig et al, 2002).

2. A second lesson is that it is possible for patients to fully recover from their eating disorder. In general, 50% of the patients with anorexia and bulimia nervosa recover, 30% improve, and 20% stay ill (Steinhausen, 1999, 2002). The percentage of recovered patients with bulimia and binge eating disorder is somewhat higher. Recently, the percentage of recovered patients has been increasing because of earlier diagnosis and better treatment. For adolescent eating disorders recovery percentages of 85% are found (Nillson & Haglöff, 2006).

3. A third lesson is that it is very difficult for eating disorder patients to become motivated to improve food intake and weight, because this is seen as very threatening. A more effective strategy is to motivate them to improve their quality of life, their self-esteem and body image, and their social relations. According to Spaans & Bloks (2008), strategies to motivate eating disorder patients should be the first part of the treatment.

4. A fourth lesson is that eating disorder patients are not yet recovered when food intake and weight have been normalized. After a treatment that only focused on increasing food intake and weight, eating disorder patients often feel bad because they have lost both their self-respect and their sense of control over their body and their life (Bruch, 1978; Windauwer et al, 1993). There is often a high risk of relapse if the underlying psychological factors have not improved (Fennig et al, 2002; Strober et al, 1997).

5. A fifth lesson is that in eating disorder patients body and mind cannot be addressed separately, because they are always closely related. Treatment directed only at recovery from the physical consequences of the eating disorder is not effective if patients still have many disturbed cognitions about food and weight, and are still obsessed by these factors. However, therapy directed only at changing their cognitions without improving food intake and weight is not effective either. When the body is in a very bad condition because of severe starvation, eating disorder patients are no longer able to think clearly and cannot take advantage of psychotherapy (Bruch, 1978).

6. A sixth lesson is that eating disorder patients are not recovered if only the most visible symptoms of the eating disorder have improved. Strober et al. (1997) define the reduction of symptoms as only *partial recovery*. For *full recovery* from eating disorders it is not only the symptoms that have to be reduced, but also the underlying factors which contributed to the development of the eating disorder. Full recovery implies eating healthy amounts of food and keeping a healthy weight, having a

positive body attitude, enough self-esteem, and better emotional and social coping strategies (Björk & Ahlström, 2008; Noordenbos & Seubring, 2006; Noordenbos, 2011; Petterson & Rosenvinge, 2002; Vanderlinden et al,2007)

7. A seventh lesson to be drawn from the interviews with fully recovered patients is that none of them mentioned one specific treatment which had helped them to recover; it was always a combination of different therapies that had proved helpful for them, such as psycho-education about the relationship between food and emotions (Jantz & Mc Murray, 2002), Cognitive Behaviour Therapy (CBT) (Fairburn et al, 2003; Fairburn, et al., 2008); Acceptance and Commitment Therapy (ACT) (Hayes et al, 1999; Heffner & Eifert, 2004), and Mindfulness (Baer, Fischer & Huss, 2005; Kristeller, Baer & Wolever, 2006).

References

Amianto, F., Caroppo, P., D'Agata, F., Spalatro, A. Lavagnino, L., Caglio, M., Righi, D., Bergui, M., Abbate-Daga, G., Rigardetto, R., Mortara, P., Fassino, S. (2013) Brain volumetric abnormalities in patients with anorexia and bulimia nervosa: A Voxel-based morphometry study. *Psychiatry Research*, 30, (3), 210-216.

Abbate-Daga, G., Gramaglia, C., Malfi, G., Pierò A., Fassino, S. (2007) Eating problems and personality traits. An Italian pilot study among 992 high school students. *European Eating Disorder Review*, 15 (6), 471-478.

American Psychiatric Association (2000) *DSM-IV: Diagnostic and Statistical Manual of Mental Disorders (4th ed, text revision)*. Washington, DC.

American Psychiatric Association (2013) *DSM-5: Diagnostic and Statistical Manual of Mental Disorders (5th edition)*. Washington, DC.

Agras, W. S. & Apple, R. F. (1997) *Overcoming Eating Disorders. A Cognitive-Behavioral Treatment for Bulimia Nervosa and Binge Eating Disorder. Therapist Guide*. The Psychological Corporation, Hartcourt Brace & Company. San Antonio.

Baer, R. A., Fischer, S. & Huss, D. B. (2005). Mindfulness-based cognitive therapy applied to binge eating: A case study. *Cognitive and Behavioral Practice*, 12, 351-358.

Barran, S. A. Weltzin, T. E. & Kaye, W. H. (1995) Low discharge weight and out-come in anorexia nervosa. *American Journal of Psychiatry, 152*, 1070-1072.

Beales, D. L., & Dolton, R. (2000). Eating disordered patients: personality, alexithymia, and implications for primary care. *British Journal of General Practice, 50*, 21-26.

Björk, T., & Ahlström, G. (2008). The Patients' Perception on having recovered from an Eating Disorder. *Health Care for Women International 29*, 926-944.

Bruch, H. (1978). *The golden cage: The enigma of anorexia nervosa*. Cambridge, MA: Harvard University Press.

Cervera, S., Lahortiga, F., Martinez-Gonzalez, M. A., Gual, P., Irala-Estevez, J., de & Alfonso, Y. (2003). Neuroticism and low self-esteem as risk factors of incident eating disorders in a prospective cohort study. *International Journal of Eating Disorders*, 33, 271-280.

Claude-Pierre, P. (1997) *The Secret Language of Eating Disorders*. Random House.

Elburg, A. A. van (2007) Changes in mood states during recovery from anorexia nervosa. In: A. A. van Elburg: *Psychoneuroendocrinological aspects of anorexia nervosa: predictors of recovery*. Thesis. (pp. 131-148). Gildeprint Drukkerijen BV, Enschede.

Elburg, A. A. (2007) Outcome of Anorexia Nervosa: results of a 5 year follow-up study. In: A. A. val Elburg: *Psychoneuro- endocrinological aspects of anorexia nervosa: predictors of recovery*. Thesis. (pp. 149-172). Gildeprint Drukkerijen B.V. Enschede.

Fairburn, C. G., Welch, S. I., Doll, H. A., Davies, B. A. & O'Connor, M. E. (1997). Risk factors for Bulimia Nervosa: A community-based case-control study. *Archives of General Psychiatry*, 54,509-517.

Fairburn, C. G., Cooper, Z., & Shafran, (2003). Cognitive behaviour therapy for eating disorders: a 'transdiagnostic' theory and treatment. *Behaviour Research and Therapy, 41*, 509-528.

Fairburn, C. G., Cooper, Z., & Shafran, R., Hawker, D. M., Murphy, R & Straebler, S. (2008). Enhanced Cognitive behaviour therapy for eating disorders: the core protocol. In: C.G. Fairburn (Ed.) *Cognitive behaviour therapy for eating disorders*. New York, Guilford.

Fennig, S., Fennig, G., & Roe, D. (2002). Physical recovery in anorexia nervosa: Is this the sole purpose of a child and adolescent medical psychiatric unit? *General Hospital Psychiatry, 24*, 87-92.

Fodor, V. (1997) *Desperately Seeking Self. An Inner Guidebook for People with Eating Disorders*. Gürze Books, Carlsbad.

Hayes, S. C., Strosahl, K. D. & Wilson, K. G. (1999) *Acceptance and Commitment Therapy*. New York; Guilford Press.

Heffner, M. & Eifert, G. H. (2004) *The Anorexia Workbook. How to Accept Yourself, Heal Your Suffering, and Reclaim Your Life*. New Harbinger Publications, Inc. Oakland.

Jacobi, C., de Zwaan, M., Hayward, C., Kraemer, H. C. & Agras, W. S. (2004). Coming to terms with risk factors for eating disorders: application of risk factors terminology and suggestions for a general taxonomy. *Psychological Bulletin*, 130, 19 -65.

Jantz, G. L. & Mc Murray, A. (2002) *Hope and Healing for Eating Disorders*. A New Approach to Treating Anorexia, Bulimia and Overeating. Colorado, Waterbrook Press.

Jimerson, D. C., Wolfe, B. E., Franko, D. L., Colvino, N. A., Sifneos, P. E. (1994). Alexithymia ratings in bulimia: Clinical correlates. *Psychosomatic Medicine*, 56, 90-93.

Keel, P. M. (2005) *Eating Disorders*. Pearson. Prentice Hall, New Jersey.

Kortink, J. (2008) *Breaking the Spell of Binge-Eating. A road to balance in Your Life*. Academy Chicago Publishers, Chicago.

Kristeller, J. L., Baer, R. & Wolever, R. Q. (2006) Mindfulness based approaches to eating disorders. In: R. Baer (ed.) *Mindfulness and acceptance-based interventions: Conceptualization, application, and empirical support*. San Diego, CA: Elsevier.

Kristeller, J. L. & Wolever, R. Q. (2011) Mindfulness-based awareness training for treating binge eating disorders: the conceptual foundation. *Eating disorders, The Journal of Treatment and Prevention* 19, 49-61.

Levine, M. P. & Smolak, L. (1998). The mass media and disordered eating: Implications for primary prevention. In: W. Vandereycken & G. Noordenbos (Eds) *Prevention of Eating Disorders* (pp. 23-56). London, Athlone Press.

Nilsson, K. &. Hägglöff, B. (2006) Patients Perspectives of Recovery in Adolescent Onset Anorexia Nervosa. *Eating Disorders, The Journal of Treatment and Prevention* 14,. 305-311.

Noordenbos, G., Oldenhave, A., Muschter,J. & Terpstra, N. (2002) Characteristics and treatment of patients with chronic eating disorders. *Eating Disorders, The Journal of Treatment and Prevention* 10, 5-29.

Noordenbos, G. & Seubring, A. (2006). Criteria for Recovery from Eating Disorders according to Patients and Therapists. *Eating Disorders: The Journal of Treatment and Prevention, 14*, 41-54.

Noordenbos, G. (2013) *Recovery from Disorders. A Guide for Clinicians and Their Clients.* Wiley-Blackwell, Oxford.

Pettersen, G. & Rosenvinge, J. H. (2002). Improvement and recovery from eating disorders: a patient perspective. *Eating Disorders, The Journal of Treatment and Prevention, 10*, 61-71.

Pinhas, L., Toner, B. A., Garfinkel, P. E. & Stuckless, N. (1999) effects of the ideal of female beauty on mood and body satisfaction. *International Journal of Eating Disorders*, 25, 223-226.

Rorty, M., Yager, J. & Rosotto, E. (1993). Why and how do women recover from Bulimia Nervosa. The Subjective Appraisals of Forty Women Recovered for a Year or More. *International Journal of Eating Disorders, 14*, 249-160.

Rorty, M, Yager, J., Buckwalter, J. G. & Rossotto, E. (1999). Social support, social adjustment, and recovery status in bulimia nervosa. *International Journal of Eating Disorders, 26*, 1-2.

Serpell, I., Treasure, J., Teasdale, J. & Sullivan, V. (1999). Anorexia Nervosa: friend or foe? *International Journal of Eating Disorders*, 25 (2) 177-186.

Serpell, I. & Treasure, J. (2002). Bulimia Nervosa:, friend or foe? The pros and cons of bulimia nervosa. *International Journal of Eating Disorders*, 32 (2) 164-170.

Spaans, J. & Bloks, H. (2008) Motivation for change. In: W. Vandereycken, W. & G. Noordenbos (Eds). *Handbook Eating Disorders* (pp. 115-144). Utrecht, De Tijdstroom. In Dutch.

Speranza, M., Loas, G., Wallier, J., & Corcos, M. (2007). Predictive value of alexithymia in patients with eating disorders: a 3-year prospective study. *Journal of Psychosomatic Research, 63*, 365-371.

Sterk, F. & Swaen, S. (2006) *Positive Selfmotivation.* Utrecht, Antwerpen, Lifetime, Kosmos –Z&K Uitgevers.

Steinhausen, H-C (1999) Eating Disorders. In H.-C. Steinhausen & F. C. Verhulst (Eds.) *Risks and outcomes in developmental psychopathology* (pp. 210-230). Oxford: Oxford University Press.

Steinhausen, H-C. (2002). The outcome of Anorexia Nervosa in the 20th Century. *American Journal of Psychiatry, 159*, 284-1293.

Stice, E. (2002) Risk and maintenance factors for eating pathology; a meta-analytic review. *Psychological Bulletin*, 128, 825-848.

Striegel-Moore, R. H. & Bulik, C. M. (2007). Risk Factors for Eating Disorders. *American Psychologist*, 62, 181-198.

Strober, M., Freeman, R. & Morrell, W. (1997). The long term course of severe anorexia nervosa, in adolescents: Survival of recovery, relapse & outcome predictors over 10-15 years in a prospective study. *International Journal of Eating Disorders, 25,* 135-142.

Tenwolde, A. A. M. (2000) *From thin to fat. Psychosocial and biological aspects of anorexia nervosa, bulimia nervosa and obesitas.* Houten/Diegem. Bohn Stafleu Van Loghum. (In Dutch Van dun tot dik).

Tierney, S. & Fox, J. R. E. (2010) Living with the 'anorexic voice': A thematic Analysis. *Psychology and Psychotherapy: Theory, Research and Practice, 83,* 243-254.

Vanderlinden, J., Buis, H., Pieters, G. & Probst, M. (2007). Which elements in the treatment are 'necessary' ingredients in the recovery process. A comparison between patient's and therapist's view. *European Eating Disorders Review, 15,* 357-365.

Windauer, U., Lennerts, W., Talbot, P. Touyz, S. W. & Beumont, P. J. (1993) How well are 'cured' anorexia nervosa patients? An investigation of 16 weight recovered anorexic patients. *British Journal of Psychiatry, 163,* 195-200.

Zonnevijlle-Bender, M. J. S., van Goozen, S. H. M., Cohen-Kettenis, P. T., van Elberg, A., & van Engeland, H. (2004). Emotional functioning in adolescent anorexia nervosa patients: a controlled study. *European Child & Adolescent Psychiatry, 13,* 28-34.

In: New Developments in Anorexia Nervosa Research
Editors: Carla Gramaglia and Patrizia Zeppegno

ISBN: 978-1-63117-551-0
© 2014 Nova Science Publishers, Inc.

Chapter 8

What about "Hungry Attention"? Spatial and Temporal Characteristics of Attentional Bias in Eating Disorders

Małgorzata Starzomska[*]
Institute of Psychology, Cardinal Stefan Wyszynski University, Warsaw, Poland

Abstract

Attentional biases have an important place in both the theory and the treatment of eating disorders, and they may consist of facilitated attention to relevant stimuli, difficulty disengaging attention from them, or their attentional avoidance. Despite suggestions about the importance of attentional biases in the maintenance of eating disorder psychopathology, research on this topic is limited. The majority of studies in this field have used the modified Stroop task which is at best a weak test of attention, as delayed color-naming latencies can arise from attention directed either towards or away from relevant stimuli. On the other hand, the second popular (though less than the previous one) test of attentional bias, namely the dot probe task, does not differentiate between vigilance and difficulty to disengage attention. The spatial cueing task is the third popular paradigm to measure attentional bias, but does not allow any individual to identify differences in the tendency to initially prioritize the assignment of attention to relevant stimuli. A perspective on using a new paradigm of measuring attentional bias in eating disorders is proposed, to make it possible differentiating between three components of attentional bias. Beyond the analysis of these spatial phenomena, the chapter includes the analysis of their temporal characteristics.

[*] Corresponding author: Institute of Psychology, Cardinal Stefan Wyszynski University, Woycickiego 1/3, building No. 14, 01-938 Warsaw. Email: eltram@life.pl.

Introduction

Many authors suggest that eating disorders are associated with selective processing of stimuli which are relevant to patients' concerns (e.g. Mathews & MacLeod, 1994). Williamson, Muller, Reas and Thaw (1999) suggested that the intensive over-concern with eating, shape, weight and their control results especially in cognitive biases of attention. A long series of studies demonstrated that eating disordered patients selectively allocate attention to food, shape and weight stimuli (e.g. Rieger, Schotte, Touyz, Beumont, Griffiths, & Russell, 1998; Shafran, Lee, Cooper, Palmer, & Fairburn, 2007, 2008; Lee & Shafran, 2008; Veenstra & de Jong, 2012; Faunce, 2002; Dobson & Dozois, 2004, Lee & Shafran, 2004, for review).

This chapter is focused on attentional bias to food stimuli in eating disordered patients, in the attempt to answer the question whether we can (metaphorically speaking) talk about "hungry attention" within this group of patients. The term "hungry" here is synonymous with "craving", which denotes the Author's intention to find out whether the attention of eating disordered patients is directed towards food-related stimuli. Some suggestions are made about possible improvements in research methodology as well.

Eating Disordered Patients' Attitude towards Food

Anorexia nervosa is characterized by an unusual attitude towards food. Although the term anorexia literally means "loss of appetite", this definition is misleading, because anorexic patients are often hungry but refuse food anyway. People with anorexia nervosa have intense fears of becoming fat and sees themselves as fat even when they are very slender.

Noteworthy, the underlying cause behind anorexia nervosa is rarely about the food itself. Many researchers (e.g. Minuchin, Rosman, & Baker, 1978; Blinder, Chaitin, & Goldstein, 1988; Selvini-Palazzoli, Cirillo, Selvini, & Sorrentino, 1988) claim that anorexic families may appear to have a perfect or ideal environment on the surface, but upon close observation little expression of warmth is seen. It has been suggested that parents of anorexic offspring put high expectations on their children in order to make up for the missing affection in their dysfunctional marriages (Blinder, Chaitin & Goldstein, 1988). The overinvolved parent unconsciously stops the child from exerting his emotional autonomy. This in turn leaves the child powerless and prevents him from developing his own, separate identity. Restricting the food intake is the only way by which the anorexic child manages to exert autonomy and control. Sometimes, the anorexic uses the illness in a desperate effort to mend his/her parents' dysfunctional marriage. Some authors describe attitudes towards food among anorexic patients from a symbolic rather than a literal perspective. This kind of description is extremely helpful in that it analyses the anorexic patients' perception of food in a great detail.

From the symbolic perspective: to people who suffer from eating disorders, in particular from anorexia, food looks "foreign" (Levens, 1995, p. 94) and "alive" (Levens, 1995, p. 61). In order to understand this perception, one has to imagine food as something which triggers a "dirty" movement inside the body. While the food and liquids are in transit through their body, patients suffer immensely (Warin, 2004). The transiting food can cross the fragile boundary of their bodies and attack them unexpectedly (Shipton, 1999; Warin, 2003); it can also encroach upon one's "self" boundaries and strike at the "core of self" by contaminating it (Levens, 1995, p. 22; p. 45). People suffering from anorexia consider food dangerous, threatening, dirty, disgusting, repugnant, disgraced, and infectious (Malson, 1998; Warin, 2003). They often tend to associate food with dirt, garbage, trash, faeces, junk and even urine (Warin, 2003). As a result, the refusal of eating means "clean" (Warin, 2003). Ellen West, an anorexic patient described by L. Binswanger, considered food lethal. For her, the act of eating revolved around a symbolic meaning of life and death. Having a full stomach meant an existential emptiness to this patient. Feeling full meant withering, rotting, dying in "the stupid world filled with marshes and coffins", and was associated with an explicit sense of guilt and bad feelings (Stobiecka, 2000, p. 241). Ellen West, like "many other anorexic patients, had probably, at the unconscious level, associated food with the death of soul. Giving up eating was the only way to avoid it. It would cause the death of the body, which in her eyes was just 'a useless, lifeless material, an empty husk" (Stobiecka, 2000, p. 241). Sabina, one of H. Thomy's patients, described by Stobiecka (2000), "has drawn a picture of an ideal woman who looked like a ghost and a phantom. She often repeated that she had felt as if she had been dead and that she wished she had been a doll, which neither eats nor defecates" (p. 241). According to Latzer and Hochdorf (2005), the "horror of eating" (p. 1) is the scariest factor to people suffering from anorexia. Therefore, these people will do their best in order to avoid food. In their minds, food appears either "clean" or "dirty". "Innocent" foods include vegetables, fruit, milk and yoghurt (the phrase "good food" is sometimes used by people experiencing eating disorders; Eiber, Mirabel-Sarron and Urdapilleta, 2005, p. 643). On the other hand, oils, butter, sugar and meat belong to the "unclean" category of foods (Bobowska, 1988; Warin, 2003). One of the sufferers self-portrayed herself as a "set" of different foods, and in her picture, she substituted the legs and the torso, the key body parts for people suffering from anorexia, with two fishes and a chicken body, accordingly (Levens, 1995, p. 21). Another patient described how she felt "dirty, polluted and disgusting, as if something bad had gotten inside her", after eating sugar (Bordo, 1988, p. 95; see also Warin, 2003, p. 78). Eating "dirty" food makes anorexia sufferers feel "tainted". Such contamination happens in two ways: either due to a contact with calories or with fats. In the jargon used by people with eating disorders, the phenomenon is best described in terms of "a calorie girl" and "a fat girl" (Warin, 2003, p. 83). "Calorie girls" fear most of all an airborne contagion of food calories, which tend to "attack" through the sense of smell, better described by the sufferers as "the smell molecules" and "the flying calories" (Warin, 2003, p. 83). In these people's houses one can most often smell the antiseptic cleaning liquids and air fresheners. The research literature often refers to "the smell calories" in terms of "miasmatic calories" (Warin, 2003, p. 77). The term alludes to the times of the Middle Ages, when the vapours of miasma from marshes and bogs, produced by decomposing plants as well as animal and human waste, were believed to cause many dangerous epidemics in the adjacent cities. On the other hand, making contact with food, in particular touching it, is the greatest fear of the "fat girls". They feel nauseous just at the thought of it. They think of fats in terms of snakes which slither through their skin into the body. In that respect, fats are even more dangerous than calories. While calories attack through the smell molecules, via nose and mouth, the fats can sneak in through the whole surface of the body, and once they are in, they can stick and solidify like cement. The perspective of fat coagulation inside their bodies is intolerable to anorexic patients.

Problems with Reliability of Self-Report Data Obtained from Eating Disordered Patients

It must be underlined that the sole description of the eating disordered patients' perception of food, based on proper guided interviews and psychotherapy sessions, including art therapy, can only be used as a theoretical basis of empirical research.

To overcome problems with reliability of self-report data in eating disorder patients, researchers are using indirect techniques for exploring biased patterns of cognitive processing (Vitousek, Daly, & Heiser, 1991; Fauce, 2002; Placanica, Faunce, & Soames Job, 2002; Vandereycken, 2006a, 2006b). Cognitive psychology, and particularly the study of eating disordered patients' selective attention, is likely to lead to a better understanding of patients' extremely aversive attitude towards food.

Regrettably, cognitive etiological models have received significantly less empirical scrutiny than the treatment methods they underlie, which are both widespread and effective in the treatment of eating disorders (e.g. Garner, Fairburn, & Davis, 1987). According to Vitousek and Hollon (1990), cognitive assessment of eating disorders has been restricted to the low level of abstraction represented by self-statements about eating and weight, while the higher-order cognitive elements hypothesized by theorists remain unexamined (Vitousek & Hollon, 1990; see also Garner & Davis, 1986). Vitousek & Hollon (1990) point out that the process of collecting thoughts (most frequently concerning food, body shape and weight) of eating disordered patients resembles gathering the exact information about the number of times and variety of ways that a paranoid individual perceives that others are trying to harm him-instead of trying to determine how this theme has arisen in his life and how it is perpetuated (see also Cameron, 1974). According to Vitousek and Hollon (1990), it is obvious that someone who has organized her life around weight control will think a great deal about food and weight, will try to restrict her intake, and will experience considerable emotion as she encounters success and failure in pursuing her goal. In summary, these authors criticise the traditional methods of collecting thoughts of eating disordered patients and claim "on a higher level, techniques inspired by cognitive psychology could also be employed to draw nonobvious conclusions from the superficial content of the eating disorders, or to connect such material with aspects of 'deep' cognitive structure" (p. 199). Faunce (2002) deems that this area of research may have a significant clinical importance, because selective attention may be one way in which eating disorder symptomatology is maintained.

The State-of-the-Art Regarding Selective Attention to Food-Related Stimuli in Eating Disordered Patients

The existing research on selective attention regarding food-related stimuli in people with eating disorders is very limited. The research conducted so far had several limitations: first, it has typically failed to address the role that hunger may play in determining attentional biases to food stimuli (see Vitousek and Orimoto, 1993, for review). Second, it often has employed the Stroop colour naming task (Stroop, 1935) that is a weak test of selective attention, because delayed color-naming latencies can arise from attention directed either toward or away from disorder-relevant stimuli (Rieger, Schotte, Touyz, Beumont, Griffiths, & Russel, 1998). Thus we still don't know how to interpret the interference effects – as evidence of a mood-congruent attentional bias or as evidence of cognitive avoidance (De Ruiter & Brosschot, 1994; Lee & Shafran, 2004). Third, with the exception of the research conducted by Lee and Shafran (2008), changes in patients' cognitive content and processing over time have not been tracked (Vitousek & Hollon, 1990). Finally, during the research (e.g. Channon, Hemsley, & de Silva, 1988; Perpina, Hemsley, Treasure, & de Silva, 1993; Long, Hinton, & Gillespie, 1994; Lovell, Williams, & Hill, 1997), high- and low-calorie food-related stimuli have not been separated. Lavy and Van den Hout (1993; see Faunce, 2002, for a review) have only split positive and negative food-related words without referring to their calorie count.

Recently, systematic attempts have been made to examine the time course of emotional information processing using the visual dot probe task (MacLeod, Mathews, & Tata, 1986). It is a methodologically stronger test of attentional bias than does the Stroop colour naming task (MacLeod et al., 1986; Placanica et al., 2002), because it is able to detect whether or not attention is directed toward or away from a given stimulus. The dot probe task requires subjects to attend simultaneously to two separate stimuli, rather than different attributes of the same stimulus as in the Stroop colour naming task (Placanica et al., 2002). A detailed description can be found in the next sections.

For example, the research of Shafran et al. (2007) relying on the dot probe task revealed that people with eating disorders focused their attention on negative, food-related stimuli (i.e. high-calorie food-related), presented in a time span of 1000 ms (Stimulus-Onset Asynchrony or SOA, also known as Interstimulus Interval or ISI; it measures time that lapses between the presentation of the prime stimulus and a target stimulus). However, the researchers did not consider the fact that by manipulating SOA the results will be altered, for example: when SOA=100 ms the subjects demonstrate vigilance to threat. Instead, with longer time lapses, SOA=2000 ms, the subjects avoid threat. (see also Lee & Shafran, 2008).

Placanica et al. (2002) employed a modified dot probe task to assess attentional biases for low- and high-calorie food-related words (SOA=500 ms). However, the choice of participants, consisting of healthy individuals, scoring high versus low on the Drive for Thinness and Body Dissatisfaction subscales of the EDI-2 (Garner, 1991), was a significant limitation. In spite of this serious shortcoming, the results are still worth mentioning. The authors found that fasting increased attentional bias towards high calorie food words across all healthy subjects (interestingly: both high and low EDI-2 scorers), and that high EDI-2 scorers also showed an attentional bias towards low calorie food words, but only when they were not fasting.

These findings suggest that when they are not hungry because they do not fast, individuals with high eating-related concerns exhibit a peculiar cognitive pattern: they selectively attend to nonforbidden (low-calorie) food-related stimuli as opposed to forbidden (high-calorie) food-related stimuli. Subsequently, this may suggest that preoccupation with food-related stimuli may not simply reflect an ongoing hunger state, but hunger may rather play an important role in determining the type of food stimuli that attracts attention. It is worth emphasizing that the researchers noticed a shift in focus among high EDI-2 scorers away from low-calorie foods with increasing hunger, which may explain the binge-purge cycle found in patients with bulimia nervosa. According to Placanica et al. (2002), as hunger increases as a consequence of self-induced starvation, attention increasingly focuses on high-calorie food-related stimuli. This increasing focus on high-calorie food-related stimuli may lead to the breaking of dietary restraint and the onset of a binge eating episode. This, in turn, may lead to feelings of guilt because of perceived loss of control and anxiety over possible weight gain, which result in purging behaviour and a subsequent return to severe dietary restraint. As restraint progresses, attention is again increasingly focused on high-calorie food-related stimuli, triggering a vicious binge-purge cycle. It is highly probable that serious eating disorders may be, at least at a cognitive level, self-perpetuating.

Mogg, Bradley, Hyare, & Lee (1998) employed the dot probe task and proved that healthy subjects with high levels of hunger showed a greater attentional bias for high-calorie food-related words presented in a suprathreshold exposure condition (SOA=500 ms), in comparison with those with low hunger. There was no evidence in this study of a hunger-related bias in pre-attentive processes (i.e. when words were shown for 14 ms and masked). Anyway, sample selection was a limitation of their study as well.

Lee and Shafran (2008) were the only researchers who have tested eating disordered people through a combination of the dot probe task and the time manipulation of SOA. In one format of the task, the time between the image pairs disappearing and the probe appearing was 500 ms. In the other, this time was 2,000 ms. The results have revealed that eating disordered patients continued to display a bias in the processing of weight, but not eating or shape-related stimuli. However, the test did not separate low-calorie from high-calorie food-related stimuli and, therefore, it was completely unhelpful to the research of processing food-related stimuli.

In conclusion, the results of the research on selective attention to food-related stimuli in eating disorder patients are limited by several methodological flaws. However, they tend to indicate that eating disordered patients, as well as people in the risk group, i.e. women with high weight and shape concerns, direct attention to food-related stimuli in a distinctive way.

There are two key aspects which have been neglected in the existing research on selective attention to food stimuli so far. First, for several years, researchers studying the selective attention have been engaged in a discussion about differentiating between two attention biases: facilitated attention to food stimuli and difficulty in disengaging attention away from them (Koster, Crombez, Verschuere, & de Houwer, 2004). To the author's best knowledge, the existing research on selective attention to food stimuli in patients with eating disorders has not taken this aspect into consideration yet. Second, the results have been usually determined by relying most often on just one SOA, typically of 500 ms. It was originally assumed that the reaction time, with SOA of 500 ms, reflects the direction of the initial orienting towards affective stimulation. This, however, proved unfounded because the processes of stimulus evaluation, as well as unfocusing, shifting and focusing the attention on a new object, last less than 500 ms and their direction and force are likely to fluctuate within the given time frame (Posner, 1994; Asanowicz & Wolski, 2007).

500 ms are sufficient for a twofold reorientation of attention: after initial focusing of attention on emotional stimuli, it can be shifted on neutral stimuli (Asanowicz & Wolski, 2007). The research on inhibition of return (IOR) (Posner and Cohen, 1984) proved that if the attention is drawn by exogenous factors, the reaction facilitation takes place when SOA does not exceed 250-300 ms. When longer SOA is required, inhibition process makes the centre of attention return to fixation point (Asanowicz & Wolski, 2007; see Fox, Russo, & Dutton, 2002). The existing research regarding selective processing of food-related stimuli have not yet established whether the patients' reactions reflect attention drawing towards these

stimulus or difficulty in disengaging attention from them. Moreover, with the exception of the research by Lee and Shafran (2008), which failed to separate low- and high-calorie food-stimuli, the prevailing research did not examine the influence of SOA (e.g. subthreshold conditions when SOA=14 ms) on the attentional biases. These two fundamental flaws in the research area should encourage a general reflection on what needs to be done in order to improve the existing methodology.

At the opening of the chapter, we established that "hungry attention" means "craving attention". The results of the tests have unanimously showed that supraliminally (not subliminally) presented high-calorie food-related stimuli in hunger draw attention. In contrast, low-calorie food-related stimuli draw attention in lack of hunger. At this point, there comes a key question: could it be that the researchers who had come to these conclusions were trapped by the over interpretation, in particular by the biases of the selective attention research?

New Research Perspectives on the "Hungry Attention"

In this section I would like to suggest two options (i.e. differentiating between various components of attentional bias and SOA influence on the type of bias) on which could potentially improve the research on attentional bias in eating disorders. This should really help to determine whether the "hungry attention" is present within this patients' group. First, I am going to suggest a reliable way in which the three components of attentional bias (facilitated attention, difficulty in disengaging attention, attentional avoidance) concerning food-related stimuli can be researched. Second, I am going to propose the research on changes of attentional bias in processing of these stimuli, which are the results of SOA manipulation.

Study Proposal of the Three Components of Attentional Bias Concerning Food-Related Stimuli

Research in anxiety disorders (MacLeod et al., 1986) has found the dot probe task to be sensitive to attentional biases (Rieger et al., 1998). In this task two stimuli are presented on a screen with one at the top and one at the bottom (alternatively, the words may appear on the left and right side of the screen). Following a brief stimulus presentation duration (e.g. 500 ms), the stimuli disappear and a probe appears in a location previously occupied by one of the stimuli. Participants are instructed to indicate the location of the probe as quickly as possible, either via keyboard or response box. Latency is measured automatically by the computer. The logic behind this task is that subjects will be quicker to detect or classify probes that replace attended rather than nonattended stimuli (Faunce, 2002; Lee & Shafran, 2004). Thus, participants are faster to respond to probes that appear in the same spatial location as the stimulus to which they are paying attention (Shafran et al., 2007). Attentional biases are inferred from different response times towards probes that replace threatening stimuli (i.e., congruent trials) compared to probes that replace neutral stimuli (i.e. incongruent trials)

(Cisler & Koster, 2010). If an individual's attention is systematically drawn to the threat stimulus, response times will be shorter for probes that replace threatening stimuli compared to probes that replace neutral stimuli (Lee & Shafran, 2004; Koster, Verschuere, Crombez, & van Damme, 2005; Cisler & Koster, 2010). Thus selective attention for threat based on these reaction times (RTs) is interpreted as facilitated detection of threatening stimuli compared to neutral stimuli that reflects a tendency to "shift attention to emotionally threatening stimuli" (MacLeod et al., 1986, p. 18; Klumpp & Amir, 2009, p. 284). On the other hand, slower probe detection when it replaces the threatening stimulus than when it replaces the neutral one, reflects avoidance of the stimulus (Lee & Shafran, 2004; Koster et al., 2005; Cisler & Koster, 2010). In summary, the dot probe task has the advantage of being able to detect whether or not attention is directed toward or away from a given class of stimulus words (Placanica et al., 2002).

Noteworthy, the interpretation of the pattern of results observed in the probe detection task has been challenged. Derryberry and Reed (2002) have suggested that the facilitated response to probes at the threat location may also arise from a difficulty to disengage from the threat location rather than vigilance to threat. Fox et al. (2002) have argued that the presence of threat-related stimuli may affect the attentional dwell time or the ability to disengage attentional resources from threatening stimuli in anxious people. According to these authors in the probe detection task, because both locations are task-relevant, and presentation times are relatively long (usually SOA=500ms), participants may attend alternately to both locations and then continue to dwell on threat-related stimuli once they have been detected. Thus, the traditional probe detection task does not seem to allow distinguishing between initial orienting and attentional dwell, followed by difficulty in disengaging attention.

A task which may allow a better assessment of disengage mechanisms is the spatial cueing task (Posner, 1980). On each trial, a single stimulus (e.g., angry or neutral face) is presented in one of two possible locations. The stimulus is replaced by a probe, which appears in either the same location (valid cue condition) or opposite location (invalid cue condition). The invalid trials are critical because reaction times can be compared following neutral, positive, and threat-related cues, giving a fairly direct measure of disengagement from threatening stimuli. For example, if a person with anxiety has difficulty with disengaging attention from threat-related stimuli then he/she should be slower in detecting a target on invalid trials following a threat-related cue, relative to a positive or neutral cue (Fox et al., 2002). Unfortunately, according to Fox et al. (2002), this task cannot measure enhanced attentional orienting towards a threat stimulus, because only one stimulus is presented prior to the probe on each trial. Thus, the research relying on this test shows only effects that reflect differential disengagement of attention from alternative emotional stimulus classes (e.g. angry vs neutral face) (Fox et al., 2002).

In summary, both the dot probe task and the spatial cueing task, as a measure of attentional bias, show significant limitations since none of them is able to discriminate between vigilance to a given stimulus and difficulty in disengaging attention from it (Klumpp & Amir, 2009).

Koster et al. (2004) propose that a probe detection task may be modified in such way that vigilance for threat and disengagement from threat may be differentiated. They propose an alternative way of analysing responses obtained in the dot probe task. They suggest that the inclusion of baseline trials (e.g. neutral-neutral pictures) should allow the measurement of these components of attention. The authors underscore that previous versions of this task have never compared reaction times (RTs) on trials containing neutral information (e.g. two neutral pictures) with reaction times on trials containing threatening information (e.g. a threatening picture and a neutral one). For this reason a positive attentional bias, which represents the difference between reaction times on the subsequent congruent and incongruent trials, could result from faster response to congruent trials (vigilance) or slower response to incongruent trials (difficulty to disengage). According to the authors, a comparison to neutral trials seems necessary to determine which of the two components of visual attention is measured. Koster et al. (2004) propose that the RT data obtained in this modified dot probe procedure should be analysed in two ways: first, by a comparison between RTs on congruent and incongruent threatening trials. Second, by a comparison between RTs on trials that contained two neutral stimuli with RTs on trials that contained one threatening and one neutral stimulus. The second comparison makes it possible to test whether the congruency effect reflects vigilance for threat or a difficulty to disengage attention from threat. Vigilance for threat should lead to faster responses on congruent threatening trials compared to neutral trials. Difficulty to disengage attention from threat should lead to slower responses on incongruent threatening trials compared to neutral trials. Longer RTs on the incongruent threatening trials are caused by the time needed to shift attention from the threatening to the neutral location. Such innovative and enhancing the research reliability modification of dot probe task would be extremely beneficial for the research on attentional bias concerning food-related stimuli in patients with eating disorders.

Innovative Research Proposal for the Assessment of Attentional Bias in Processing of Food-Related Stimuli and Their Changes over Time

By using the modified dot probe task described by Koster and co-workers (2004) and manipulating the exposure duration of the stimuli, it is possible to index the time course of three components of attentional bias, namely: vigilance towards a given stimulus, difficulty in disengagement attention from it and avoidance of it (see Koster et al., 2005).

In the dot probe tasks, SOA of 500 ms, and SOA of 1000 ms have been usually applied, and in the case of subliminal stimuli, SOA of 14 and 17 ms (Asanowicz & Wolski, 2007). As mentioned previously, only one study so far (Lee & Shafran, 2008) has manipulated the exposure duration of the stimuli in the eating disordered patients' group. When planning the research on processing food-related stimuli, it is worth taking into consideration the conclusions of the studies on IOR (inhibition of return) phenomenon. These demonstrated that 500 ms are sufficient for the double reorientation of attention. If attention is drawn by exogenous factors, the reaction facilitation occurs when SOA is not longer than 250-300 ms. This is due to the fact that with longer SOA, the inhibition process makes the centre of attention return to a fixation point. The examination of the temporary dynamics of attentional bias through the dot probe task, where the stimuli last 100, 200 and 500 ms, subsequently, would provide a very valuable study in the future.

Second, we should not overlook, the extremely short, subliminal stimuli presentation (e.g. for 14 and 17 ms, see Mogg et al., 1998; Asanowicz & Wolski, 2007), which is unregistered by the conscious. It makes the discussion about the automatic and controlled mechanisms in the information processing more meaningful.

At the same time, it is also worth remembering the advantages of using SOA longer than 500 ms. Koster et al. (2005) have tested the changes in the course of the processing of threatening and nonthreatening stimuli, using the dot probe task. Three SOA of 100, 200 and 1250 ms were used in the test. They found out that with SOA=100 ms all tested individuals, regardless of the anxiety level, had focused on the area where the threatening stimulus occurred. Whereas, with SOA=500 ms, the differences between high anxiety and low anxiety groups, (i.e. trait-anxiety), were traced. According to the authors, participants in the anxiety group found it more difficult to disengage attention from threatening stimuli compared to the non-anxious group of individuals.

Conversely, with SOA=1250 ms, individuals with high anxiety levels used to avoid both threatening and nonthreatening stimuli. Alternatively, Rohner (2002) presented the low trait anxious and high trait anxious individuals with pairs of angry, neutral and happy faces, grouped in different sequences. The direction of their gaze was constantly monitored. For the first 1000 ms, both groups were found to look at the angry faces more than neutral and happy faces. For the next 2000 and 3000 ms, the subjects averted their gaze from angry faces. The results seem to support the vigilant-avoidant theory in relation to the repressors (i.e. individuals who use the repressive coping style) proposed by Derakshan, Eysenck, & Myers (2007). According to the theory, "there are two successive stages of processing when repressors are exposed to self-relevant threats. The initial stage (vigilance stage) occurs rapidly and may involve automatic and non-conscious processes, whereas the second stage (avoidance stage) involves controlled and strategic processes and an emphasis on possible coping strategies" (p. 1589).

In conclusion, we may consider that a greater level of SOA manipulation (e.g. from 14, 100, 200, 500, 1000, 1250, up to 1500 ms) will allow us to learn more about changes of attentional bias over the relevant time stimuli. However, we should keep in mind the following statement by Mogg and Bradley (1998): „In any individual study, it is difficult to sample more than two or three exposure durations (e.g., 500 or 1000 ms), without the task becoming excessively long and fatiguing, particularly for clinical samples" (p. 33). This statement also applies to patients with eating disorders. Nonetheless, one has to remember that an exhaustive study of the influence of the SOA changes on the patients' attentional functioning is simply invaluable.

Conclusion

Unfortunately, the existing research on attentional bias in eating disordered people (also and perhaps mainly) in the field of food-related stimuli, still supports the claim of Vitousek & Orimoto (1993) that the "eating disorder field lags consistently behind research in the affective and anxiety disorders in the maturity of [its] questions and techniques" (p. 207). Bearing in mind that the nature of the attentional bias varies as a function of the time course in the processing of informations (Calvo & Alvero, 2005), it would be invaluable to be able to explore "the temporal dynamics of emotional responding" (see Davidson, 1998, p. 310). Such innovative research project should examine what kind of attentional biases (e.g. facilitated attention to food stimuli, difficulty in disengaging attention away from them and attentional avoidance of them, Cisler & Koster, 2010) can occur at any given stage in the information processing. Such research would propel the field forward, bringing it closer to the levels of the research on anxiety disorders. By exposing the mechanisms of the prevalence, and perhaps the etiology, of eating disorders, the research could contribute to the development of more efficient future interventions for affected patients.

References

Asanowicz, D. & Wolski, P. (2007). Attention in anxiety, emotional disorders and phobias. Methodological issues of the dot-probe task. In *Psychology and medicine. Shared areas of common interests*, (5-16). Warsaw: VIZJA PRESS & IT.

Blinder, B. J., Chaitin, B. F. & Goldstein, R. S. (1988). *The Eating Disorders*. New York PMA Publishing.

Bobowska, A. (1988). Eve and the forbidden fruit. In M. Sokolik (Ed.), *Selected problems of psychotherapy. Methods and healing process, study cases*, (163-191). Warsaw: Warsaw University Press.

Bordo, S. (1988). Anorexia nervosa: psychopathology as the crystallization of culture. In I. Diamond, & L. Quinby (eds.), *Feminism and Foucault*, (87-117). Boston MA: Northeastern University Press.

Calvo, M. G. & Avero, P. (2005). Time course of attentional bias to emotional scenes in anxiety: Gaze direction and duration. *Cognition and Emotion, 19*, 433-451.

Cameron, N. (1974). Paranoid conditions and paranoia. In S. Arieti (Ed.), *American handbook of psychiatry*, (2nd ed., vol. 3) (676-693). New York: Basic Books.

Channon, S., Hemsley, D. & de Silva, P. (1988). Selective processing of food words in anorexia nervosa. *British Journal of Clinical Psychology, 27*, 259-260.

Cisler, J. M. & Koster, E. H. W. (2010). Mechanisms of attentional biases towards threat in anxiety disorders: An integrative review. *Clinical Psychology Review, 30*, 203-216.

Davidson, R. J. (*1998*). Affective style and affective disorders: perspectives from affective neuroscience. *Cognition and Emotion, 12*, 307-320

de Ruiter, C. & Brosschot, J. F. (1994). The emotional Stroop interference effect in anxiety: attentional bias or cognitive avoidance? *Behaviour Research and Therapy, 32*, 315-319.

Derakshan, N., Eysenck, M. W. & Myers, L. B. (2007). Emotional information processing in repressors: The vigilance-avoidance theory. *Cognition and Emotion, 21*, 1585-1614.

Derryberry, D. & Reed, M. A. (2002). Anxiety-related attentional biases and their regulation by attentional control. *Journal of Abnormal Psychology, 111*, 225–236.

Dobson, K. S. & Dozois, D. J. A. (2004). Attentional biases in eating disorders: A meta-analytic review of Stroop performance. *Clinical Psychology Review, 23*, 1001-1022.

Eiber, R., Mirabel-Sarron, C. & Urdapilleta, I. (2005). Cognitions in eating disorders and their assessment. *Encephale, 31*, 643-652.

Faunce, G. (2002). Eating disorders and attentional bias: A review. *The Journal of Treatment and Prevention, 10*, 125-139.

Fox, E., Russo, R. & Dutton, K. (2002). Attentional bias for threat: Evidence for delayed disengagement from emotional faces. *Cognition and Emotion, 16*, 355-379.

Garner, D. M., Fairburn, C. G. & Davis, R. (1987). Cognitive-behavioral treatment of bulimia nervosa. *Behavior Modification, 11,* 398-431.

Garner, D. M. & Davis, R. (1986). The clinical assessment of anorexia nervosa and bulimia nervosa. In P. A. Keller & L. Ritt (Eds.), *Innovations in clinical practice: A source book,* (vol. 5), (5-28). Sarasota, Florida: Professional Resource Exchange.

Garner, D. M. (1991). *Eating Disorder Inventory–2 manual.* Odessa, FL: Psychological Assessment Resources.

Klumpp, H. & Amir, N. (2009). Examination of vigilance and disengagement of threat in social anxiety with a probed detection task. *Anxiety, Stress, and Coping, 22,* 283-296.

Koster, E. H. W., Crombez, G., Verschuere, B. & de Houwer, J. (2004). Selective attention to threat in the dot probe paradigm: Differentiating vigilance and difficulty to disengage. *Behaviour Research and Therapy, 42,* 1183-1192.

Koster, E. H. W., Verschuere, B., Crombez, G. & van Damme, S. (2005). Time-course of attention for threatening pictures in high and low trait anxiety. *Behaviour Research and Therapy, 43,* 1087-1098.

Latzer, Y. & Hochdorf, Z. (2005). Attachment to life in anorexia nervosa. *Eating Disorders Review, 16,* 1-2.

Lavy, E. H. & van den Hout, M. A. (1993). Attentional bias for appetitive cues: Affects of fasting in normal subjects. *Behavioural and Cognitive Psychotherapy, 21,* 297-310.

Lee, M. & Shafran, R. (2004). Information processing biases in eating disorders. *Clinical Psychology Review, 24,* 215-238.

Lee, M. & Shafran, R. (2008). Processing biases in eating disorders: The impact of temporal factors. *International Journal of Eating Disorders, 41* 372-375.

Levens, M. (1995). *Eating disorders and magical control of the body. Treatment through art therapy.* London: Routledge.

Long, C. C., Hinton, C. & Gillespie, N. K. (1994). Selective processing of food and body size words: Application of the Stroop test with obese restrained eaters, anorexics and normals. *International Journal of Eating Disorders, 15,* 279-283.

Lovell, D., Williams, J. M. G. & Hill, A. B. (1997). Selective processing of shape related words in women with eating disorders and those who recovered. *British Journal of Clinical Psychology, 36,* 421-432.

MacLeod, C., Mathews, A., & Tata, P. (1986). Attentional bias in emotional disorders. *Journal of Abnormal Psychology, 95,* 15 - 20.

Malson, H. (1998). *The thin woman: feminism, post-structuralism and the social psychology of anorexia nervosa.* London: Routledge.

Mathews, A. & MacLeod, C. (1994). Cognitive approaches to emotion and emotional disorders. *Annual Review of Psychology, 45,* 25-50.

Minuchin, S., Rosman, B. L. & Baker, L. (1978). *Psychosomatic Families.* Mass. Harvard University Press.

Mogg, K. & Bradley, P. B. (2005). Attentional Bias in Generalized Anxiety Disorder Versus Depressive Disorder, *Cognitive Therapy and Research, 29,* 29-45.

Mogg, K., Bradley, B. P., Hyare, H. & Lee, S. (1998). Selective attention to food-related stimuli in hunger: Are attentional biases specific to emotional and psychopathological states, or are they also found in normal drive states? *Behaviour Research and Therapy, 36,* 227-237.

Perpina, C., Hemsley, D., Treasure, J. & de Silva, P. (1993). Is the selective information processing of food and body words specific to patients with eating disorders? *International Journal of Eating Disorders*, *14*, 359-366.

Placanica, J. L., Faunce, G. J. & Soames Job, R. F. (2002). The effect of fasting on attentional biases for food and body shape/weight words in high and low Eating Disorder Inventory scorers. *International Journal of Eating Disorders*, *32*, 79-90.

Posner, M. I. (1980). Orienting of attention. *Quarterly Journal of Experimental Psychology*, *32*, 3-25.

Posner, M. I. (1994). Attention: The mechanisms of consciousness. *Proceedings of the National Academy of Sciences USA*, *91*, 7398–7403

Posner, M. I. & Cohen, Y. (1984). Components of visual orienting. In H. Bouma, & D. Bowhuis (Eds.), *Attention and performance X*, (531–556). Hove, UK: Lawrence Erlbaum Associates Ltd.

Reiger, E., Schotte, D. E., Touyz, S. W., Beumont, P. J. V., Griffiths, R. & Russel, J. (1998). Attentional Biases in eating disorders: A visual probe detection procedure. *International Journal of Eating Disorders*, *23*, 199-205.

Rohner, J. C. (2002). The time-course of visual threat processing: High trait anxious individuals eventually avert their gaze from angry faces. *Cognition and Emotion*, *16*, 837-844.

Selvini Palazzoli, M., Cirillo, S., Selvini, M. & Sorrentino, A. M. (1988). *I giochi psicotici della famiglia*. Milano: Raffaello Cortina.

Shafran, R., Lee, M., Cooper, Z., Palmer, R. L. & Fairburn, C. G. (2007). Attentional bias in eating disorders. *International Journal of Eating Disorders*, *40*, 369-380.

Shafran, R., Lee, M., Cooper, Z., Palmer, R. L. & Fairburn, C. G. (2008). Effect of psychological treatment on attentional bias in eating disorders. *International Journal of Eating Disorders*, *41*, 348-354.

Shipton, G. (1999). Anorexic space. *Journal of Community & Applied Social Psychology*, *9*, 435- 448.

Stobiecka, M. (2000). The hunger of death. Preoccupation with the subject of death in anorexia nervosa. In A. Suchanska (Ed.), *Individual and social factors in anorexia nervosa*, (237–276). Poznan: Humaniora Foundation Publishing.

Stroop, J. R. (1935). Studies of interference in serial verbal reactions. *Journal of Experimental Psychology*, *18*, 643-661.

Vandereycken, W. (2006a). Denial of illness in anorexia nervosa – a conceptual review: Part 1 Diagnostic significance and assessment. *European eating Disorders Review*, *14*, 341-351.

Vandereycken, W. (2006a). Denial of illness in anorexia nervosa – a conceptual review: Part 2 Different Forms and Meanings. *European eating Disorders Review*, *14*, 352-368.

Veenstra, E. M. & de Jong, P. J. (2012). Attentional bias in restrictive eating disorders. Stronger attentional avoidance of high-fat food compared to healthy controls? *Appetite*, *58*, 133-140.

Vitousek, K. B., Daly, J. & Heiser, C. (1991). Reconstructing the internal world of the eating-disordered individual: Overcoming distortion in self-report. *International Journal of Eating Disorders*, *10*, 647-666.

Vitousek, K. B. & Hollon, S. D. (1990). The investigation of schematic content and processing in eating disorders. *Cognitive Therapy and Research*, *14*, 191-214.

Vitousek, K. B. & Orimoto, L. (1993). Cognitive-behavioral models of anorexia nervosa, bulimia nervosa and obesity. In K.S. Dobson, & P.C. Kendall (Eds.), *Psychopathology and cognition*, (191-234). San Diego: Academic Press.

Warin, M. (2003). Miasmatic calories and saturating fats: fear of contamination in anorexia. *Culture, Medicine and Psychiatry, 27,* 77-93.

Warin, M. (2004). Primitivising Anorexia: The Irresistible Spectacle of Not Eating, *Australian Journal of Anthropology, 15,* 95-104.

Williamson, D. A., Muller, S. L., Reas, D. L. & Thaw, J. M. (1999). Cognitive bias in eating disorders: Implications for theory and treatment. *Behavior Modification, 23,* 556-577.

In: New Developments in Anorexia Nervosa Research
Editors: Carla Gramaglia and Patrizia Zeppegno

ISBN: 978-1-63117-551-0
© 2014 Nova Science Publishers, Inc.

Chapter 9

A Review of the Use of Acupuncture in the Treatment of Anorexia Nervosa

Sarah Fogarty[*1] *and Sloane Madden*[2]
[1] University of Western Sydney, Australia
[2] Children's Hospital at Westmead, Australia

Abstract

Anorexia Nervosa is serious illness with significant morbidity. The evidence base for existing psychological and pharmacological interventions to manage Anorexia Nervosa is not strong, particularly in adults, and use of new adjunctive therapies that improve the effectiveness of existing treatments and lead to improved mental health outcomes for this patient group is highly desirable. Even the best evidenced based treatments are not successful in a substantial minority of patients, with relapses common, leading to chronic illness for many individuals. A review of the literature on acupuncture and Anorexia Nervosa was undertaken and a summary of the findings of the literature review is presented.

The review found that the small pilot studies done so far with acupuncture and eating disorders suggest acupuncture may have benefit as an adjunct therapy, particularly around symptoms of eating disorders including mood, anxiety and quality of life. Larger randomized controlled trials are needed to confirm these findings.

Keywords: Anorexia Nervosa, Acupuncture, Traditional Chinese Medicine, Eating Disorders

[*] Corresponding Author Address Sarah Fogarty, Centre for Complementary Medicine, University of Western Sydney. Locked Bag 1797, Penrith, NSW, 2751, Australia, Email: s.fogarty@uws.edu.au.

Introduction

Research investigating the use of acupuncture as an adjunct in the treatment of Anorexia Nervosa (AN) is a recent phenomenon. Research into AN, however, is well established with substantial evidence contributed over the last decade. Severe and enduring AN has been acknowledged and investigated (Robinson, 2009; Touyz, Le Grange, Lacey, Hay, Smith, Maguire, Bamford, Pike & Crosby, 2013) and the evidence has supported Family Based Treatment as the treatment of choice for adolescents with AN (Hay, 2013). Despite this, response to treatment for many with AN remains poor. It is critical that complementary therapies including acupuncture be rigorously evaluated so any potential treatment benefits can be utilized and that AN sufferers' considerable interest in and desire to use complementary medicine in their recovery, can be informed by evidence. This chapter examines the current evidence for the use of acupuncture/acupressure in the treatment of those suffering from AN.

Acupuncture is characterized by the insertion of needles into specific body points to impact the flow of qi (vital energy), a therapeutic relationship, individualized treatment and active engagement of patients in self care or management (NCCAM, 2013). The acupuncture consultation is a complex therapeutic intervention involving not just needling but a more holistic experience (Shi, Yang, Liu & Wang, 2012). There is emerging evidence identifying an adjunctive role for the use of acupuncture to treat some mental health disorders (Pilkington, Kirkwood, Rampes, Cummings & Richardson, 2007; Smith, Hay & MacPherson, 2010), however, research evaluating the effect of acupuncture as an adjunctive treatment for eating disorders is sparse.

Acupuncture has been identified as being used in eating disorders for the treatment of anxiety and quality of life (Smith, Fogarty, Touyz, Madden, Buckett & Hay, 2014; Fogarty, Harris, Zaslawski, McAinch & Stojanovska, 2010; Clarke, 2009; Cristina Stefanini, Menicalli, Troiani, Vuono, Baccetti & Traversi, 2012), emotional support, stress, menstrual irregularities, depression and digestive complaints (Clarke, 2009).

The evidence for acupuncture and AN is informed by one clinical pilot trial and one uncontrolled observational study (Smith, Fogarty, Touyz, Madden, Buckett & Hay, 2013; Cristina Stefanini, Menicalli, Troiani, Vuono, Baccetti & Traversi, 2012; Fogarty, Smith, Touyz, Madden, Buckett & Hay, 2013). There is also one clinical pilot trial, one uncontrolled observational study, one case series and two cross sectional study investigating AN and other eating disorders (EDs) (Fogarty, Harris, Zaslawski, McAinch & Stojanovska, 2010; Clarke, 2009; Hogberg, 1998; Fogarty, Harris, Zaslawski, McAinch & Stojanovska, 2012; Fogarty, McIntire & Clydesdale Waldron, 2013). These sources of evidence are reviewed below.

Acupuncture/Acupressure and Anorexia Nervosa

Smith et al. (2014) conducted a mixed methods pilot randomized controlled trial (RCT) and a qualitative study with a clinical in-patient population suffering from AN. Twenty-five females and one male aged between 17 and 38 years receiving treatment at a private hospital eating disorder facility in Sydney, Australia were randomized to acupuncture plus treatment as usual (TAU) or acupressure/massage plus TAU. TAU involved treatment by a multidisciplinary team comprising a consultant psychiatrist, clinical psychologists, intern clinical psychologists, dietitian, occupational therapist and specially trained nursing staff. Patients attended group therapy for several hours each day with a cognitive behavioural focus. All meals and snacks were supervised by members of the clinical team. The study intervention was administered twice a week for the first three weeks followed by weekly treatment for three weeks. At the end of the intervention differences were found for one item on a sub scale of Eating Disorder Examination-Questionnaire (EDE-Q) outcome (Fairburn, Cooper & O'Connor, 2008). Participants in the control group demonstrated reduced eating concerns on the EDE ($p<0.05$). Over time both groups reported changes for Eating Disorder Inventory-3 (EDI-3) Bulimia (Garner, 2004) and total quality of life and in the physical/cognitive domain of the Eating Disorder Quality of Life (EDQoL) Scale (Engel, Wittrock, Crosby, Wonderlich, Mitchell & Kolotkin, 2005). Within group comparisons found significant improvement in symptomatology for the acupuncture group in relation to EDQoL psychological, EDE shape and EDE weight. A similar improvement was found for the control group with improvements over time for the EDE including total score, restraint, and eating concerns (Smith, Fogarty, Touyz, Madden, Buckett & Hay, 2014).

The qualitative study involved patient interviews following their completion of the trial (Smith, Fogarty, Touyz, Madden, Buckett & Hay, 2014). Saturation was reached at 9 acupuncture and 6 massage participants. Both groups reported positive experiences and benefit from treatment and the interventions were viewed as a welcome supplementary activity from usual care. The overarching theme from the data was seeking and obtaining therapeutic support, this covered two sub-themes of seeking support and a positive response to treatment. An improvement in mood and feeling relaxed and calm were the most common reported benefits for those receiving acupressure. Those receiving acupuncture reported a broader range of outcomes including an improvement in mood, feeling relaxed and calm, sleeping better, less 'churning of thoughts', less anxiety and stress and being more communicative. Participants also valued the therapeutic relationship, in particular establishing a trusting relationship, sensitivity to their clinical condition, a non-judgmental attitude, feeling nurtured and being able to talk with someone independent of their treating team. The limitations of this mixed method study included the small sample size and the lack of a usual care group.

Further analysis of data from the study questionnaires examined the characteristics of what participants' valued as part of their therapeutic encounter (Fogarty, Smith, Touyz, Madden, Buckett & Hay, 2013). Eighteen participants (69%) completed a post study questionnaire exploring participant views of the study consultation, aspects of the therapeutic relationship, the clinical care encounter and treatment perceptions. Participants in both groups scored empathy and the therapeutic relationship highly. They valued the therapeutic encounter and in particular the practitioner characteristics of empathy, positive regard, acceptance, non-judgmental responses and trust. Having someone to talk to, feeling less stressed and more relaxed and contact with the study staff were identified as important. The strong therapeutic relationship provided by the study practitioner may contribute to the beneficial effects from adjunctive therapies. Interpretation of data from this study is limited by the small study size, and potential bias from the low response rate and drop out.

A small uncontrolled observational pilot study of 5 adolescent females aged 13-18 with a BMI range of 14-16.5 with restrictive subtype AN received a Traditional Chinese Medicine (TCM) treatment. The participants were receiving treatment at the Pediatric ward at the

University Hospital of Careggi, Florence, Italy. Participants were either in-patients or attending as day patients and their treatment involved therapeutic group sessions, eating rehabilitation, psychotherapeutic educational groups and music, theatre and pet therapy. The TCM treatment included a two phased treatment involving individual acupressure/Chinese massage for 20 minutes, Qi Gong exercises, Seven Star needling, moxibustion and auricular acupuncture. Treatment was once weekly for a period of 6 months. Participants also attended group static Qi Gong exercise groups once a week. Treatment sessions were pragmatic depending upon specific presenting TCM symptoms. One participant dropped out so results are reported on four participants. Following the six month intervention participants reported an average weight gain of 15% and a body mass index (BMI) gain of 14%. 3 of the 4 participants transitioned to a diet without supplementation and 3 of 4 resumed school attendance. The study limitations include the small study size, the lack of a control group and the involvement of multiple TCM interventions which make the specific TCM treatment benefits unattainable. The study was presented at a conference, not as a published paper, and many of the conventions of reporting research are not applicable or were not reported in this framework such as psychometric outcome measures, the STandards for Reporting Interventions in Clinical Trials of Acupuncture (STRICTA) (MacPherson, White, Cummings, Jobst, Rose & Niemtzow, 2002) guidelines and Consolidated Standards of Reporting Trials (CONSORT) statements (Zwarenstein, Treweek, Gagnier, Altman, Tunis, Haynes, Oxman & Moher, 2008).

Acupuncture, Anorexia Nervosa and Bulimia Nervosa

Fogarty et al. (2010) conducted an open label randomized crossover design pilot study to examine the role of acupuncture in the treatment of eating disorders (AN and Bulimia Nervosa (BN)). The two interventions were i) treatment as usual (TAU) and ii) TAU plus acupuncture with a two week wash out period in between phases. Participants with AN or BN were recruited from an outpatient private eating disorder clinic in Melbourne, Australia. Nine females average age 23.7 years, enrolled in the study and received ten 60-minute sessions of acupuncture. The analysis for cross-over design studies accounted for possible carry-over effects and period effects and this was reported in the results (Fogarty, Harris, Zaslawski, McAinch & Stojanovska, 2010). Significant improvements were found for state anxiety using the State Trait Anxiety Inventory (STAI) (Spielberger, 1983) (p=0.017), an improvement in quality of life as measured by the Eating Disorder Quality of Life Scale (EDQoL) (p=0.007), and a significant change in the Physical/Cognitive domain of the EDQoL (p=0.0009). There was a trend for an improvement in the EDI-3 subscale of Perfectionism (p= 0.0597) and for the Psychological domain of the EDQoL (p= 0.0557). No other significant findings were found between the phases. A limitation of the study was the small sample size. The inclusion of both AN and BN in the study sample makes systematic reviews and meta-analysis by eating disorder type more complex.

A small observational study of 26 females with AN or BN was conducted in Angelhom, Sweden. Twenty-one of the 26 participants had previous treatment for their eating disorder and were not eating disorder symptom free at the time of their admission to the study. The treatment intervention was electro-acupuncture. The electro-acupuncture treatment involved trans-cutaneous stimulation of acupuncture points according to a given schedule. Neither the acupuncture points used nor the course of treatment is reported. Each treatment lasted between 1-3 hours and the practitioner employed the practice of active listening. The average number of treatments per patient was seven and the interval between each treatment varied. Data for this study was obtained from post-treatment interview.

It was reported that the average follow up period was three and a half years, however, it is not clear if the participants were followed up after the interview or that three and a half years later is when the interview took place. The study found some benefits from electrical acu-stimulation including 21 of the 26 participants reported being free from their eating disorder and living a 'normal social life'. Five participants reported no effect from the treatment intervention and none became worse. Participants described the treatment similarly, experiencing a feeling of tiredness in the body which was replaced by a sense of joy which lead to a removal of obsessional thoughts about food and exercise. Appetite returned and there were reports of changes in mood and cognition. The mechanisms behind these changes were reported to be due to either a placebo effect or a biological effect of acu-stimulation or both. Limitations of the study include the lack of use of the guidelines for reporting acupuncture studies such as COREQ (Consolidated Criteria for reporting Qualitative Research). The original article was in Swedish and translated into English. It is possible that the translation and the limited reporting on methodology and use of COREQ have led to a misinterpretation of the data. The author of the report was contacted for clarification but did not reply.

Eating Disorders and Acupuncture Treatment

A 2014 retrospective case-series design involved eating disorder patients who sought acupuncture treatment during their illness. The aim of the case-series was to inform clinicians and guide further research questions by providing a better understanding of how eating disorders present in TCM practice and how they are treated. Three acupuncturists with experience treating eating disorders contributed cases to this study. Two of the acupuncturists are from the United States and one from Australia. Forty-three individuals with an eating disorder (ED) sought treatment with the three different practitioners from 2002 to 2012. Patients were either private patients of the acupuncture clinicians or undertaking acupuncture treatment as part of a research project involving one of the acupuncturists. TCM style manual acupuncture was used most commonly in these cases. Of the 43 cases there were 26 in-patients and 17 out-patients. The majority suffered from AN (33 of the 43) with 7 suffering from BN and 3 from ED not otherwise specified (EDNOS). The characteristics of the in-patients seeking acupuncture are: majority female (96.2%), aged in their early twenties, suffering from a co-morbid disease such as depression, anxiety and or irritable bowel syndrome, single, living with their parents and studying. The in-patients, on average, had their eating disorder for 5.2 years (SD 6.2) and out-patients for 7.5 years (SD 7.5). Almost a quarter of participants had previously used complementary medicine or therapies. The characteristics of the out-patient group are female (100%), aged in their early twenties, single, suffering from a co-morbid disease and many were studying. The majority of cases in this study sought acupuncture to help issues related to their eating disorder rather than specifically for their eating disorder (ED). The majority of in-patients wanted help for digestive and mood concerns. The majority of out-patients wanted help with sleep and digestive concerns. The case-series found that mood issues were more important for those in in-patient care whereas sleep issues were more important in out-patient care. The points most commonly used by the three acupuncturists were reported. The commonly used points reflect the issues the patients requested treatment for such as sleep, mood or digestive complaints. The point selection presented in this case series may be used to guide future acupuncture and eating disorder research protocols. The findings also reiterate that acupuncture is being used as a complementary therapy not a primary treatment modality and future research designs should continue to reflect this.

Understanding Eating Disorders According to Traditional Chinese Medicine (TCM)

A 2012 cross sectional study was used to systematically evaluate, identify and quantify TCM patterns relevant to eating disorders. 196 female participants (142 with a self-reported eating disorder and 54 with no eating disorder) completed an online survey. ED participants were recruited via invitation from several international and national eating disorder organizations (Beating Eating Disorders UK, Eating Disorder Foundation of Victoria, Australia, Centre for Excellence for Eating Disorders, Australia). Those without an eating disorder were recruited in a similar method as a comparator control group. The survey questionnaire included a list of signs and symptoms associated with eating disorders. In addition there were also questions on the individual's age, gender as well as questions on general health (e.g. sleep, menstruation, headache and so on). The answers to the questionnaire enabled the researchers to extrapolate the signs and symptoms into TCM Patterns of Disharmony (PoD). There were 333 respondents, 132 were excluded because they completed less than half of the survey and 5 because they were male (due to the possible differences in presentation between males and females, the small numbers of males made making meaningful conclusions about this population group challenging). A TCM diagnosis (PoD) was determined for each individual and for each ED. This data was summarized as a mean and standard deviation for each eating disorder type (AN, BN, EDNOS and Binge Eating Disorder [BED]) and those with no ED. A regression model was computed to determine whether there was any significant difference between the means for each eating disorder subtype and those with no ED. There were statistically significant differences between all TCM PoD presenting in AN and no ED and also for BN and no ED. EDNOS had just over 75% significant difference in TCM PoD and no ED and BED had just over 50% significant difference in TCM PoD and no ED. The TCM presentation of AN, BN and EDNOS were similar however the TCM presentation of BED was very different. Although a highly debated topic, research suggests that EDNOS is a progression from (or to) AN or BN and that BED is a stand-alone ED (Grilo, 2006; Grilo, White & Masheb, 2009). This study's findings indicate that TCM diagnosis and presentation of ED present in the same way as Grilo's (2006 and 2009) theory of relationship and progression. In psychiatry, as well as TCM there exists a school of thought that suggests that EDs are not an autonomous illness but part of other illnesses such as depression (Agras, Crow, Mitchell, Halmi & Bryson, 2009), however, this study demonstrated significant differences in the presentation and diagnosis of the ED subtypes suggesting that ED can be classified as separate autonomous TCM syndromes. The study had a number of limitations: a) the self-reported surveys, some respondents may have under- or- over-reported their symptoms and b) the possibility of multiple responses from a single individual.

Acupuncture and Eating Disorders According to the Acupuncturists

Views on the role of acupuncture and eating disorders were reported by acupuncturists and ED patients in a mixed method study from the United Kingdom (Clarke, 2009). The study involved two observational studies and in-depth interviews. One survey was posted to 500 British Acupuncture Council (BAcC) acupuncturists. This was used to gather information on the practices of acupuncturists with experience of treating patients with ED. The second survey was sent to 270 Beat Eating Disorders (BEAT) members. This was used to gather information on their experiences of acupuncture and ascertain if a demand existed for acupuncture. In addition three BAcC respondents and six BEAT members completed a semi structured telephone interview. The interviews were conducted to expand on the responses to the relevant surveys and to discuss key points which arose from the survey findings. The interviews were transcribed and analysed for themes using Thematic Framework Analysis. The BAcC survey response rate was 39% and the BEAT survey was 30%. One hundred and ten of the 195 BAcC respondents had experience of treating patients with ED with most of the treatments related to eating disorder symptoms rather than primarily treating the eating disorder. The findings from the acupuncturist survey included an overall belief that acupuncture was helpful. Patients reported to their acupuncturists' decreased signs and symptoms associated with their ED, reduced stress and or depression and improved menstrual irregularities and self-esteem. While acupuncturists believed that acupuncture was partly successful in treating the symptoms of an eating disorder (72/110), barriers to successful treatment included patients not being able to afford ongoing treatment, patient inability to engage in standardized ED treatment and an inability to confirm with the advice given by the acupuncturist. The findings from the BEAT member surveys did not specifically ask for participant's ages. Instead they asked for age ranges, these age ranges included two open-ended categories at either end of the age ranges (less than 12 years old and greater than 30 years old). The middle ranges included 12-16 years, 16-18 years and 18-30 years. The majority of respondents fell into the 18-30 year old range (35/80). Interestingly no BEAT members surveyed between the ages of 18-30 years of age had received acupuncture (for any ailment). BEAT members who had received acupuncture most commonly received it from an acupuncturist (20/23) rather than a medical practitioner or physiotherapist. BEAT members' reason for having acupuncture mirrored the results from the BAcC responders, with the majority receiving acupuncture for symptoms related to their ED such as stress, emotional wellbeing and for relaxation. The interviews with the acupuncturists found that two elements of the therapeutic relationship, trust and rapport, were key elements of a successful eating disorder treatment as was the involvement of a mental health care physician or therapist (psychiatrist, psychologist, counselor, etc). The finding from the BEAT member interview found benefits from the acupuncture consultation/treatment including feeling relaxed and generally better post treatment. Interviews with both the BEAT members and the BAcC members further strengthened the finding that acupuncture was not sought specifically to 'cure' an eating disorder but to assist with co-occurring symptoms and it was viewed as a useful adjunct and as a resource to manage their life and their eating disorder (Clarke, 2009).

Limitations of the study include not surveying other major acupuncture associations in the UK, the small sample size of the interviewees and a poor response rate with some questions in the surveys.

Acupuncture, Anorexia Nervosa and Safety

A 1990 case study published in a French journal presented the case of a 13 year old girl with a BMI of 13.6 suffering from anorexia nervosa and diabetes mellitus who developed a pneumothorax twelve days after receiving thoracic wall acupuncture (Huet, Renard, Blotman & Jaffiol, 1990). She presented with ketoacidosis, chest pain and dyspnea and was diagnosed with a right sided pneumothorax. She was hospitalized, observed and treated with oxygen therapy. She took a several days to recover. There was no report regarding a follow up to assess any related recurrences or re-admissions post injury. The underlying cause of her pneumothorax was not determined to be the acupuncture procedure and was undetermined in the publication.

Summary

Despite anecdotal reporting of improvements to mental health outcomes and ED symptomatology, acupuncture treatment for AN and other ED has not been subject to rigorous evaluation. Research into acupuncture therapies and AN is in its infancy, though research capacity is developing. Although small sample sizes are appropriate when conducting pilot studies future research studies must address this limitation. Preliminary findings from evaluations of acupuncture show promise. An appropriately powered RCT investigating the effects of acupuncture on AN symptomatology is needed concentrating on the improving co-occurring symptoms of the eating disorder such as anxiety, stress, sleep, mood and subsequently quality of life. There is limited evidence of general benefits to AN sufferers' wellbeing reported in the pilot studies and patient views.

Current studies have investigated mixed eating disorder diagnoses and future research should investigate individual eating disorder types. Men also suffer from eating disorders and future studies should ensure they represent clinical populations.

Current evidence suggests that acupuncture is being used (both by patients and clinicians) as a complementary therapy which addresses symptoms associated with the eating disorder rather than the eating disorder specifically. Future research studies should ensure they use appropriate outcome measures that assess eating disorder symptomatology and its effect on mental health outcomes such as anxiety, depression, and quality of life.

Conclusion

Further high quality research is needed to consolidate preliminary findings, and address previous methodological limitations before recommendations can be made for clinical practice.

Acknowledgment

The authors declare no conflicts of interest.

REFERENCES

Agras WS, Crow S, Mitchell JE, Halmi K, Bryson S. A 4-Year Prospective Study of Eating Disorder NOS compared with Full Eating Disorder Syndromes. *International Journal of Eating Disorders.* 2009;42(6):565-70.

Clarke L. *Exploring the basis for Acupuncture Treatment of Eating Disorders;* A Mixed Methods Study: Northern College of Acupuncture (NCA). 2009.

Cristina Stefanini M, Menicalli C, Troiani MR, Vuono C, Baccetti S, Traversi A, et al., editors. TCM and Serious Eating Disorders: A pilot trial. *5th European Congress for Integrative Medicine: The future of comprehensive patient care*; 2012; Palazzo dei Congressi, Florence

Engel SG, Wittrock DA, Crosby RD, Wonderlich SA, Mitchell JE, Kolotkin RL. Development and psychometric validation of an eating disorder-specific health-related quality of life instrument. *International Journal of Eating Disorders.* 2005;Volume 39 (Issue 1):Pages 62 - 71.

Fairburn C, Cooper Z, O'Connor M. Eating Disorder Examination. In: Fairburn C, editor. *Cognitive Behaviour.* 16 ed. New York: Guilford Press- 2008.

Fogarty S, Harris D, Zaslawski C, McAinch AJ, Stojanovska L. Acupuncture as an Adjunct Therapy in the Treatment of Eating Disorders: A Pilot Study. *Complementary Therapies in Medicine.* 2010;18(6):227-76.

Fogarty S, Harris D, Zaslawski C, McAinch AJ, Stojanovska L. Development of a Chinese Medicine Pattern Severity Index for Understanding Eating Disorders. *The Journal of Alternative and Complementary Medicine.* 2012;18(6):597-606.

Fogarty S, Smith C, Touyz S, Madden S, Buckett G, Hay P. Patients with anorexia nervosa receiving acupuncture or acupressure; their view of the therapeutic encounter. *Complementary Therapies in Medicine.* 2013: 21: 675-681.

Fogarty S, McIntire N, Clydesdale Waldron D. *A case series: How do patients with an eating disorder, seeking acupuncture treatment present (patterns of disharmony), and how are they treated?* 2014.

Garner DM. EDI-3 *Eating Disorder Inventory-3-Professional Manual.* Florida: PAR Psychological Assessment Resources Inc- 2004.

Grilo CM. Eating and weight disorders. *London: Psychology Press.* 2006.

Grilo CM, White M, Masheb R. DSM-IV Psychiatric Disorder Comorbidity and Its Correlates in Binge Eating Disorder. *International Journal of Eating Disorders.* 2009;42(3):228-34.

Hay P. A systematic review of evidence for psychological treatments in eating disorders: 2005–2012. *International Journal of Eating Disorders.* 2013;46(5):462-9.

Hogberg G. Has electrical acu-stimulation an impact on anorexia and bulmia? *Lakartidningen.* 1998;95(45):4963-5.

Huet R, Renard E, Blotman M, Jaffiol C. Unrecognized pneumothorax after acupuncture in a female patient with anorexia nervosa. *La Presse Médicale*. 1990;Sep 22, 19(30):14-5

MacPherson H, White A, Cummings M, Jobst K, Rose K, Niemtzow R. Standards for Reporting Interventions in Controlled Trials of Acupuncture: The STRICTA recommendations. *Journal of Alternative & Complementary Medicine*. 2002;8(1):85-9.

(NCCAM). NCfCaAM. Acupuncture: An Introduction. NCCAM; August 2011 [updated August 2011; cited 2013 12 March]; *NCCAM Pub* No:D404].

Pilkington K, Kirkwood G, Rampes H, Cummings S, Richardson J. Acupuncture for anxiety and anxiety disorders--a systematic literature review. *Acupuncture in Medicine*. 2007;25:1-10.

Robinson P. *Severe and Enduring Eating Disorder:* JohnWiley & Sons, Ltd; 2009.

Shi G-X, Yang X-M, Liu C-Z, Wang L-P. Factors contributing to therapeutic effects evaluated in acupuncture clinical trials. *Trials*. 2012;13(42):1-5.

Smith CA, Hay PPJ, MacPherson H. Acupuncture for depression. *Cochrane Database of Systematic Reviews*. 2010;1.

Smith C, Fogarty S, Touyz S, Madden S, Buckett G, Hay P. Acupuncture and acupressure health outcomes for patients with anorexia nervosa: findings from a pilot randomised controlled trial and patient interviews.*The Journal of Alternative and Complementary Medicine*. 2014; 20 (2): 103-112.

Spielberger C. State-Trait Anxiety Inventory for Adults, Sampler Set.Manual, Test Booklet and Scoring Key. *Consulting Psychologists Press, Inc: Mind Garden*- 1983.

Touyz S, Le Grange D, Lacey H, Hay P, Smith R, Maguire S, Bamford B, Pike KM, Crosby RD.Treating severe and enduring anorexia nervosa: a randomized controlled trial. *Psychological Medicine*. 2013;FirstView:1-11

Zwarenstein M, Treweek S, Gagnier J, Altman D, Tunis S, Haynes B, Oxman AD, Moher D. Improving the reporting of pragmatic trials: an extension of the CONSORT statement. *British Medical Journal (BMJ)*. 2008;337(20 December):1-8.

In: New Developments in Anorexia Nervosa Research   ISBN: 978-1-63117-551-0
Editors: Carla Gramaglia and Patrizia Zeppegno   © 2014 Nova Science Publishers, Inc.

Chapter 10

Alexithymia, Emotion Identification and Social Inference in Anorexia Nervosa

Carla Gramaglia[*] *and Patrizia Zeppegno*

Institute of Psychiatry, Department of Translational Medicine, Università del Piemonte
Orientale "Amedeo Avogadro", Novara, Italy

Abstract

An impaired emotional functioning and alexithymic traits are core elements of Eating Disorders (EDs), and particularly of Anorexia Nervosa. ED patients have difficulties identifying feelings and often mislabel adverse emotional states as feeling fat. Emotional and relational problems fade behind the extreme concreteness of ED symptoms, with the ED becoming a "concretised metaphor". The aim of this chapter is to describe the theoretical background concerning anorexic patients' difficulties in identifying emotions. In conclusion, a research approach which may add to the existing knowledge about alexithymic traits, facial emotion recognition and social inference skills in ED patients will be briefly outlined.

Introduction

Impaired emotional functioning and alexithymic traits are suggested to be core elements of Eating Disorders (EDs), and particularly of Anorexia Nervosa (AN).

Alexithymia may be defined as the inability to identify, describe, regulate and express one's emotions (Sifneos, 1976; Taylor & Doody, 1985). According to current literature, this feature is particularly prominent in AN, while as far as Bulimia Nervosa (BN) is concerned, the relationship with affect dysregulation is the leading feature. It is still debated whether there are different patterns of emotional processing deficiencies in different subtypes of EDs,

---

[*] Corresponding author: Email: carla.gramaglia@gmail.com.

and whether emotional regulation and emotional processing difficulties are a unique hallmark of EDs, since these have been acknowledged to play an important role in the development and maintenance of various mental disorders, including also Depression.

Present researches suggest that individuals with AN have deficits in emotion regulation across a variety of domains and theoretical models suggest such difficulties are a maintaining factor for the disorder. Currently, little is known about how different factors might maintain emotion regulation difficulties, and research still fails to provide a detailed insight into their possible disorder-specificity. For instance, a possible overlapping between AN and autism spectrum disorders has been suggested, not only as far as central coherence and executive functions are concerned, but also with respect to social and empathy difficulties, which may be assessed by means of the Theory of Mind and emotional Theory of Mind (ToM and eToM; Oldershaw et al., 2010).

An early study of alexithymia in AN suggested that a specific subgroup of AN patients might exist, whose features are high scores on the Toronto Alexithymia Scale (TAS), together with a clinical evidence and diagnosis of empathy disorder (Råstam et al., 1997). Approximately in the same period, a study dealing with the structure of alexithymia in ED patients and healthy controls found four factors according to the TAS: inability to identify feelings, paucity of fantasy, non-communication of feelings, and concrete thinking (Troop et al., 1995). Overall, the ED group showed poorer skills than healthy controls at identifying their own feelings. Specifically, patients with restrictive AN (AN-R) had a poorer fantasy life when compared to BN patients and controls, and showed a lower tendency to express their feelings. The TAS differences observed between EDs subtypes were hypothesized to be somehow specific, rather than simply a consequence of general psychopathology.

It is a common clinical observation that starved individuals with AN have poor awareness of their feelings and problems identifying them (alexithymia), reduced understanding of others' mental states (cognitive empathy), and difficulty regulating personal emotions (self-regulation), which may lead them to mislabel adverse emotional states as "feeling fat". Moreover, possible comorbidity with depression and anxiety has been shown to impact on elevated levels of alexithymia in AN and emotion regulation deficits may depend on illness duration as well.

The compromission of AN patients spans from recognition of facial emotions, especially negative ones (i.e. sadness and fear), to recognition of emotions in voices, both positive and negative (particularly happiness and sadness) (Kucharska-Pietura et al., 2004). On the contrary, no significant difference was found as far as neutral vocal stimuli are concerned. In the study by Kucharska-Pietura and coworkers (2004), the impairment in facial emotion recognition was still significant after controlling for confounding variables including depression, age, and educational level, while the impairment of vocal recognition lost significance.

Alexithymic traits, comorbidity and starvation effects together are likely to contribute to the deficits in the recognition of nonverbal emotional cues both from faces and voices in AN patients, thus influencing the patients' social functioning. Difficulties identifying and expressing feelings, problems in emotional recognition, lack of empathy and poor interpersonal communication may be related to a poor social functioning and interaction, and a diminished drive for social pleasure, which, in turn, may explain the entanglement between AN and socio-relational problems.

However, several unanswered questions still surround this issue. First of all, as previously stated, it is still unclear whether subtypes of ED differ in their emotion regulation profile and whether emotion regulation difficulties are specific for ED rather than a transdiagnostic factor (Svaldi et al., 2012). In other words, it is not clear whether emotion regulation difficulties in EDs reflect a central abnormality in emotional processing, which may be shared by people within the internalizing spectrum of psychopathology (i.e. mental disorders with primary symptoms involving inner emotions as opposed to outward behavior; Thackery & Harris, 2003), or whether such patients have a specific impairment in attending closely to specific stimuli. Second, it is still not clear whether alexithymia and emotion regulation difficulties are state or trait-related, and whether a purely symptomatic improvement (i.e. weight gain or weight restore) in AN patients goes together with an improvement of alexithymia, emotional empathy, and self-regulation (Beadle et al., 2013).

Although alexhithymia in EDs and particularly in AN is raising growing interest, literature concerning the use of structured measures of emotional empathy and social interaction is still scant and full of contradictions. Hence the need to address the exact nature of problems in interpersonal relationships as an important topic for clinicians and researchers in the field of EDs has been suggested. Since these interpersonal issues may have a role as maintaining factors for EDs, addressing them is not only relevant from a theoretical point of view, but also as far as treatment is concerned (Tchanturia et al., 2012).

When the Body Speaks Instead and in Spite of Patients

The human body has a complex meaning and role in everybody's life and experience. It is object and subject; it does not mechanically respond to environmental stimuli, yet it constantly interacts and dialogues with the world. It is the individual, but somehow the individual also transcends the boundaries of the body. Our bodily being-in-the-world describes an existential position where the body is a subjective and intersubjective ground of and for experience. The body is existential in its ongoing experiencing and acting in the world. The body is extremely concrete and extremely symbolic at the same time. We use it as a mean and a language to communicate both with others and with ourselves beyond corporeality itself.

A striking clinical feature of EDs, and in particular of AN, is the extreme concreteness of symptoms. In such disorders, a psychic equivalence between physical and psychic reality takes place, and ED symptoms may be considered as "concretised metaphors" which also stand in for emotions (Enckell, 2002; Skårderud, 2007). A metaphor can be described as a word or phrase for one thing which is used to refer to something else, and metaphors allow understanding and experiencing a phenomenon through another with their indirect, mediational power, and the images they evoke. Specifically, the phrase "concretised metaphor" refers to situations where the metaphor loses its property of standing for something else, and is experienced as a direct and bodily revelation of a concrete reality, as an immediate equivalence between bodily and emotional experience (Enckell, 2002). Enckell (2002) describes a collapse of the symbolic gap between body and emotion/cognition, and bodily sensations give shape to both inner and external world.

As a consequence of their impaired reflective function, AN patients have decreased symbolic skills, which are replaced by an extremely concrete attitude. Despite most issues in this field of research are still open to debate, it is a common clinical observation that ED patients' emotional and relational problems fade behind the extreme concreteness of symptoms, with the "concretised metaphors" clearly standing for something else. From this point of view, the body in AN is certainly not only something slimming down, and starvation is not just a matter of losing weight. Campbell & Enckell (2006) highlight the meaning of concretised metaphors as "restitutional efforts" to maintain, albeit at a concrete level, a cohesive mental configuration, as a reaction to a perceived threat of inner fragmentation. The starting point from this perspective would be a vulnerable or distorted self-organization in AN. Hence EDs often reflect the individual's wish to change, although this attempt is highly self-destructive. Acknowledging the meaning patients give to their symptoms may help understanding their affection for AN and their unwillingness or their ambivalence to give up the disorder (Schmidt & Treasure, 2006; Nordbø et al., 2006).

Skårderud (2007) described these body metaphors as instances where bodily qualities and phenomena are the immediate translation of emotional, social or moral ones. In AN bodily expressions and "concretised metaphors" do not play their usual role of experience-containing representations, but turn into concrete facts here-and-now which can no longer contain anything. The "as if" of the metaphor is replaced by a concrete "is", which is difficult to negotiate with. Being perceived as foreign, overwhelming, unacceptable, or unbearable, emotions are concretised and turned into something bodily. Through the manipulation of their body and their body weight, patients gain an illusion of mastery and relief from anguish and "negative" emotions, but also from "positive" ones (provided that emotions can be "positive" and "negative"…). Skårderud (2007) identified the following metaphors:

1. emptiness and fullness: sensations referring to one's body or stomach may stand for difficulties handling emotions, and the sensation of being overwhelmed;
2. purity: reflects patients' desire for a plain, certain and simple life;
3. spatiality: the physical space occupied by the body also stands for the emotional space occupied by oneself and the others in the relationships;
4. heaviness and lightness: feeling heavy is the concretization of feeling burdened and experiencing "negative" feelings; on the contrary, lightness is a relief from these overwhelming experiences;
5. solidity: the hardness of bones represents a certainty, something predictable which can help feeling relief from anxiety;
6. removal: the lost body weight may stand for something negative patients wish to remove from their lives; the body change concretely represents the patients' strive for change, for the reconstruction of a new self;
7. control: control over body, food, and appetite foster the illusion of having control over all the unpredictable aspects of one's life;
8. vulnerability and protection: AN may play the role of a sort of armor/shell to protect a vulnerable self; such belief is supported by a paradox and a deep denial, since the starved body, although extremely fragile, is thought to be tough and strong. Bones are boundaries and certainties challenging the feeling of being unprotected.

Due to regression and poor symbolic skills, AN patients have little awareness of the metaphoric connections between the concrete symptoms and emotions, self-esteem, sense of self. Anyway all these issues can and should certainly be addressed in therapy in order to allow patients to start gaining a broader perspective on their symptoms and on the "costs" and losses they entail. Striving for change may be a good thing *per se*, but the paradox of AN is that the patients' wish for change, which is dynamic in origin, loses its dynamic power and leads to a deadly static situation. The patients' desire to reconstruct a new self finds a quick, "toxic" fulfillment in the anorectic identity, but this fulfillment is not long-lasting and leads to a paralysis in the possibility to truly develop one's identity. The patients' desire to achieve a psychological distinction between self and others is pursued without considering the price of AN, which is to eventually lose exactly what they meant to preserve, i.e. the distinction between body, thoughts and feelings, and the possibility of independence and real distinction from the others.

A different and complementary perspective about the body speaking in place of patients is offered by models of female socialization highlighting that women, despite being open communicators, socialize to suppress negative feelings and needs in order to preserve close relationships (Gilligan et al., 1991). According to these models, women would focus on others' feelings and needs more than their owns, and they would specifically inhibit their negative feelings, thus failing to explore and acknowledge their personal experiences. Jack & Dill (1992) have identified four cognitive schemas to describe these patterns of socialization:

1. conflict avoidance through the inhibition of self-expression;
2. putting the needs of others before the self so as to secure attachments;
3. judging the self on the basis of external standards;
4. displaying an outer compliant self, opposed to an inner self who grows hostile and angry.

Inhibiting one's self-expression leads to an increased risk of health problems and psychological disorders (Pennebaker & Hoover, 1986; Jack & Dill, 1992). Such issue is particularly relevant in AN patients, who tend to silence negative affect and to replace it with a concrete communication style through starvation and ED symptoms. The tendency of AN patients to avoid expressing negative emotions may be related to an over-anticipation of their possible consequences in terms of distress and discomfort. Moreover, AN patients may be unusually sensitive to others' feelings and needs, and are likely to prefer stable, invariant, and emotionally temperate environments. Anyway, as for alexithymia, one should consider that whether this avoidance of negative emotion is typical and specific of AN or rather a shared phenomenon across other psychiatric groups is still not clear.

By the way, it is an undeniable clinical observation that patients often talk about their ideal socio-relational environments in terms of "harmony" and "agreement". AN patients seem to overvalue the importance of putting to silence any potential disagreement and negative emotion. They seem to believe that a sort of ideal relational Eden exists where being fond of each other equals feeling nothing negative and always think and want the same things. While striving to reach this impossible goal, patients are compelled to deny and inhibit any negative feeling; otherwise their model of relationships would crush. Anyway, since negative feelings exist and do need space, they are displaced and substituted by something less conflicting. The displacement of negative self-feelings onto the body was suggested by Hilde

Bruch (1973, 1978) and the role of the anorectic symptom in the maintenance of a sort of balance, albeit disturbed, in families, was discussed by Minuchin and coworkers (1975, 1978). Instead of experiencing negative feelings, such as anger, the individual suffering from AN denies and displaces them, and rather turns to concretised metaphors and might say she feels fat or full.

Despite clinical examples of this phenomenon are common, there is a lack of empirical studies dealing with the relationship between body dissatisfaction and inhibited expression of negative emotions. Moreover, the relationship between the tendency to suppress and inhibit negative emotions and perfectionism should be further investigated. Extremely perfectionistic individuals, such as AN patients (Treasure et al., 2011), are likely to believe that experiencing and, even more, expressing negative feelings or needs means having something wrong with one's character (Stroe-Kunold et al., 2012). Hence avoiding discussions about negative experiences is a way to avoid exposing what are supposed to be "imperfections".

The study by Geller and coworkers (2000) supports the hypothesis that AN individuals tend to suppress negative feelings as well as to minimize their own needs according to the belief that such attitude would preserve close relationships. Women with AN were found to avoid expressing feelings and thoughts when conflicting with those of others; in other words, they tended to give priority to others' feelings over their own. This pattern of silencing one's own thoughts and feelings is likely to be considerably energy-consuming for AN patients. Moreover, the inhibited expression of thoughts and feelings was related to negative feelings and thoughts about the body. Given the patients' poor interoceptive awareness (Garner & Bemis, 1985), it is likely that body dissatisfaction stands for confusion in identifying feelings, or it might stem from the avoidant attitude towards the expression of impulses and feelings perceived as threatening. Body dissatisfaction and ED symptoms may hence be an outburst for unexpressed hostility and sadness.

The patients' social functioning is therefore impaired, as previously highlighted. Failure in expressing one's emotions, thoughts and needs may deprive the individual of needed validation and understanding of feelings, it negatively impacts on the possibility of making sense of personal experiences, and compromises the opportunity of resolving areas of discordance. While not expressing his own feelings and needs, the individual misses the opportunity to receive care and support in difficult situations. Moreover, the false belief that the thoughts, feelings, and difficulties experienced are unique to oneself and unacceptable to others may trap the patient in shame and stigma. Finally, the priority patients seem to give to others' thoughts, beliefs, feelings and needs is a façade. It is not an authentic attention to the others, but rather a distorted attempt to read their minds, which does not allow a real "space" for the relationship. Of course, in order to overcome these distorted patterns, the possibility to "risk" in the relationship should be accepted and tolerated, so as the risk of showing others what the patients may believe is a flaw, an unattractive trait or even a guilt. From this point of view, a treatment approach addressing perfectionism and its self-defeating nature may be helpful to disclose the "traps" of these relational patterns. Moreover, improving the patients' skills in identifying, tolerating and accepting feelings, thoughts and needs may improve their comfort with social situations.

Cognitive-Affective Division and Emotion-Coupling in EDs

Jenkins & Connor (2012) have suggested the phrase "cognitive-affective division" to describe the often observed but seldom understood phenomenon of the difficulty ED patients show and face when trying to translate what they "think" cognitively to what they "feel" emotionally (and maybe also to put into words and share what they feel).

Findings in this field of research are contradictory and sometimes have failed to fully support what described above. For instance, Torres and coworkers (2010) explored the cognitive processing of emotions in AN (N=80, compared to 80 healthy controls), including both the emotions felt and the assessment of meta-emotional abilities. Although higher levels of alexithymia were found in AN, their meta-emotional abilities seemed to be preserved, with patients proving able to imagine emotions in hypothetical situations and to identify and label them. Results from this study therefore suggest that the patients' impairment in emotional processing may show up in specific stressful situation, for example food and weight-related ones. In such circumstances, AN patients may indeed feel more intense and internally based negative emotions than control subjects.

Other Authors (Parling et al., 2010) also suggested the need to rethink the measurement of alexithymia in AN, based on the observation that in the sample they studied, the alexithymia levels no longer showed differences between the AN and healthy controls groups after controlling for depression or anxiety (but not for perfectionism). It is likely that although AN patients believe that they have difficulties in identifying and reporting emotions, they actually perform as well as controls at the task of identifying and reporting emotions according to the Levels of Emotional Awareness Scale (LEAS). Moreover, the Authors suggest that the assessment of the alexithymic dimension should be performed with instruments and under circumstances that are not sensitive to the patients' mood.

Emotional deficits in AN can also show up in autobiographical memory recall and have been investigated in order to test whether they specifically concern negative or positive emotional values (Nandrino et al., 2006). Results from this study showed no deficits in explicit memory tests, but a specific pattern for AN patients, who tended to recall more general memories than controls in an autobiographical memory test, both for negative and positive cues. This pattern had no relation to depression, alexithymia, or anxiety severity, but increased significantly with illness duration. Such results seem to suggest a difficulty of AN patients integrating negative and positive emotional experiences, which worsens together with the increasing duration of illness.

Emotion regulation strategies in AN have also been investigated with a specific focus on the concept of "emotion coupling" between anger and disgust, according to suggestions that this might help explain some of the specific symptoms of AN (Fox et al., 2012), such as overestimation of body size.

On the contrary, Fox and Power (2009) examined the relationship between emotions, depression and EDs and tried to integrate it within a version of the multi-level model of emotion proposed by Power and Dalgleish. In accordance with the Schematic Propositional Analogical Associative Representation System model, they highlighted the importance of anger and disgust in EDs and the role of the ED itself as an inhibitor of emotions within the self. Considering also Enckell's concretised metaphors, it is likely that the ED may "replace" something unpleasant or unbearable from an emotional point of view with something allowing an illusion of concrete control.

As far as verbal expression of emotions in EDs is concerned, AN subjects were found to use fewer words when describing their emotional experiences and fewer positive affect words than controls, while no significant difference was found between BN and controls (Davies et al., 2012). As already stressed, emotion inhibition in AN may be a maintaining factor of the illness, and patterns of emotion regulation in EDs may contribute to an increased negative mood and a poorer social functioning.

Emotion Regulation Difficulties: ED-Specific or Rather a Transdiagnostic Factor?

A recent study (Svaldi et al., 2012) supported the latter hypothesis. The Authors assessed a mixed sample of psychiatric patients and healthy controls. The psychiatric diagnoses assessed included EDs (N=20 AN; N=18 BN; N=25 Binge Eating Disorder [BED]), Borderline Personality Disorder and Major Depressive Disorder. Overall, AN, BN and BED patients scored higher on level of emotion intensity, self-reported emotion related problems, and lower on acceptance of emotion, emotional awareness and clarity, compared to controls. No difference was found among the ED subgroups, apart from a slightly more adaptive pattern of emotion regulation in BED subjects than in AN and BN. On the other hand, the Authors found a similar performance on the emotion regulation variables in all clinical groups, hence suggesting that emotion regulation difficulties are higher in patients than in healthy controls but do not discriminate among diagnostic categories.

Other Authors (Zonnevylle-Bender et al., 2004) also found an altered processing of emotional information both in AN and other psychiatric patients (outpatients suffering from Depressive and/or Anxiety Disorders) compared to healthy controls, while no difference emerged as far as cognitive tasks were concerned. Anyway, in this study, deficits in emotional functioning showed some diagnosis-specific differences. Higher levels of alexithymia were found in AN, while the group of depressed/anxious patients had greater difficulties memorizing responses to auditory emotional stimuli than the other two groups.

In the matter of differences in alexithymia and depression between ED subgroups, differences were found by Corcos and coworkers (2000), with AN scoring higher than BN both at the TAS and the Hospital Anxiety and Depression Scale (HADS). Anyway, these disorder-specific differences failed to maintain significance after accounting for depression as a confounding variable.

A study comparing AN (N=20) and BN (N=20) patients and healthy controls (N=20) (Gilboa-Schechtman et al., 2006) supported the hypothesis of an emotional deficiency in ED subjects and of a mediational role of emotional distress between emotional processing and ED, but only partial support was offered to disorder specificity.

A recent study (Racine & Wildes, 2013) investigated associations between specific difficulties with emotion regulation and the core symptoms of AN, using the multidimensional Difficulties in Emotion Regulation Scale, and examining its association with several clinical variables. Lack of emotional awareness independently related to some clinical variables, including body mass index (BMI) at admission, eating disorder cognitions, objective binge eating, subjective binge eating, and purging. Impulse control difficulties when upset were associated with recurrent objective binge eating and recurrent purging in AN. Differential associations between specific emotion regulation deficits and core symptoms of AN are supported, as well as the role of ED symptoms as an attempt to achieve a sort of emotion regulation.

Another recent study by Manuel & Wade (2013) found that, compared to controls, women with AN had significantly greater difficulties with emotion regulation, depression, and negative affective memory bias, as well as lower bias for anger-threat. Negative affective memory emerged as a mediator, accounting for about one-third of the total effect a diagnosis of AN can have on difficulties with emotion regulation. Suggestions were raised about shared risk factors with depression, and the association between high levels of alexithymia and depression in patients with EDs is currently debated. A study about alexithymia and depressive experiences in ED patients (Speranza et al., 2005), including restricting AN, purging AN and BN, found high levels of alexithymia and depressive symptoms in patients. In particular, they used the Depressive Experiences Questionnaire, which allows the identification of two types of depressive personality style: dependent and self-critical. BN patients and controls showed differences as far as the TAS Difficulty Identifying Feelings factor is concerned; moreover, restricting AN patients and controls showed differences in the TAS Difficulty Describing Feelings factor. Self-critical depressive personality style scores were higher in BN than in AN-R and controls, and were associated with the TAS Difficulty Identifying Feelings factor in all EDs, although the association was stronger in AN than in BN. Dependent depressive personality style was associated with the TAS Difficulty Identifying Feelings factor only in AN. A specific profile of alexithymic and depressive dimensions was supported in ED subtypes.

Apart from the role of depression in predicting alexithymic features of ED patients, Axis II psychopathology and its relation to alexithymia have been investigated as well (Sexton et al., 1998). After controlling for depression, only the TAS factor "difficulty expressing feelings" was significantly higher in AN-R than in BN patients. This factor was suggested to be a relatively stable personality characteristic in AN-R, and total alexithymia score was mainly predicted by depression and the presence of avoidant personality disorder.

Another approach to the possible disorder-specificity of emotion regulation difficulties was proposed (Brockmeyer et al., 2012), through the assessment of specific emotion regulation difficulties in female samples with Major Depression, AN, and healthy controls. Compared to healthy controls, both AN and depressed patients showed greater emotion regulation difficulties as far as experience, differentiation, attenuation and modulation of emotions are concerned. Anyway, depressed patients performed worse on the last two dimensions (attenuation and modulation), compared to AN. Evidence from this study supported the hypothesis that emotion regulation difficulties are a transdiagnostic phenomenon, with depression being likely to present greater emotion regulation difficulties than AN. Such observation should be remembered, in respect of the frequent comorbidity between AN and depressive symptoms or full-criteria Major Depression.

Emotion Regulation Difficulties: State- or Trait-Related?

A recent longitudinal study (Beadle et al., 2013) tested acute (N=26) and weight-restored (N=20) AN patients, and compared them with a control sample of age-matched healthy women. Higher levels of alexithymia and emotional empathy in the domain of personal distress (vicarious negative arousal to others' suffering) were found in starved as well as in weight-restored AN compared to healthy controls. This finding suggests that alexithymia and personal distress may be trait features of AN, since they do not seem to improve after weight restoration. On the strength of the positive correlation between personal distress and alexithymia and the negative one between personal distress and self-regulation, it is likely that personal distress may be a function of poor emotional awareness and regulation in AN.

Tchanturia and coworkers (2012) explored social anhedonia, described as a reduced feeling of pleasure from social stimulation, in ED patients and healthy controls. Their clinical sample included 72 patients with acute AN and 14 recovered patients. Acutely ill AN reported higher social anhedonia than healthy controls, and clinical severity and alexithymia were found to be associated with social anhedonia. Contrary to the results by Beadle et al. (2013) recovered AN showed an intermediate profile in between AN and controls, thus suggesting this dimension might be somehow state-related.

Emotion recognition and emotion regulation may also be assessed via other instruments such as the Reading the Mind in the Eyes (RME) task and the Difficulties in Emotion Regulation Scale (DERS), respectively. Harrison et al. (2009) observed that AN (N=20) women compared to healthy controls (N=20) performed worse on the RME and had greater difficulties with emotion regulation. In greater detail, a significant negative correlation between total DERS score and correct answers at the RME was found. Although the study design of this research did not allow to discriminate whether the deficits found are a result of starvation and whether they can be reversed by weight gain alone, the need to target these difficulties in treatment is once again pointed out.

Furthermore, perceived changes in sensation have been linked to emotional intensity and dysregulation and are believed to be a crucial constituent of emotional experience. The disturbed experience of the body in AN has led to hypotheses about patients' sensory sensitivity and emotion regulation (Merwin et al., 2013). Both acute and weight-restored AN were found to have an increased sensory sensitivity and greater difficulty regulating emotions compared to controls, with self-perceived sensory sensitivity being associated with greater emotion dysregulation. The Authors suggest that hypersensitivity and impaired skills in coping with sensations may be an enduring feature in AN, which may be only in part improved by weight gain.

A study dealing with emotion recognition skills in acute and recovered AN and healthy controls found a better performance in recovered patients than in currently ill ones as far as emotional inference in the self and the others are concerned (Oldershaw et al., 2010). Nonetheless, recovered patients compared to healthy controls still showed some slight impairment, particularly in recognizing positive emotions. The impairment showed by patients with current AN in determining their own emotions (Oldershaw et al., 2010) supported at least in part the state-dependency of this trait, since normal performance on the eToM was found in recovered, weight-restored patients. This finding is also consistent with previous reports (Miller et al., 2003) of state-related diminished emotional experience and emotional avoidance in AN. The results by Oldershaw and coworkers (2010) also highlighted the fact that AN patients, both currently ill and recovered, may actually be making greater efforts than healthy controls despite their poorer performance in recognizing emotions. It is not clear whether emotion recognition claims a greater effort from these patients, and if so, why? Is this likely to be related to AN patients' perfectionism?

On the other hand, Brockmeyer and coworkers (2012) failed to support the state-dependency of emotion regulation difficulties in AN. They found a specific association between body weight and emotion regulation: the lower the first in acute AN, the lesser the difficulties in emotion regulation. From this standpoint, emotion regulation difficulties do not seem to be state-dependent, at least not as far as their worsening is concerned. On the contrary, one may suggest that the dysfunctional behavior of self-starvation and the consequent weight loss may serve to attenuate and regulate negative affective states and aversive emotions in AN. These findings indicate that, at least in some cases, it is likely that no specific neurobiological impairment is responsible for AN patients' emotion regulation difficulties. On the contrary, these rather have a specific meaning in the psychological functioning of the individual, for instance, attenuation and regulation of negative affect.

Moreover, there are hypotheses about emotional difficulties being trait markers and possible endophenotypes for a broader range of psychiatric disorders. For instance, poor social cognition skills are typical of autism spectrum disorders, and may be trait markers for these and other related disorders, including AN, which also have a genetic determination (Oldershaw et al., 2010). Reasons suggested to support social cognitive deficits being a trait marker include the fact that social functioning deficits, social phobia and continued post-recovery social impairments are common in AN. Hence, these social cognitive impairments are likely to represent predisposing and enduring factors. Of course, this does not mean that the severe physical and cognitive consequences of starvation can be underestimated.

Anyway, the temporal pattern of these changes is still not clear. Do patients show improved emotional recognition skill because they recover from AN? Or, conversely, do they start recovering because their emotional regulation improves? In other words, are emotional deficits and impairments really state-dependent, meaning they are biologically determined by some starvation-related factor? Or are they state-dependent, in the sense that they have a time-relation with acute AN, yet this relation consists in a defensive pattern which can be explained according to a psychodynamic approach rather than in neurobiological alterations?

Neurobiological Correlates of Alexithymia in AN

This section aims at offering some brief hints from the neurobiological point of view, which is complementary to some of the psychodynamic suggestions described above. The processing of emotions in AN has also been addressed with the aim of identifying possible biological markers, which may be crucial for the development of new treatment approaches. For instance, differences in brain dynamics might contribute to difficulties in AN patients' correct recognition of facially expressed emotions, deficits in social functioning, and consequently the maintenance of EDs. Nonetheless, little is known about the underlying neurobiological relationships between alexithymia and AN.

Some Authors (Hatch et al., 2010) raised the issue whether an association between AN and disturbances in the nonconscious neural processing of innate signals of emotion exists and whether such disturbances are state-dependent, hence decreasing after weight gain. Event-related potentials (ERPs) during overt and covert presentation of emotion expressions were altered in AN (both underweight and weight-restored), compared to healthy controls. These findings support the hypothesis of a persistent disruption of the early automatic appraisal of salient emotional signals, and a core, generic disturbance in AN in the early "automatic" neural processing of emotion irrespective of weight or nutritional status.

A functional magnetic resonance imaging study of AN and healthy controls (Miyake et al., 2012) examined the relationship between alexithymia levels and brain activation in AN. Neuroimaging results highlighting an activation of the prefrontal cortex suggest that AN patients tend to cognitively process negative words concerning interpersonal relationships. A lower activation of the amygdala, posterior cingulate cortex (PCC) and anterior cingulate cortex (ACC) in response to negative words concerning interpersonal relationships may contribute to the impairments of emotional processing that are hallmarks of alexithymia, and may be involved in the emotional processing impairments in AN patients as well.

Another study investigating the relationship between alexithymia levels and brain activation in patients with AN (Miyake et al., 2009) was performed in 30 patients, who were assessed with the TAS and with functional magnetic resonance imaging in order to identify the brain regions displaying abnormal hemodynamic activity in patients engaged in an emotional decision-making task. A significant activation in the amygdala during the task was found, as well as a correlation between PCC and ACC activation and alexithymia levels.

Emotional face recognition involves the amygdala for fear and anger, the insula and basal ganglia for disgust, and the cingulate, medial frontal and parietal cortices for happiness (Kilts et al., 2003). Anyway, imaging data about face perception in EDs are still lacking, but current studies found functional abnormalities during the processing of food, emotional, and body image stimuli in the prefrontal, cingulated and temporal cortices (Frank et al., 2002; Gordon et al., 2001; Uher et al., 2004).

Facially Expressed Emotions and Social Behaviors

The facial expression of emotions has a powerful influence on social behavior. The human face plays an important role as an instrument for social signaling, provided that the observer is capable of decoding the complexity of facial expressions (Kilts et al., 2003). Studies of facial expression emotion identification often used static displays of such expressions, namely photographs. Anyway, the network of brain regions decoding these social signals is likely to be much more complex, since facial emotional expressions are highly dynamic signals that encode the emotion message in facial action patterns. The question whether different neural correlates underlie the encoding and decoding of facial expressions of emotion by static or dynamic displays is still unanswered. Suggestions have been made (Kilts et al., 2003) that static displays of facial emotional expression may represent non-canonical stimuli that are processed for emotional content by mental strategies and neural events which are distinct from their more relevant dynamic counterparts.

ED patients with either AN and BN have been described as highly alexithymic and having difficulties in recognizing facially displayed emotions, but the relationship between these two dimensions is far from being clear, and although alexithymia is supposed to be a relevant variable in the interrelation between EDs and emotion recognition skills, it is not known whether facial emotion recognition is independent from alexithymia. The literature broadly addressing the issue of alexithymia and emotion regulation in AN is still full of unanswered questions, contradictions and multiple methodological biases, and data about classification and recognition of emotional faces in EDs is even poorer.

A research by Kessler and coworkers (2006) suggested that alexithymia is a complex and independent construct from basic facial emotion recognition. On the other hand, impairments in decoding and recognition of emotional facial expressions have been described in various psychopathological conditions, e.g. Major Depression (Mendlewicz et al., 2005).

Pollatos and coworkers (2008) compared AN patients (N=12) and matched healthy controls as far as visual-evoked potentials (VEPs) to emotional faces and classification performance are concerned, with the aim of understanding the relationship between classification of emotional faces and impaired central processing in EDs and the potential mediatory role of alexithymia and depression. Overall, AN patients made more mistakes than controls in emotional faces recognition, especially for neutral, sad, and disgust contents. Moreover, marked differences were found between AN and controls in evoked potentials and emotion recognition performances (significantly increased N200 amplitudes in response to all emotional categories and decreased VEPs in response to unpleasant emotional faces in the P300 time range). It is likely that in AN patients the processing of facial emotions leads to an increase in attentional demands or the need to shift attentional resources to the appropriate emotional category. AN patients seem to process neutral faces deeper than healthy controls, and to fail in modulating their central activity in response to this category of facial information, which is " not harmful". The Authors supposed that social interactions are exhausting for ED patients, because of several flaws in facial information processing including neutral expressions. In ED patients, the complexity and variety of facial expressions and related information encountered in social contexts and environments are connected with a series of misunderstanding and misclassifications of their emotional content. Moreover, alexithymic traits and depression may further impact on processing of neutral faces, which may be particularly difficult because of their ambiguous emotional content.

On the other hand, a study comparing ED patients and healthy controls, performed with the Reading the Mind in the Eyes task, the Difficulties in Emotion Regulation Scale (DERS) and a computerized pictorial (angry and neutral faces) Stroop task (Harrison et al., 2010), found that although both AN and BN patients showed attentional biases to faces in general, this bias was specific to angry faces over neutral faces. Emotion regulation difficulties were greater in ED patients, and emotion recognition was worse in ED patients as well, particularly in restricting AN.

Kucharska-Pietura and coworkers (2004) proposed that an impairment of facial emotion recognition may contribute to poor personal communication and lack of empathy in AN. Anyway, results in this field of research are not univocal.

Theory of Mind and Social Inference

Theory of Mind (ToM) refers to the individual's mentalizing skills, i.e. the ability to make inferences about another person's beliefs, desires and intentions. ToM concept can be extended to include inference about one's feelings, and this specific skill can be referred to as affective or emotional ToM. ToM is what enables the individual to take and understand other ones' perspective, hence understand and predict their behavior. ToM skills allow an effective management of social interactions, which are relevant for the achievement of individual and shared goals as well. Poor social skills and deficits in social perception can be found in several neurological and psychiatric conditions, including for example schizophrenia, autism and learning disabilities. If untreated, these impairments might restrict social independence and quality of life.

Deficits in social skills and social perception compromise the possibility to understand socially conveyed messages and emotional expressions. All these impairments contribute to the difficulty integrating the contextual information that is part of normal social encounters. Understatement, sarcasm, deception, and polite hints are just a few examples of everyday communication that rely upon social context to convey meaning.

As already described, identification of facial information and emotional expression is a core component of social life and interpersonal communication. Consequently, impaired skills in this cognitive processing ability, particularly with respect to negative emotional contents, may lead to social difficulties and hence contribute to maintenance of the ED. Deficits in social functioning in AN have been related to underlying problems in recognizing emotions in others and also own emotions. AN individuals show social functioning deficits, social phobia, and persistent social impairments even after recovery (Kaye et al., 2004; Nilsson et al., 1999), social isolation and avoidance. These social difficulties are at least partly related to the personality changes and diminished desire for social interaction in the starved state (Keys et al., 1950). Although it is necessary to acknowledge that there is still limited and contradictory evidence about these issues, attention is growing on the role of disrupted social cognition and interpersonal experience in the pathogenesis of AN. Whether these deficits represent a social endophenotype and how they could be properly addressed by treatment are still unanswered questions.

Conclusion

As described above, the research about alexithymia, emotion identification, social inference and Theory of Mind in EDs is still full of unanswered questions. In the attempt to add to the existing literature, a case-control study is currently being performed at the University Institute of Psychiatry, AOU Maggiore della Carità, Novara. AN patients are recruited from the outpatient service for EDs, and healthy controls are recruited on a community basis. The assessment of the variables of interest is performed with the Facial Emotion Identification Test (FEIT), The Awareness of Social Inference Test (TASIT), and the Toronto Alexithymia Scale (TAS). Data collection is still ongoing, but we expect to find healthy controls showing fewer alexithymic traits, and overall greater skills as assessed by both FEIT and TASIT, than ED patients. Moreover, we believe that results will allow to identify which of these instruments assessing - broadly speaking - the patients' skill to put themselves in someone else's shoes and to recognize emotions (a self-administered test: the TAS; a "static" one: the FEIT; and a "dynamic" one: the TASIT) best discriminates between ED and control subjects.

Brief Description of the Assessment

Facial Emotion Identification Test

The FEIT (Kerr & Neale, 1993) consists of 55 black-and-white photographs of 19 different faces, each depicting one of seven different emotions (happiness, sadness, anger, surprise, disgust, shame, neutral), shown one at a time for 15 seconds, with 10 seconds of blank screen between each stimulus presentation. After each stimulus, the participant makes a forced choice by selecting which of the seven emotions is depicted. 32 photographs depict negative emotions (sadness, anger, fear, and shame), while 16 photographs depict positive emotions (happiness, and surprise), and 7 photographs depict neutral faces. The score is the sum of the number of correct emotion identifications.

The administration of FEIT in this study was performed with the aid of a laptop computer screen to present each participant with the photographs of facial emotions. After each stimulus the participant was required to select which of the seven emotions was depicted on the picture and to mark it on a form which appeared under each photograph on the laptop screen.

The Awareness of Social Inference Test (TASIT)

The Awareness of Social Inference Test (TASIT) provides a systematic examination of social perception.
It consists of videoed vignettes and standardised response probes based upon recent theoretical accounts of how social cues provide meaning. The TASIT is articulated in 3 sections assessing different components of social perception; each section takes 10-15 minutes to view.

Section 1
The Emotion Evaluation Test. This is designed to assess interpretation of naturalistic emotional displays including facial movement, tone of voice and gestures. In each form, 28 vignettes of neutral scripts are enacted by professional actors to represent seven basic emotional categories: Fear, Anger, Sadness, Disgust, Surprise, Happiness and Neutral.

Section 2
Social Inference - Minimal (SI-M). Emotional demeanor can significantly alter the meaning of social messages. For example, 'You have been a great help!' may be said sincerely or in a derisive and sarcastic manner using facial expression and other paralinguistic features to imply the opposite.

A set of scripts are enacted either sincerely or sarcastically, with the ability to understand the meaning of each script being assessed by four standardised probe questions.

Section 3

Social Inference - Enriched (SI-E). This assesses the ability to use additional contextual cues in assigning conversational meaning. All vignettes entail scripts in which a speaker is making an assertion that is literally untrue. In eight of these, the speaker is speaking sarcastically, i.e. amplifying the truth. In the remainder the speaker is attempting to deceive the other by concealing the truth. In addition to the demeanor of the speaker, there are additional visual or verbal clues that provide information about the speaker's real intentions. Each vignette is assessed via four questions.

Toronto Alexithymia Scale

The TAS (Bagby et al., 1994; Caretti & La Barbera, 2005) is a widely used measure of alexithymia. The TAS-20 consists of three subscales.
Factor 1 assesses the difficulty of identifying feelings; factor 2 assesses the difficulty of describing feelings; factor 3 assesses externally oriented thinking. Total score ranges from 20 to 100 points. In accordance with Taylor et al. (1991), we judged scores of 61 and above as indicating an alexithymic state.

The importance of this field of research depends on the fact that difficulties identifying feelings may play the role of maintaining factor for AN and negatively impact on prognosis. Alexithymia has been shown to have a predictive value for the outcome of AN. A 3-year longitudinal study aimed at evaluating the long-term prognostic value of alexithymic features in a sample of ED patients was performed (Speranza et al., 2007), with assessment including the Toronto Alexithymia Scale (TAS-20) and the Beck Depression Inventory. At follow-up, 74% of the sample still presented asyndromal or subsyndromal EDs, and the Difficulty Identifying Feelings factor of the TAS-20 was found to significantly predict treatment outcome, independent of depressive symptoms and ED severity.

Improving identification of own emotions may ease the recovery process. The difficulties in emotional management not only maintain AN, but represent its core. Due to these difficulties, patients feel bound to replace their feelings with bodily situations, and are stuck with concretised metaphors.

Being aware of poor skills in emotional identification and expression in ED patients is necessary to address such problems with specific treatment strategies aimed at encouraging identification, labeling and sharing of emotions. Indeed, a shared conclusion of all studies in this field, independent of the results found, is that an approach supporting and fostering the identification and expression of feelings in ED patients may be a particularly useful treatment.

References

Bagby, RM; Parker, JDA; Taylor, GJ. The twenty-item Toronto Alxithymia Scale – Item selection and cross-validation of the factor structure. *Journal of Psychosomatic Research*, 1994, 38, 23-32.

Beadle, JN; Paradiso, S; Salerno, A; McCormick, LM. Alexithymia, emotional empathy, and self-regulation in anorexia nervosa. *Annals of Clinical Psychiatry*, 2013 May, 25(2), 107-20.

Berthoz, S; Perdereau, F; Godart, N; Corcos, M; Haviland, MG. Observer- and self-rated alexithymia in eating disorder patients: levels and correspondence among three measures. *Journal of Psychosomatic Research*, 2007 Mar, 62(3), 341-7.

Brockmeyer, T; Bents, H; Holtforth, MG; Pfeiffer, N; Herzog, W; Friederich, HC. Specific emotion regulation impairments in major depression and anorexia nervosa. *Psychiatry Research*, 2012 Dec 30, 200(2-3), 550-3.

Brockmeyer, T; Holtforth, MG; Bents, H; Kämmerer, A; Herzog, W; Friederich, HC. Starvation and emotion regulation in anorexia nervosa. *Comprehensive Psychiatry*, 2012 Jul, 53(5), 496-501.

Bruch, H. Eating disorders: obesity, anorexia, and the person within. New York: Basic Books, 1973.

Bruch, H. The golden cage: the enigma of anorexia nervosa. Cambridge, MA: Harvard University Press, 1978.

Campbell, D; Enckell, H. Metaphor and the violent act. In H Enckell (Ed), Metaphor and the psychodynamic functions of the mind. Doctoral dissertation. Finland: Department of Psychiatry, University of Kuopio, 2006.

Caretti, V; La Barbera, D (Eds). Alessitimia: valutazione e trattamento. Roma: Astrolabio, Ubaldini Editore, 2005.

Corcos, M; Guilbaud, O; Speranza, M; Paterniti, S; Loas, G; Stephan, P; Jeammet, P. Alexithymia and depression in eating disorders. *Psychiatry Research*, 2000 Apr 10, 93(3), 263-6.

Davies, H; Swan, N; Schmidt, U; Tchanturia, K. An experimental investigation of verbal expression of emotion in anorexia and bulimia nervosa. *European Eating Disorders Review*, 2012 Nov, 20(6), 476-83.

Enckell, H. Metaphor and the psychodynamic function of the mind. Doctoral dissertation. Kuopio, Finland: KuopionYliopisto, 2002.

Fox, JR; Power, MJ. Eating disorders and multi-level models of emotion: an integrated model. *Clinical Psychology & Psychotherapy*, 2009 Jul-Aug,16(4), 240-67.

Fox, JR; Smithson, E; Baillie, S; Ferreira, N; Mayr, I; Power, MJ. Emotion Coupling and Regulation in Anorexia Nervosa. *Clinical Psychology & Psychotherapy*, 2012 Nov 20; doi:10.1002/cpp.1823. [Epub ahead ofprint]

Frank, GK; Kaye, WH; Meltzer, CC; Price, JC; Greer, P; McConaha, C; Skovira, K. Reduced 5-HT2A receptor binding after recovery from anorexia nervosa. *Biological Psychiatry*, 2002, 52, 896-906.

Garner, DM; Bemis, KM. Cognitive therapy for anorexia nervosa. In DM Garner & PE Garfinkel (Eds). Handbook of psychotherapy for anorexia nervosa and bulimia (107-146). New York: Guilford Press, 1985.

Gilboa-Schechtman, E; Avnon, L; Zubery, E; Jeczmien, P. Emotional processing in eating disorders, specific impairment or general distress related deficiency? *Depression and Anxiety*, 2006, 23(6), 331-9.

Gilligan, C; Rogers, AG; Tolman, DL. Women, girls, and psychotherapy. New York, Haworth Press, 1991.

Gordon, CM; Dougherty, DD; Fischman, AJ; Emans, SJ; Grace, E; Lamm, R; Alpert, NM; Majzoub, JS; Rauch, SL. Neural substrates of anorexia nervosa, a behavioral challenge study with positron emission tomography. *Journal of Pediatrics*, 2001,139, 51-57.

Harrison, A; Sullivan, S; Tchanturia, K; Treasure, J. Emotion recognition and regulation in anorexia nervosa. *Clinical Psychology & Psychotherapy*, 2009 Jul-Aug,16(4), 348-56.

Harrison, A; Sullivan, S; Tchanturia, K; Treasure, J. Emotional functioning in eating disorders: attentional bias, emotion recognition and emotion regulation. *Psychological Medicine*, 2010 Nov, 40(11), 1887-97.

Harrison, A; Tchanturia, K; Treasure, J. Attentional bias, emotion recognition, and emotion regulation in anorexia: state or trait? *Biological Psychiatry*, 2010 Oct 15, 68(8), 755-61.

Hatch, A; Madden, S; Kohn, MR; Clarke, S; Touyz, S; Gordon, E; Williams, LM. Emotion brain alterations in anorexia nervosa: a candidate biological marker and implications for treatment. *Journal of Psychiatry and Neuroscience*, 2010 Jul, 35(4), 267-74.

Jack, DC; Dill, D. The Silencing the Self Scale: Schemas associated with depression in women. *Psychology of Women Quarterly*, 1992, 16, 97-106.

Jenkins, PE; O'Connor, H. Discerning thoughts from feelings: the cognitive-affective division in eating disorders. *Eating Disorders*, 2012, 20(2), 144-58.

Kaye, WH; Bulik, CM; Thornton, L; Barbarich, N; Masters, K. Comorbidity of anxiety disorders with anorexia and bulimia nervosa. *American Journal of Psychiatry*, 2004, 161, 2215-2221.

Kerr, SL; Neale, JM. Emotion perception in schizophrenia: a specific deficit or further evidence of generalized poor performance? *Journal of Abnormal Psychology*, 1993, 102, 312-318.

Kessler, H; Schwarze, M; Filipic, S; Traue, HC; von Wietersheim, J. Alexithymia and facial emotion recognition in patients with eating disorders. *International Journal of Eating Disorders*, 2006, 39(3), 245-251.

Keys, A. The residues of malnutrition and starvation. *Science*, 1950, 112, 371-373.

Kilts, CD; Egan, G; Gideon, DA; Ely, TD; Hoffman, JM. Dissociable neural pathways are involved in the recognition of emotion in static and dynamic facial expressions. *Neuroimage*, 2003, 18, 156-168.

Kucharska-Pietura, K; Nikolau, V; Masiak, M; Treasure, J. The recognition of emotion in the faces and voice of Anorexia Nervosa. *International Journal of Eating Disorder*, 2004, 35, 42-47.

Manuel, A; Wade, TD. Emotion regulation in broadly defined anorexia nervosa: Association with negative affective memory bias. *Behaviour Research and Therapy*, 2013 May 1, 51(8), 417-424.

Mendlewicz, L; Linkowski, P; Bazelmans, C; Philippot, P. Decoding emotional facial expressions in depressed and anorexic patients. *Journal of Affective Disorders*, 2005, 89(1-3), 195-199.

Merwin, RM; Moskovich, AA; Wagner, HR; Ritschel, LA; Craighead, LW; Zucker, NL. Emotion regulation difficulties in anorexia nervosa: Relationship to self-perceived sensory sensitivity. *Cognition & Emotion*, 2013, 27(3), 441-52.

Miller, SP; Redlich, AD; Steiner, H. The stress response in anorexia nervosa. *Child Psychiatry & Human Development*, 2003, 33, 295–306.

Minuchin, S; Baker, BL; Rosman, BL; Liebman, R; Milman, L; Todd, TC. A conceptual model of psychosomatic illness in children: family organization and family therapy. *Archives of General Psychiatry*, 1975, 32, 1031-1038.

Minuchin, S; Rosman, BL; Baker, BL. *Psychosomatic families: anorexia nervosa in context*. Cambridge, MA: Harvard University Press, 1978.

Miyake, Y; Okamoto, Y; Onoda, K; Shirao, N; Mantani, T; Yamawaki, S. Neural correlates of alexithymia in response to emotional stimuli: a study of anorexia nervosa patients. *Hiroshima Journal of Medical Sciences*, 2009 Mar, 58(1), 1-8.

Miyake, Y; Okamoto, Y; Onoda, K; Shirao, N; Okamoto, Y; Yamawaki, S. Brain activation during the perception of stressful word stimuli concerning interpersonal relationships in anorexia nervosa patients with high degrees of alexithymia in an fMRI paradigm. *Psychiatry Research*, 2012 Feb 28, 201(2), 113-9.

Nandrino, JL; Doba, K; Lesne, A; Christophe, V; Pezard, L. Autobiographical memory deficit in anorexia nervosa: emotion regulation and effect of duration of illness. *Journal of Psychosomatic Research*, 2006 Oct, 61(4), 537-43.

Nilsson, EW; Gillberg, C; Gillberg, IC; Rastam, M. Ten- year follow-up of adolescent-onset anorexia nervosa: personality disorders. *Journal of the American Academy of Child and Adolescent Psychiatry*, 1999, 38, 1389-1395.

Nordbø, RH; Espeset, EM; Gulliksen, KS; Skårderud, F; Holte, A. The meaning self-starvation: qualitative study of patients' perception of anorexia nervosa. *International Journal of Eating Disorders*, 2006, 39(7), 556-564.

Oldershaw, A; Hambrook, D; Stahl, D; Tchanturia, K; Treasure, J; Schmidt, U. The socio-emotional processing stream in Anorexia Nervosa. *Neuroscience & Biobehavioral Reviews*, 2011 Jan, 35(3), 970-88.

Oldershaw, A; Hambrook, D; Tchanturia, K; Treasure, J; Schmidt, U. Emotional theory of mind and emotional awareness in recovered anorexia nervosa patients. *Psychosomatic Medicine*, 2010, 72, 73-79.

Parling, T; Mortazavi, M; Ghaderi, A. Alexithymia and emotional awareness in anorexia nervosa: time for a shift in the measurement of the concept? *Eating Behaviors*, 2010 Dec, 11(4), 205-10.

Pennebaker, JW; Beall, SK. Confronting a traumatic event: toward an understanding of inhibition and disease. *Journal of Abnormal Psychology*, 1986, 95, 274-281.

Pollatos, O; Herbert, BM; Schandry, R; Gramann K. Impaired central processing of emotional faces in anorexia nervosa. *Psychosomatic Medicine*, 2008 Jul, 70(6), 701-8.

Racine, SE; Wildes, JE. Emotion dysregulation and symptoms of anorexia nervosa: the unique roles of lack of emotional awareness and impulse control difficulties when upset. *International Journal of Eating Disorders*, 2013 Jun 11, doi, 10.1002/eat.22145. [Epub ahead of print]

Råstam, M; Gillberg, C; Gillberg, IC; Johansson, M. Alexithymia in anorexia nervosa: a controlled study using the 20-item Toronto Alexithymia Scale. *Acta Psychiatrica Scandinavica*, 1997 May, 95(5), 385-8.

Rollins, J; Flanagan, S; McDonald, S. 2002 TASIT

Sexton, MC; Sunday, SR; Hurt, S; Halmi, KA. The relationship between alexithymia, depression, and axis II psychopathology in eating disorder inpatients. *International Journal of Eating Disorders*, 1998 Apr, 23(3), 277-86.

Schmidt, U; Treasure J. Anorexia nervosa: valued and visible. A cognitive-interpersonal maintenance model and its implications for research and practice. *British Journal of Clinical Psychology*, 2006, 45(Pt 3), 343-366.

Sifneos, PE. The prevalence of "alexithymic" characteristics in psychosomatic patients. *Psychotherapy and Psychosomatics*, 1976, 22, 255-262.

Skårderud, F. Eating one's words, part I: "concretised metaphors" and reflective function in anorexia nervosa – an interview study. *European Eating Disorder Review*, 2007, 15(3), 163-174.

Speranza, M; Corcos, M; Loas, G; Stéphan, P; Guilbaud, O; Perez-Diaz, F; Venisse, JL; Bizouard, P; Halfon, O; Flament, M; Jeammet, P. Depressive personality dimensions and alexithymia in eating disorders. *Psychiatry Research*, 2005 Jun 15, 135(2), 153-63.

Speranza, M; Loas, G; Wallier, J; Corcos, M. Predictive value of alexithymia in patients with eating disorders: a 3-year prospective study. *Journal of Psychosomatic Research*, 2007 Oct, 63(4), 365-71.

Stroe-Kunold, E; Wesche, D; Friederich, HC; Herzog, W; Zastrow, A; Wild, B. Temporal relationships of emotional avoidance in a patient with anorexia nervosa: a time series analysis. *International Journal of Psychiatry in Medicine*, 2012, 44(1), 53-62.

Svaldi, J; Griepenstroh, J; Tuschen-Caffier, B; Ehring, T. Emotion regulation deficits in eating disorders: a marker of eating pathology or general psychopathology? *Psychiatry Research*, 2012 May 15, 197(1-2), 103-11.

Taylor, GJ; Doody, K. Verbal measures of alexithymia: what do they measure. *Psychotherapy and Psychosomatics*, 1985, 43, 32-37.

Tchanturia, K; Davies, H; Harrison, A; Fox, JR; Treasure, J; Schmidt, U. Altered social hedonic processing in eating disorders. *International Journal of Eating Disorders*, 2012 Dec, 45(8), 962-9.

Thackery, E; Harris, M. The gale encyclopedia of mental disorders. New York, Thomson Gale, 2003

Torres, S; Guerra, MP; Lencastre, L; Roma-Torres, A; Brandão, I; Queirós, C; Vieira, F. Cognitive processing of emotions in anorexia nervosa. *European Eating Disorders Review*, 2010 Oct 6, 19 (2), 100-111.

Treasure, J; Crane, A; McKnight, R; Buchanan, E; Wolfe, M. First do no harm: iatrogenic maintaining factors in anorexia nervosa. *European Eating Disorders Review*, 2011Jul-Aug, 19(4), 296-302.

Troop, NA; Schmidt, UH; Treasure, JL. Feelings and fantasy in eating disorders: a factor analysis of the Toronto Alexithymia Scale. *International Journal of Eating Disorders*, 1995 Sep, 18(2), 151-7.

Uher, R; Murphy, T; Brammer, MJ; Dalgleish, T; Phillips, ML; Ng, VW; Andrew, CM; William, SCR; Campbell, IC; Treasure, J. Medial Prefrontal cortex activity associated with symptom provocation in eating disorders. *American Journal of Psychiatry*, 2004, 161, 1238-1246.

Zonnevylle-Bender, MJ; van Goozen, SH; Cohen-Kettenis, PT; van Elburg, TA; van Engeland, H. Emotional functioning in adolescent anorexia nervosa patients: a controlled study. *European Child & Adolescent Psychiatry*, 2004 Feb, 13(1), 28-34.

In: New Developments in Anorexia Nervosa Research
Editors: Carla Gramaglia and Patrizia Zeppegno

ISBN: 978-1-63117-551-0
© 2014 Nova Science Publishers, Inc.

Chapter 11

Epidemiological Data on Eating Disorders in Japan

Yoshikatsu Nakai, M.D.[*1], *Kazuko Nin, Ph.D.*[2],
and Shunichi Noma, M.D.[3]

[1]Kyoto Institute of Health Sciences, Kyoto, Japan
[2]Human Health Sciences, Kyoto University Graduate School of Medicine, Kyoto
[3]Department of Psychiatry, School of Medicine, Kyoto University, Kyoto, Japan

Abstract

To study transcultural differences in eating disorders, we examined the time trend of eating disorder symptoms and eating disorders in clinical and non-clinical samples in Japan from the early 1980s to the present. Study on Anorexia Nervosa (AN) in Japan dates from the end of the 1950s. The number of patient with AN rapidly increased during the early 1980s in Japan. Then, cross-sectional prevalence studies started in 1981. National surveys on eating disorders in major hospitals were conducted by a Research Group for Eating Disorders in 1981, 1992 and 2000. The incidence of AN and Bulimia Nervosa (BN) increased dramatically in 2000. Epidemiological studies of AN in female students were conducted with the two-stage screening approach in 1983, 1993 and 2000. The prevalence rate of AN was 0.12%-0.23% in 1983, 0.16%-0.41% in 1993 and 1.5%-2.0% in 2000. We collected questionnaire information on body image perception, eating behaviors and menstruation from a total of 10,599 female students, aged 16 to 23 years, in Kyoto city and conducted a survey of AN, BN and Eating Disorder Not Otherwise Specified (EDNOS) in these subjects in 1982, 1992 and 2002. On almost all measures, there were significant increases of disordered attitude about fear of gaining weight, body perception disturbance and problematic eating behaviors over time. The point prevalence of AN, BN and EDNOS significantly increased over time. These results suggest that the prevalence of eating disorder symptoms and eating disorders is still increasing among Japanese female students. Changing socio-cultural factors in Japan may explain a dramatic increase of eating disorders over time.

* Address for correspondence: Yoshikatsu Nakai M.D., Kyoto Institute of Health Sciences, Miyako Bldg 5F, Karasuma Oike Agaru, Nakagyo-ku, Kyoto 604-0845, Japan (E-mail: ynakai@helen.ocn.ne.jp)

Keywords: Epidemiology, eating disorders, anorexia nervosa, bulimia nervosa, eating disorder symptoms

Introduction

Descriptive epidemiological studies provide information about the occurrence of disease and trends in the frequency of disease over time. The most commonly used descriptive measures in epidemiology are incidence and prevalence. Studies of the prevalence and incidence of eating disorders seek to identify the number of affected individuals in a given time period (prevalence) and new-onset or newly identified cases (incidence). The validity and generalizability of results from epidemiological studies are influenced by the selection of target populations and methods of case detection (Hsu 1996; Hoek and van Hoeken 2003). Differential availability of services and variable methods of case detection may be interpreted as changes in occurrence. Only a fraction of patients will seek professional help or receive a referral to specialized health care services, therefore studies limited to clinical settings may underestimate the occurrence of eating disorders in the community. Large population-based studies are more representative of the source population and less biased in their conclusion, but they are often extremely expensive and time-consuming to conduct (Keski-Rahkonen, Raevuori and Hoek, 2008).

Japan differs from Western countries in terms of customs regarding food, housing, religion, and family, including women's issues (Vardaman, 2006). However, during the past half-century, there has been a growth in the influence of Western culture, which has brought many changes to the traditional Japanese lifestyle and cultural standards. These changes are associated with an increase in eating disorders over the past 30 years (Nakai, 2003a; Nogami, 1997). There were 3 reviews on eating disorders in Japan, written in English (Chisuwa & O'Dea, 2010; Kuboki, Nomura, Ide, Suematsu, Araki, 1996; Nogami, 1997). However, there was no description on the methodological details of cross-sectional studies conducted in Japan in these reviews. The details of these studies were written in the Annual Report of the Research Group into Eating Disorders in Japanese.

There has been considerable debate regarding whether the prevalence of eating disorders has been increasing in Western countries from the1960s to the present (Hoek 2006; Keski-Rahkonen et al., 2008; Striegel-Moore, Franko and Ach, 2006). After the 1970s, the incidence of anorexia nervosa (AN) in Europe stabilized (Currin, Schmidt, Treasure and Jick 2005; Milos, Spindler, Schnyder, Martz, Hoek and Willi, 2004). Currin et al. (2005) reported a decline in bulimia nervosa (BN) incidence following its dramatic increase in the UK. Although eating disorder not otherwise specified (EDNOS) is the most prevalent eating disorder in clinical and community settings at present, there are limited data on how this transformation occurred (Striegel-Moore et al., 2006). The incidence of AN and BN has remained stable, but the age-standardized incidence of EDNOS increased in primary care between 2000 and 2009 in the UK (Micali, Hagberg, Petersen and Treasure, 2013). These studies used primary-care databases to identify cases.

Since it is well known that patients with eating disorders tend to conceal their illness and avoid professional help, study of the prevalence in non-clinical samples is essential. Fombonne (1995) reported that, in meta-analysis, there was no evidence of an increase in AN.

Pawluck and Gorey (1998) reported that integrative evidence across population-based epidemiological studies covering 40 years suggests that the incidence of AN has not increased significantly. In the Netherlands, the overall incidence of AN has been generally stable, but increased significantly among 15-19-year-old females from 1985-1989 to 1995-1999 (van Son, van Hoeken, Bartelds, van Furth and Hoek, 2006). Point prevalence of BN in college women significantly decreased from 1982 to 2002 (Keel, Heatherton, Dorer, Joiner, and Zalta, 2005). Some recent evidence suggests that the incidence of BN is decreasing, but atypical forms of eating disorders, such as binge eating disorder (BED) and EDNOS, appear to be common in the community in Western countries (Machado, Machado, Gonçalves & Hoek, 2007).

In addition to the prevalence of eating disorders, examination of the prevalence of eating disorder symptoms is important because symptoms may represent the first signs of the development of a full syndrome disorder and data on their prevalence thus give an indication of the size of the at-risk group (Striegel-Moore et al., 2006). There were significant reductions of problematic eating behaviors and disordered attitudes about body weight and shape in the United States from 1982 to 2002 (Heatherton Nichols, Mahamedi, and Keel, 1995; Keel et al., 2005). Researchers affiliated with Radcliffe College examined changes in prevalence of dieting behavior and eating disorder symptoms among college students from 1982 to 2002. On almost all measures there were significant reductions of problematic eating behaviors and disordered attitudes about body weight and shape in both women and men from 1982 to 2002 (Heatherton et al., 1995; Keel et al., 2005).

Keel and Klump (2003) explored the extent to which eating disorders represent culture-bound syndromes and discussed the implications for conceptualizing the role genes play in their etiology. Eating disorders have been described as culture-bound syndromes associated with Western or Caucasian societies and are thought to be rare in Asian and non-Western societies (Tsai, 2000; Striegel-Moore et al., 2006). However, perceptions of overweight and attempts to lose weight were highest in Asian countries in a self-reported survey on 18,512 college students administered in 22 Countries, including Asian countries, European countries, Mediterranean countries and the USA, in their native languages (Wardle, Haase and Steptoe, 2006). Accordingly, epidemiological studies on eating disorder symptoms and eating disorders in non-Western countries are useful for understanding factors triggering eating disorders.

The purpose of the present study was to investigate transcultural differences in eating disorders. For this, we examined the time trend of eating disorder symptoms and eating disorders in clinical and non-clinical samples in Japan from the early 1980s to the present.

Prevalence of Eating Disorders in Clinical Samples

Although "Fushoku-byo", a form of AN, had been described by physicians of Oriental medicine during the last quarter of the 18th century (Otsuka, 1955), modern study on AN in Japan dates from the end of the 1950s (Nogami, 1997). The number of patients with AN rapidly increased during the early 1980s in Japan (Nakai, 2003a; Nogami, 1997). Then, cross-sectional prevalence studies started in 1981, when the Ministry of Health and Welfare established a Research Group for Eating Disorders. National surveys on eating disorders in major hospitals were conducted in 1981, 1992 and 2000 (Kuboki, et al., 1996; Nakai, 2003a).

Table 1. Epidemiological study on anorexia nervosa and bulimia nervosa in clinical samples in Japan

	1980-1981	1985	1992	2000
number of surveyed institutions (rate of response)	1,030 (33.0%)	5,283 (64.3%)	5,057 (37.4%)	23,041 (61.0%)
reported number of AN patients	980	2,391	2,068	5,417
prevalence of AN per 10^5 of general population	2.2-2.8	2.9-3.7	3.6-4.5	8.3-11.9
prevalence of AN per 10^5 of 13-29-year-old female population	14.4-18.0	20.4-25.3	20.4-25.3	51.6-73.6
reported number of BN patients			699	3,201
prevalence of BN per 10^5 of general population			1.3-2.5	4.3-5.9
prevalence of BN per 10^5 of 13-29-year-old female population			12.8-13.6	27.7-37.7

AN: anorexia nervosa BN: bulimia nervosa.
Institutions included the departments of psychiatry, internal medicine, gynecology, psychosomatic medicine and pediatrics at all medical colleges and university hospitals, and general and psychiatric hospitals having more than 200 beds.

The incidence of AN and BN in Japan increased dramatically in 2000 (Table 1). The estimated incidence of AN in 1981, 1992 and 2000 was 2.5, 4.0 and 10.1 per 100,000 of the total population and 16.2, 22.9 and 62.6 per 100,000 females aged 13-29 years, respectively. The estimated incidence of BN in 1992 and 2000 was 1.8 and 5.1 per 100,000 of the total population and 13.0 and 32.7 per 100,000 females aged 13-29 years, respectively (Kuboki, et al., 1996; Nakai, 2003a). These studies were conducted in the departments of psychiatry, internal medicine, gynecology, psychosomatic medicine and pediatrics at all medical colleges and university hospitals and general and psychiatric hospitals having more than 200 beds. Clinics and hospitals having less than 200 beds were not included in these studies.

Then, a questionnaire, asking about the number of patients with an eating disorder treated in 2008, was sent to the physicians of psychiatry, psychosomatic medicine and internal medicine in Kyoto city (Nakai, et al., 2009). Data were collected from 357 (37%) of the 965 medical facilities surveyed. In 333 medical facilities, no patients with an eating disorder were reported. In the remaining 24 institutions, 532 patients with an eating disorder were reported. Out of 532 cases, 88 (16.5%) were treated in all the 2 university hospitals and 325 (61.1%) were treated in 3 private clinics. In these medical facilities, more than 50 patients were treated in each facility. The remaining 119 (22 %) patients were treated in 19 medical facilities, where less then 10 patients were treated.

Table 2. Proportion of the types of eating disorders in 2 university hospitals and 3 private clinics in Kyoto City

	University hospitals	Private clinics	Total
	n = 88	n = 325	n = 413
ANOREXIA NERVOSA	57%	26%	32%
BULIMIA NERVOSA	34%	50%	47%
EDNOS	9%	24%	21%

EDNOS: eating disorder not otherwise specified.

Out of 88 cases in 2 university hospitals, 50 (57%) were categorized as having AN and 33 (37.5%) as having BN. On the other hand, out of 352 cases in 3 private clinics, 81 (25%) were categorized as having AN and 169 (52%) as having BN (Table 2).Prevalence rate of BN patients may have been underestimated in the national surveys on eating disorders, because private clinics were not included in these surveys (Kubobki, et al., 1996; Nakai, 2003a). Accordingly, we should be cautious for the interpretation of the national surveys on eating disorders conducted in major hospitals by the Research Group for Eating Disorders in 1981, 1992 and 2000 (Kuboki, et al., 1996; Nakai, 2003a).

Prevalence of Eating Disorders in Non-Clinical Samples

Currently, the two-stage screening approach is the most widely accepted procedure for the identification of the prevalence of cases with eating disorders (Hoek & van Hoeken, 2003). First, a large population is screened for the likelihood of eating disorders by a screening questionnaire such as the Eating Attitudes Test (EAT: Garner & Garfinkel, 1979) or the Eating Disorder Examination Questionnaire (EDE-Q: Fairburn & Beglin, 2008) that identifies an at-risk population (first stage). Second, definite cases are established on the basis of a personal interview with subjects from this at-risk population and from a randomly selected sample of subjects not at risk (second stage; Williams, Tarnopolsky and Hand, 1980). Methodological problems of two-stage studies are poor response rates, the sensitivity and specificity of the screening instrument, and the restricted size of the groups interviewed, particularly of those not at risk (Fairburn & Beglin, 1990).

In Japan, epidemiological studies of anorexia nervosa in female students were conducted with the two-stage screening approach by the members of a Research Group for Eating Disorders in 1983 and in 1993 (Kuboki et al., 1996; Nakai, 2003a, 2012). In 2000, two research groups conducted a survey of anorexia nervosa in females students with the two-stage screening approach (Hisamatsu, Tuboi, Tsutsui & Shinoda, 2000; Watanabe, 2002). They used low BMI of less than 17.5 kg/m^2 for the 1st stage screening for AN, because sensitivity of the EAT was poor for the diagnosis of AN in Japan (Nagata, et al., 1989; Nakai, 2003b; Ujiie & Kono, 1994). Compared with the North American standardization sample, the Japanese anorexia nervosa, restricting type （AN-R） group reported lower levels of the EAT. On the other hand, non-eating disordered group reported higher levels of the EAT. The sensitivity and specificity of the EAT were 0.51 and 0.95 for AN-R (Nakai, 2003b). In the second stage, specialists in eating disorders conducted a direct interview with subjects from this at-risk population.

Table 3. Two-stage studies of the prevalence of eating disorders in community samples of female subjects in Japan

Study	district	age of subjects	sample size	type	prevalence rates (%)
Mizushima (1983)	Fukui	12-15	12,179	AN	0.18
Nakai (1983)	Kyoto*	12-15	5,005	AN	0.23
Mizuno (1983)	Fukui	15-18	12,674	AN	0.12
Azuma (1983)	Kyoto*	15-18	19,250	AN	0.18
Nakai (1983)	Kyoto**	15-18	14,967	AN	0.14
Yamamoto (1993)	Fujieda	12-15	2,525	AN	0.32
Azuma (1993)	Kyoto*	15-18	15,609	AN	0.41
Nakai (1993)	Kyoto**	15-18	4,989	AN	0.16
Hisamatsu (2000)		18-23	357	AN	1.4
Hisamatsu (2000)	Tokyo	18-23	357	BN	1.4
Hisamatsu (2000)		18-23	357	EDNOS	8.7
Watanabe (2002)	Tokyo	15-18	1,130	AN	2.03

AN: anorexia nervosa.
BN: bulimia nervosa.
EDNOS: eating disorder not otherwise specified.
*: public schools.
**: private schools.

Results of the two-stage screening studies on eating disorders in Japanese female students are shown in Table 3. The prevalence rate of AN was 0.12%-0.23% in 1983 (Azuma & Ohishi, 1984; Mizuno & Mizushima, 1984; Mizushima & Ishii, 1983; Nakai, 1983) and 0.16%-0.41% in 1993 (Azuma & Noma, 1993; Nakai, 2012). Although the sample size was small, the prevalence rate of AN was 1.5%-2.0% in 2000 (Hisamatsu, et al., 2000; Watanabe, 2002).

Table 4. Studies of the prevalence of eating disorders with a self-reported questionnaire in community samples of female subjects in Japan

study	year	district	age of subjects	sample size	type	prevalence rates (%)
Tomita	1983	Nagoya	12-15	13,762	AN	0.07
Ozeki	1983	Sanin	12-15	18,042	AN	0.08
Nakagawa	1983	Sapporo	15-18	13,009	AN	0.02
Suematsu	1983	Tokyo	15-18	1,799	AN	0.06
Tomita	1983	Nagoya	15-18	11,084	AN	0.12
Suematsu	1983	Oita	15-18	5101	AN	0.08
Kiriike	1988	Osaka	18-20	456	Bulimia	2.9
Baba	1993	Yokohama	12-15	2406	AN	0.27
Baba	1993	Yokohama	15-18	12443	AN	0.05
Takeda	1993	Yokohama	15-18	1345	BN	1.9
Sasaki	1993	Aomori	15-18	2279	BN	1.05
Nakai	1993	Kyoto	15-18	3079	BN	1.97
Azuma	1993	Kyoto	15-18	1741	BN	0.92
Nakai	2002	Kyoto	12-15	929	AN	0.5
Nakai	2002	Kyoto	12-15	929	BN	0.3
Nakai	2002	Kyoto	12-15	929	EDNOS	17.1

AN: anorexia nervosa.
BN: bulimia nervosa.
EDNOS: eating disorder not otherwise specified.

Table 4 shows results of the studies with a self-reported questionnaire of the prevalence of eating disorders in young Japanese females. The prevalence rate of AN with a self-administered questionnaire, the EAT, was considerably lower than that with the two-stage studies (0.02-0.12% vs. 0.12-0.23%) in 1983. There have been few studies on the prevalence of BN and BED using the two-stage screening approach in Japan (Hisamatsu, et al., 2000). The Personal Information Protection Law was enacted in Japan in 2003. Thereafter, it has been very difficult to conduct an epidemiological study in Japan.

Time Trend of Eating Disorder Symptoms and Eating Disorders in Non-Clinical Samples

Few studies have examined the time trend of eating disorder symptoms and eating disorders in non-clinical samples in Japan. Accordingly, we collected questionnaire information on body image perception, eating behaviors and menstruation from Japanese female students and conducted a survey of AN, BN and EDNOS in these subjects in 1982, 1992 and 2002 (Nakai, 2010). The questionnaire was composed of 15 items that measure fear of weight gain, body perception disturbance, eating disordered behaviors (frequencies and duration of restrictive dieting and binge eating with loss of control), inappropriate compensatory behaviors to control weight (frequencies and duration of fasting for a whole day, self-induced vomiting, use of laxatives, diuretics and/or diet pills and exercise). We define here severe restrictive dieting as restrictive dieting more than twice a week for at least 3 months, severe binge eating as binge eating more than twice a week for at least 3 months and severe purging as purging more than twice a week for at least 3 months. The questionnaire was contrived to minimize the difference of threshold between self-reporting of the questionnaire and direct interview.

In the spring of 1982, a survey of eating disorder symptoms and eating disorders was conducted on 4500 Japanese female students, aged 16 to 23 years, in 10 high schools and 8 universities randomly selected from 53 high schools and 35 universities in Kyoto prefecture, located in the middle of Japan. The response rate was 82%. Replicating methods used in 1982, a survey was conducted on 4500 and 3750 female students from the same group of high schools and universities in the spring of 1992 and 2002, respectively. The number of participants decreased due to a declining birth rate in 2002. The response rate was 85% in 1992 and 80% in 2002. Hence, a total of 10,499 female students participated this study. There were no significant shifts in socioeconomic status in the participants studied over time. Informed consent was obtained from the responsible persons in the schools and the universities. All participants were asked to complete a self-reported questionnaire on an anonymous and voluntary basis. Additionally, information on age, height, current weight, and menstruation was obtained and body mass index (BMI) was calculated. In accordance with the recommendation of the Ministry of Health, Labour and Welfare, Japan (2003), subjects were divided into 3 groups based on the current BMI: underweight group (BMI < 18.5 kg/m^2), average-weight group (BMI 18.5-25.0 kg/m^2) and overweight group (BMI > 25.0 kg/m^2).

**Table 5. Prevalence of fear of weight gain, body perception disturbance, eating
disordered behaviors and amenorrhea in all subjects studied in 1982, 1992 and 2002**

	1982	1992	2002	Statistics
fear of weight gain (%)	69.9	70.0	82.3	P<0.001
body perception disturbance (%)	60.0	63.0	69.1	P<0.001
restrictive-dieting (%)	30.2	33.5	44.9	P<0.001
binge-eating (%)	12.7	32.5	33.4	P<0.001
purging (%)	3.8	9.4	11.8	P<0.001
severe* restrictive-dieting (%)	8.1	8.2	8.9	N.S.
severe* binge-eating (%)	1.2	3.8	4.7	P<0.001
severe* purging (%)	0.4	0.8	1.0	P<0.001
amenorrhea (%)	2.1	3.0	3.6	P<0.001

*: at least twice a week for 3 months.
NS: not significant.

The diagnosis of an eating disorder was made on the basis of the following operational definitions, relying exclusively on the participants' responses to the questionnaire. The criteria for AN in this study were (a) BMI of less than 17.5 kg/m^2, (b) intense fear of gaining weight, (c) overestimation of body weight and desired BMI of less than 17.5 kg/m^2 and (d) amenorrhea. The criteria for BN in this study were (a) binge eating episodes with loss of control, (b) inappropriate compensatory behaviors to control weight (self-induced vomiting, use of laxatives, diuretics, or diet pills, excessive fasting or exercise), (c) a and b occur at least twice a week for 3 months, (d) inaccurate self-evaluation of body weight and shape and (e) exclusion of AN. Since the criteria for EDNOS remain inconclusive (American Psychiatric Association, 1994), we classified EDNOS into 3 subtypes: partial AN, partial BN and binge eating disorder (BED). Partial AN was defined as AN with the absence of criterion (c) and/or criterion (d) of AN in this study. Partial BN was defined as BN with the absence of criterion (c) of BN in this study. BED was defined as BN with the absence of criterion (b) of BN in this study. We tested the validity of operational definitions used in this study using 286 patients with eating disorders (75 AN patients, 88 BN patients and 123 EDNOS patients) and 72 control subjects. Control subjects had normal BMI, regular periods and no eating disorders including history. Clinical interviews were conducted on all the patients and control subjects by the senior author and diagnosis of eating disorders was made using DSM-IV criteria (American Psychiatric Association, 1994). The self-reported questionnaire was administered to both eating disorder patients and control subjects. Test-retest reliability (r=0.85, P<0.01) was good. The sensitivity and specificity of the questionnaire used in this study were 0.80 and 0.92 for AN, 0.86 and 0.96 for BN, and 0.80 and 0.90 for EDNOS against the diagnoses obtained from clinical interviews.

The Cochran-Armitage trend test was used to examine the hypothesis that the point prevalence of eating disorders and the prevalence of body image perception disorders, eating disordered behaviors and amenorrhea increased from 1982 to 2002 (Armitage & Berry, 1987). There was no significant difference in the age, height, weight and BMI among 1982, 1992 and 2002. However, Cochran-Armitage trend test demonstrated that the percentages of underweight subjects (P<0.001) as well as overweight subjects (P<0.001) increased significantly over time. Table 5 shows the prevalence of fear of weight gain, body perception disturbance, eating disordered behaviors and amenorrhea in all the subjects studied in 1982,

1992 and 2002. Cochran-Armitage trend test demonstrated that the prevalence of fear of gaining weight (P<0.001) and body perception disturbance (P<0.001) increased significantly over time. The prevalence of restrictive dieting (P<0.001), binge eating (P<0.001), purging (P<0.001), severe binge eating (P<0.001) and severe purging (P<0.001) increased significantly over time. The prevalence of amenorrhea (P<0.001) increased significantly over time.

Table 6. Point prevalence of eating disorders among female students in 1982, 1992 and 2002

Year	1982	1992	2002	Statistics
AN (%)	0.1	0.1	0.4	P<0.05
BN (%)	0.0	0.4	2.3	P<0.001
EDNOS (%)	1.1	4.0	10.0	P<0.001
eating disorder total (%)	1.2	4.5	12.7	P<0.001

AN: anorexia nervosa.
BN: bulimia nervosa.
EDNOS: eating disorder not otherwise specified.

Table 6 shows the point prevalence of AN, BN and EDNOS in 1982, 1992 and 2002. The point prevalence of AN in 1982, 1992 and 2002 was 0.1%, 0.1% and 0.4%, respectively. The point prevalence of BN in 1982, 1992 and 2002 was 0.0%, 0.4% and 2.3%, respectively. The point prevalence of EDNOS in 1982, 1992 and 2002 was 1.1%, 4.0% and 10.0%, respectively. The point prevalence of eating disorders in 1982, 1992 and 2002 was 1.2%, 4.5% and 12.9%, respectively. Cochran-Armitage trend test demonstrated that the point prevalence of all EDs, including AN (P<0.05), BN (P<0.001) and EDNOS (P<0.001) increased significantly over time.

We revealed that the prevalence of eating disorder symptoms and the point prevalence of eating disorders increased significantly among Japanese female students over time. On the other hand, in the United States, there were significant reductions of problematic eating behaviors and disordered attitudes about body weight and shape from 1982 to 2002 (Heatherton et al., 1995; Keel et al., 2005). Although the prevalence of AN has stabilized, prevalence rates of BN are decreasing in Western countries (Hoek & van Hoeken, 2003; Currin et al., 2005; Keel et al., 2005). However, there are no data, to our knowledge, of a longitudinal study on the prevalence of EDNOS. Some recent evidence suggests that the incidence of BN is decreasing, but atypical forms of eating disorders, such as BED and EDNOS, appear to be very common in the community (Machado, et al., 2007), as well as in the primary care context (Fairburn & Bohn, 2005; Micali, et al., 2013), in Western countries.

We examined the prevalence of EDNOS as well as AN and BN in 1982, 1992 and 2002 (Nakai, 2010). Since criteria for BED in this study were different from those in research criteria for BED in the DSM-IV, we should be cautious with the interpretation of the prevalence of BED in this study. The prevalence rates of AN, BN and EDNOS in the study using a self-reported questionnaire (Nakai, 2010) were lower than those with the two-stage studies (Nakai, 2012). This is probably because all diagnoses of eating disorders were made relying on the subjects' responses to the questionnaire and some subjects with eating disorders, especially AN patients, might not have answered the questionnaire honestly in the present study.

Relationship between Sociocultural Factors and Eating Disorders

There has been a growing interest in the relationship between sociocultural factors and eating disorders. Eating disorders are most likely to occur in females from industrialized nations (American Psychiatric Association, 1994), and appear to be less common among some ethnic subgroups (Streigel-Moore et al., 2006). These patterns raise questions about how membership of a given culture, ethnic group and gender influence disordered eating (Keel & Gravender, 2008). It is well known that the rise of eating disorders in non-Western countries is correlated with industrialization and westernization (Keel & Gravener, 2008).

Japan has rapidly developed with industrial techniques along with a growing increase in the influence of Western culture (Vardaman, 2006). In the early 1960s, when Japan began to enter the stage of rapid economic development, the first series of studies on the symptomatology and etiology of AN were published (Kajiyama, 1959; Ishikawa, Iwata, Hirano, 1960; Shimosaka, 1961). Family pathology was perhaps the most significant etiological factor among Japanese researchers in the 1960s. (Nogami, 1997). Ishikawa et al. (1960) and Shimosaka et al. (1961) commented on the rearing attitudes of parents. The characteristic feature of mothers' attitude to daughters with AN was over-protection and excessive intervention. Fathers' attitudes had also received attention. They were lacking in masculinity or firmness. Some fathers were too attached to their daughters. They tended to avoid confrontation with family members if they had some consideration for them. Such attitudes failed to present a likeable male image or father figure for daughters and this might disturb their ego development. Shimosaka (1961) speculated that the origin of AN was the refusal to be a mature woman, which was probably derived from poor skills in human relationships as well as conflict with the family, especially the mother. As seen in these studies, the understanding of AN in Japan at this stage seem to correspond to the international picture (Bruch, 1973; Minuchin, Rosman & Baker 1978; Selvini-Palazzoli; 1974). Anyway, a stigmatization attitude toward the family may be an obstacle for treatment.

AN was a rare disorder in Japan in the 1960s and the 1970s. The number of patients with AN rapidly increased around 1980. In this period, women's fashion styles and the standard of their beauty were influenced by Western culture (Chisuwa & O'Dea, 2010; Keel & Gravener, 2008; Nogami, 1997). Plumpness had been a symbol of health and success for both men and women in Japan. However, a lot of Western-oriented women's magazines have been published since 1970, and these magazines have favored the development of an ideal of extreme slimness for women in Japan (Morohashi, 1993). The rapid spread of television has further spurred desire for thinness in young females (Murata, 2006; Vardaman, 2006). In the 1980s, slimness was the standard of beauty in Japanese women, under the influence of Western culture (Kiriike, Nagata, Tanaka, Nishiwaki, Takeuchi, Kawakita, 1988; Nakai, 2003a; Nakai, Satoh, Tamura, Sugiura, Hayashi, 2004). In 1982, 69.9% of the subjects reported fear of weight gain and 60% reported body perception disturbance (Nakai, 2010). In the 1980s, prevalence of AN dramatically increased in Japan (Nakai, 2003a; Nogami, 1997).

In 1992, the prevalence of AN was unchanged, but the prevalence of BN and BED increased 4 times, compared with the levels in 1982 (Nakai, 2010). In addition, the prevalence of binge eating and purging behaviors remarkably increased in 1992, compared with the levels in 1982. Because the prevalence of fear of weight gain and body perception disturbance changed less than 5% in 1992 compared with that in 1982, it may be difficult to explain the remarkably increased prevalence of BN and BED in 1992 solely by the abnormality of body image perception.

Eating habits have gradually changed from low-fat Japanese-style food to high-fat Western food since 1980. As a result, BMI increased in the 1990s in men over 20 years of age and women over 30 years of age (Ministry of Health, Labour and Welfare, Japan, 2003). Furthermore, the percentages of underweight men over 20 years of age and underweight women over 40 years of age decreased in the 1990s. On the other hand, underweight women in their 20s and 30s increased in the 1990s (Ministry of Health, Labour and Welfare, Japan, 2003). This is because slimness was still the beauty standard among young Japanese women in the 1990s. In this period, there were huge numbers of advertisements for books on diets, methods of dieting, diet pills, sports centers and exercise machines to lose weight. On the other hand, food is available 24 hours a day in convenience stores in Japan (Murata, 2006; Vardaman, 2006) and there are a lot of vending machines everywhere, even in rural areas (Murata, 2006; Vardaman, 2006). Accordingly, a conflict between abundant high-fat food and desire for thinness may exist among young Japanese females these days, which could be a factor in the development of binge eating and purging behaviors, resulting in the increase in patients with BN and BED.

In 2002, the prevalence of AN and BN increased 4 times and 5 times, respectively, compared with the levels in 1992 (Nakai, 2010). The prevalence of EDNOS also increased in 2002. All the subtypes of EDNOS increased in 2002 compared with their levels in 1992. In particular, the prevalence of BED increased remarkably in 2002. Why did the prevalence of eating disorder symptoms as well as the prevalence of eating disorders increase in 2002? The impact of Western ideals and rapid cultural transitions on disordered eating has been the focus of previous work (Grabe & Hyde, 2006; Keel & Klump, 2003). However, a new generation of studies has focused on non-Western cultural ideals that may increase the risk for eating disorders (Jackson, Keel and Ho Lee, 2006). Several articles have described risk factors for the development of eating disorders in individuals that are native to Asian cultures, including Korea (Jackson et al., 2006), Thailand (Jennings, Forbes, McDermott, Hulse and Juniper, 2006) and Japan (Kusano-Scharz and von Wietersheim, 2005). They have noted the potential influence of collectivism on the development of disordered eating in Asian culture (Kusano-Scharz and von Wietersheim, 2005; Jackson et al., 2006; Jennings et al., 2006). Collectivism emphasizes the needs and desires of the group over those of the individual, in contrast to individualism, which emphasizes autonomy and desires of the individual. Kusano-Scharz and von Wietersheim (2005) described Japanese culture as emphasizing harmony with the values of society. In Western countries, self-association, self-confidence, independence and individuality are considered important virtues. In Japanese society, attentiveness towards other people, modesty and respect are more important. They speculated that the higher levels of disordered eating in Japan may reflect greater influence of unhealthy ideals in a culture that equates self-realization with the realization of social values. Therefore, both societies might deal differently with the ideal of slimness. However, these interpretations are very speculative. Collectivism is a traditional culture in Japan in men as well as in women. Accordingly, it may be difficult to explain with collectivism why eating disorders occur mostly in females and why eating disorders have been recently increasing in Japan.

Yokoyama (1997) studied sociocultural factors contributing to the rapid rise of eating disorders in Japan. He pointed out that the number of women who studied at university and continued to work after marriage and childbirth had increased. As a result, women may experience a stressful life due to competition and conflict with others. He further pointed out that, in addition to westernization, a highly organized media-oriented culture has replaced the traditional moral concepts to offer new standards. A person whose social identity has been damaged easily adopts the standards offered by the media, such as those regarding beauty and dieting.

Young Japanese people have been stressed and powerless after the bursting of the economic bubble in about 2000 (Vardaman, 2006). Furthermore, young Japanese women were in conflict between women's liberation and discrimination against women. Although the law of equal employment opportunity was enacted in 1985, discrimination against women remains in Japanese society (Vardaman, 2006). Young Japanese women are also in conflict between individualism under the influence of Western culture and collectivism (harmony with the values of society) in traditional Japanese culture (Kusano-Scharz & von Wiestersheim, 2005). The conflict between desire for thinness and abundant high-fat food remains among young Japanese females nowadays (Ministry of Health Labour and Welfare, Japan, 2003). These conflicts may be responsible for the dramatic increase of eating disorder symptoms and, consequently, the increase of eating disorders in 2002.

The overview of eating disorders in Japan indicates that in the 1970s the focus was on a contribution of the family in classical anorexia nervosa, in the 1980s on weight and diet pressures in bulimia nervosa and in the 1990s on the awareness of female role stress in EDNOS (Nakai, 2003; Vardaman, 2006). The overview of eating disorders in Japan as well as in Western society reveals the essential issues for cross-cultural perspectives on eating disorders: not only the standard of thinness but also the role of the family, awareness of female role stress and so on.

In conclusion, the prevalence of eating disorder symptoms and eating disorders is still increasing among Japanese female students. Changing socio-cultural factors in Japan may explain a dramatic increase of eating disorders over time.

References

American Psychiatric Association (1994). *Diagnostic and Statistical Manual of Mental Disorders,* 4th edn (DSM-IV) American Psychiatric Association: Washington, DC.

Armitage, P. & Berry, G. (1987). *Statistical Methods in Medical Research,* 2nd edn. Blackwell, Publishing: Oxford, UK.

Azuma, T. & Ohishi, M. (1984). An epidemiological study of anorexia nervosa on high school students in Kyoto prefecture. *Annual Report of Research Group into Eating Disorders* 40-46 (in Japanese).

Azuma, T. & Noma, S. (1993). An epidemiological study of eating disorders on high school students in Kyoto prefecture. *Annual Report of Research Group into Eating Disorders* 55-58 (in Japanese).

Bruch, H. (1973). *Eating Disorders: Obesity, Anorexia Nervosa, and the Person Within.* New York; Basic Books.

Chisuwa, N. & O'Dea, J.A. (2010). Body image and eating disorders amongst Japanese adolescents. A review of the literature. *Appetite* 54, 5-15.

Currin, L., Schmidt, U., Treasure, J. & Jick, H. (2005). Time trends in eating disorder incidence. *British Journal of Psychiatry* 186, 132-135.

Fairburn, C.G. & Beglin, S.J. (1990). Studies of the epidemiology of bulimia nervosa. *American Journal of Psychiatry* 147, 401-408.

Fairburn, C.G. & Beglin, S. (2008). Eating Disorder Examination Questionnaire (EDE-Q 6.0) editors. In *Cognitive behavior therapy and eating disorders* (ed. Fairburn, C.G.), pp. 309-313. The Guilford Press, NY, USA.

Fairburn, C.G. & Bohn, K. (2005). Eating disorder NOS (EDNOS): an example of the troublesome "not otherwise specified" (NOS) category in DSM-IV. *Behaviour Research and Therapy* 43, 691-701.

Fombonne, E. (1995), Anorexia nervosa. No evidence of an increase. *British Journal of Psychiatry* 166, 462-471.

Garner, D.M. & Garfinkel, P.E. (1979). The Eating Attitudes Test: An index of the symptoms of anorexia nervosa. *Psychological Medicine* 9, 273-279.

Grabe, S. & Hyde, J.S. (2006). Ethnicity and body dissatisfaction among women in the United States: a meta-analysis. *Psychological Bulletin* 132, 622-640.

Heatherton, T.F., Nichols, P., Mahamedi, F. & Keel, P. (1995). Body weight, dieting, and eating disorder symptoms among college students, 1982 to 1992. *American Journal of Psychiatry* 152, 1623-1629.

Hisamatsu, Y., Tuboi, K., Tsutsui, S. & Sinoda, T. (2000). A study on primary screening method for eating disorder in female university students. *Japanese Journal of Psychosomatic Medicine* 40, 325-331 (in Japanese).

Hoek, H.W. (2006). Incidence, prevalence and mortality of anorexia nervosa and other eating disorders. *Current Opinions in Psychiatry* 19, 389-394.

Hoek, H.W. & van Hoeken, D. (2003). Review of the prevalence and incidence of eating disorders. *International Journal of Eating Disorders* 34, 383-396.

Hsu, L.K. (1996). Epidemiology of the eating disorders. *Psychiatric Clinics of North America* 19, 681-700.

Ishikawa, K., Iwata, Y. & Hirano, G. (1960). Studies on the symptoms and the pathogenesis of anorexia nervosa. *Psychiatria et Neurologia Japonica* 62, 256-272 (in Japanese).

Jackson, S.C., Keel, P.K. & Ho Lee, Y. (2006). Trans-cultural comparison of disordered eating in Korean women. *International Journal of Eating Disorders* 39, 498-502.

Jennings, P.S., Forbes, D., McDermott, B., Hulse, G. & Juniper, S. (2006). Eating disorder attitudes and psychopathology in Caucasian Australian, Asian Australian and Thai university students. *Australian and New Zealand Journal of Psychiatry* 40, 143-149.

Kajiyama, S. (1959). Anorexia nervosa. A clinical psychiatric study of 20 cases. *Psychiatria et Neurologia Japonica* 62, 256-272 (in Japanese).

Keel, P. & Gravener, J.A. (2008). Sociocultural influence on eating disorders. In *Annual Review of Eating Disorders PART 2 – 2008* (ed. S. Wonderlich, J.E. Mitchell, M. de Zwaan, H. Steiger), pp. 43-57. Radcliffe Publishing: Oxford, UK.

Keel, P.K., Heatherton, T.F., Dorer, D.J., Joiner, T.E. & Zalta, A.K. (2005). Point prevalence of bulimia nervosa in 1982, 1992 and 2002. *Psychological Medicine* 35, 1-9.

Keel, P.K. & Klump, K.L. (2003). Are eating disorders culture-bound syndromes? Implications for conceptualizing their etiology. *Psychological Bulletin* 129, 747-769.

Keski-Rahkonen, A., Raevuori, A. & Hoek, H.W. (2008). Epidemiology of eating disorders: an update. In *Annual Review of Eating Disorders PART 2 – 2008* (ed. S. Wonderlich, J.E. Mitchell, M. de Zwaan, H. Steiger), pp. 58-68. Radcliffe Publishing: Oxford, UK.

Kiriike, N., Nagata, T., Tanaka, M., Nishiwaki, S., Takeuchi, N. & Kawakita, Y. (1988). Prevalence of binge-eating and bulimia among adolescent women in Japan. *Psychiatry Research* 26, 163-169.

Kuboki, T., Nomura, S., Ide, M., Suematsu, H. & Araki, S. (1996). Epidemiological data on anorexia nervosa in Japan. *Psychiatry Research*. 62, 11-16.

Kusano-Scharz, M. & von Wietersheim, J. (2005). EDI results of Japanese and German women and possible sociocultural explanations. *European Eating Disorders Review* 13, 411-416.

Machado, P.P., Machado, B.C., Gonçalves, S. & Hoek, H.W. (2007). The prevalence of eating disorders not otherwise specified. *International Journal of Eating Disorders* 40, 212-217.

Micali, N., Hagberg, K.W., Petersen, I. & Treasure, J.L. (2013). The incidence of eating disorders in the UK in 2000-2009: findings from the General Practice Research Database. *BMJ Open* 3, doi:pii: e002646. 10.1136/bmjopen-2013-002646.

Milos, G., Spindler, A., Schnyder, U., Martz, J., Hoek, H.W. & Willi, J. (2004). Incidence of severe anorexia nervosa in Switzerland: 40 years of development. *International Journal of Eating Disorders* 35, 250-258.

Ministry of Health, Labour and Welfare, Japan (2003). *The National Nutrition Survey in Japan, 2001*, Dai-ichi-Suppan Publishing: Tokyo, Japan (in Japanese).

Minuchin, S., Rosman, B.L. & Baker, L. (1978). *Psychosomatic Families: Anorexia Nervosa in Context*. Harvard University Press, Cambridge, MA.

Mizuno Y. & Mizushima, N. (1984). An epidemiological study on middle school and high school students in Fukui prefecture. *Annual Report of Research Group into Eating Disorders* 50-62 (in Japanese).

Mizushima, N. & Ishii, Y. (1983). An epidemiological study on middle school and high school students in Ishikawa prefecture. *Annual Report of Research Group into Eating Disorders* 42-55 (in Japanese).

Morohashi, T. (1993). *The culture of Women's magazines: a Study of gender image*. Akashi Shoten, Tokyo, Japan (in Japanese).

Murata, K. (2006). *Playback the 1980s*. Bungeisynjyu, Tokyo, Japan (in Japanese).

Nagata, T., Kiriike, N., Yoshino, S., Nishiwaki, S., Takeuchi, N., Tanaka, M. & Kawakita, Y. (1989). Reliability and validity of the Eating Attitudes Test in patients with eating disorders. *Japanese Journal of Clinical Psychiatry* 18, 1279-1286 (in Japanese).

Nakai, Y. (1983). An epidemiological study of anorexia nervosa on middle school and high school in Kyoto prefecture. *Annual Report of Research Group into Eating Disorders* 42-55 (in Japanese).

Nakai, Y. (2003a). The epidemiology of eating disorders: Data from Japan. In *Eating Disorders* (ed. M. Maj, K. Halmi, J.J. Lopez-Ibor, N. Sartorius), pp.126-128. John Wiley & Sons Ltd: West Sussex, UK.

Nakai, Y. (2003b). Validity of Eating Attitudes Test (EAT). *Seishin Igaku* 45, 161-165 (in Japanese).

Nakai, Y. (2010). Changes of prevalence of eating disorders and eating disorder symptoms. *Seishin Igaku* 52, 379-383 (in Japanese).

Nakai, Y. (2012). Epidemiology. In *Guideline of eating disorders*. (ed. Japan Society for Eating Disorders), pp.18-22, Igakushoin, Tokyo, Japan (in Japanese).

Nakai, Y., Hamagaki, S., Noma, S., Takao, Y., Fujita, M., Takagi, R. & Ishikawa, T. (2009). Survey of eating disorders among medical facilities in Kyoto city. *Seishin Igaku* 51, 381-383 (in Japanese).

Nakai, Y., Satoh, M., Tamura, K., Sugiura, M. & Hayashi, J. (2004). Survey of eating disorders in junior high school, high school and university. *Seishin Igaku* 46, 1269-1273 (in Japanese).

Nogami, Y. (1997). Eating disorders in Japan: a review of the literature. *Psychiatry and Clinical Neurosciences* 51, 339-46.

Otsuka, K. (1955). 'Fushokubyo' in Edo era. *Nihon Toyo Igakukai Zasshi* 6, 10-14 (in Japanese).

Pawluck, D.E. & Gorey, K.M. (1998). Secular trends in the incidence of anorexia nervosa: integrative review of population-based studies. *International Journal of Eating Disorders* 23, 347-352.

Selvini-Palazzoli, M. (1974). *Self-starvation*. Chaucer Publising Co. Ltd., London.

Shimosaka, K. (1961). Psychiatrische studien über pubertätsmagersucht. *Psychiatria et Neurologia Japonica* 63, 1042-1082.

Striegel-Moore, R.H., Franko, D.L. & Ach, E.L. (2006). Epidemiology of eating disorders: an update. In *Annual Review or Eating Disorders Part 2 – 2006* (ed. S. Wonderlich, J.E. Mitchell, M. de Zwaan, H. Steiger), pp. 65-80. Radcliffe Publishing: Oxford, UK.

Tsai, G. (2000). Eating disorders in the Far East. *Eating & Weight Disorders* 5, 183-197

Ujiie, T. & Kono, M. (1994). Eating Attitudes Test in Japan. *The Japanese Journal of Psychiatry and Neurology* 48, 557-565.

van Son, G.E., van Hoeken, D., Bartelds, A.I., van Furth, E.F. & Hoek, H.W. (2006). Time trends in the incidence of eating disorders: a primary care study in the Netherlands. *International Journal of Eating Disorders* 39, 565-569.

Vardaman, J.M. (2006). Contemporary Japanese History: Since 1945. IBC Publishing, Tokyo, Japan.

Wardle, J., Haase, A.M. & Steptoe. A. (2006). Body image and weight control in young adults: international comparisons in university students from 22 countries. *International Journal of Obesestiy (Lond)* 30, 644-51.

Watanabe, H. (2004). *Study of the prevalence of eating disorders amongst adolescents and the prevention*. Ministry of Health and Welfare and Child Health Division Tokyo, Japan (in Japanese).

Williams, P., Tarnopolosky, A. & Hand, D. (1980). Case definition and case identification in psychiatric epidemiology: review and assessment. *Psychological Medicine* 10, 10-14.

Yokoyama, T. (1997) Changes of clinical features in eating disorder over the times. *Japanese Journal of Psychopathology*, 18, 141-150.

In: New Developments in Anorexia Nervosa Research
Editors: Carla Gramaglia and Patrizia Zeppegno

ISBN: 978-1-63117-551-0
© 2014 Nova Science Publishers, Inc.

Chapter 12

Rethinking Schema-Driven Processing in Eating Disorders: Is it Possible to Overcome Controversies?

*Małgorzata Starzomska**

Institute of Psychology, Cardinal Stefan Wyszynski University, Warsaw, Poland

Abstract

There are many cognitive theories about eating disorders. The schematic approach is among the most prominent, assuming that schemas influence the processing of information in a schema-congruent fashion. Patients with eating disorders are characterized by body-related self-schemas influencing selective attention towards eating, shape, and weight-related stimuli. Lately, this approach has been challenged by researchers trying to explore mechanisms underlying schema-driven information processing. Such partially justified criticism should be kept in mind while discussing the schematic theory of eating disorders. This chapter includes a presentation of the state of the art concerning schema processes in eating disorders and the most frequent controversies around it. Finally, we suggest how such controversies should change our attitude to eating disorders research and how such problems might be faced.

Introduction

Any theory about eating disorders bringing us one step closer to understanding these conditions is worth paying attention to. The cognitive revolution has certainly influenced clinical psychology. The rise of several cognitive theories about eating disorders was one of the outcomes of this influence. Among them, the schema-driven information processing in people suffering from eating disorders is particularly noteworthy.

* Corresponding author: Institute of Psychology, Cardinal Stefan Wyszynski University, Woycickiego 1/3, building No. 14, 01-938 Warsaw. Email: eltram@life.pl.

Defining Schemas

Although researchers have not reached an agreement yet on the definition of schemas, the majority of them would agree that schemas are functional knowledge structures based on previous experiences and have accumulated throughout life (Power & Dalgleish, 1997). Johansson (Johansson, 2006) describes schemata as "belief systems around which an individual organises and processes incoming information which subsequently serves to guide behaviour. These schemata bias information processing toward schemata-congruent information automatically by guiding processing resources toward information consistent with the schemata" (p. 20). According to Johansson (Johansson, 2006) such facilitation of information processing can be constructive and functional (e.g. schema "I can do many great things in my life"), but it can also be destructive and dysfunctional (e.g. schema "I am useless"). On the other hand, Young (Young, 1999) assumes that all schemas are dysfunctional; he defines schemas as "extremely stable and enduring themes that develop during childhood, are elaborated throughout an individual lifetime, and are dysfunctional to a significant degree" (p. 9). The author claims that they serve as "templates for the processing of later experience" (p. 9).

According to Beck (Beck, 1976), who proposed a schema theory of mood disorders, anxiety and depression are characterized by maladaptive schemata. Johansson (Johansson, 2006) states that individuals suffering from mood disorders differ from normal individuals in how they process information in a concern-centred manner, due to such dysfunction. Self-schemata appear to exert the strongest influence on the individual's everyday functioning. Markus (Markus, 1977) defined self-schemas as "cognitive generalizations about the self, derived from past experience, that organize and guide the processing of self-related information contained in an individual's social experience" (p. 64). A person who is schematic, and who develops a self-schema in a particular area, will process information related to that area completely differently from someone who is not schematic (Cash, 2002; Cash & Labarge, 1996). Such individuals process schema-consistent information efficiently, but when the information is counter-schematic, they resist them (Vitousek & Hollon, 1990).

Review of Schema-Based
Eating Disorders Concepts

One of the models I would like to present first is that by Vitousek and Hollon (Vitousek and Hollon, 1990). Researchers suggested their own schematic approach to understand of eating disorders, describing their research efforts as follows: "We have an urgent and practical need to understand more about what and how the eating disorder patient thinks if we want to affect how she behaves, and it is hoped that a schematic approach may advance our progress toward this goal" (s. 210). The authors underline that they did not strive to develop a new theory for the understanding of eating disorders, rather to propose a framework which may guide researchers into existing cognitive models. However, we should not underestimate their significant contribution in structuring and broadening our knowledge in the field of information processing in people suffering from eating disorders. The authors assume that eating disordered individuals have a particularly urgent need to simplify, organize, and stabilize their experience of the self and the external environment. Focusing on weight serves this need and, according to the authors, it reflects "a desperate struggle to restore a sense of orderliness and predictability to a world they experience as chaotic and overwhelming" (p. 195). In particular, the symptoms of anorexia, reported as alarming by relatives and doctors, are highly valued by the sufferers who perceive them as egosyntonic (see, e.g. Tan, Hope, & Steward, 2003; Lamourex & Bottorff, 2005; Rieger & Touyz, 2006; Schmidt & Treasure, 2006; Vandereycken, 2006) According to Vitousek and Hollon (Vitousek and Hollon, 1990)., the "cognitive essence" (p. 191) of eating disorders may be found in organized cognitive structures that unite views of the self with beliefs about weight, defined weight-related self-schemata (e.g. schema of overweight self) (see also Eiber, Mirabel-Sarron, & Urdapilleta, 2005), which may exert automatic effects on the processing of information. As the disorder progresses, the schemata become increasingly stereotyped (Vitousek & Hollon, 1990).

Another important schema-based theory of eating disorders is the one by Williamson, Stewart, White, & York-Crowe (Williamson, Stewart, White, & York-Crowe, 2002). The researchers proposed a cognitive information-processing model for body image in relation to eating disorders. In this model, body image is a cognitive bias resulting from a self-schema related to body size/shape and eating that is easily activated (see also Fairburn, Cooper, & Shafran, 2003). This self-schema draws the person's attention to body and food-related stimuli and leads to biased interpretations of self-relevant information and events. This model hypothesizes that body- or food-related information, ambiguous stimuli, and tasks requiring thinking-over may cause cognitive bias in susceptible people, in particular those affected by: fear of fatness, over concern with body size/shape, internalization of a thin ideal size/shape, and perfectionism or obsessiveness.

Waller (the model is presented in the article of Luck, Waller, Meyer, Ussher, & Lacey, 2005) has suggested another remarkable model of eating disorders. This model states that restrictive and bulimic disorders are characterized by various styles of coping with schemas. This suggestion was based on the notion of the schema therapy by Young (Young, 1999). The author has listed three types of dysfunctional styles of coping with schemas. The first one, schema surrender, refers to ways how people accept the schema as true and behave so as to confirm the schema. The second schema coping style refers to ways how people avoid activating schemas (schema avoidance). The third dysfunctional way of coping with schemas is schema overcompensation, when an individual behaves opposite to what the schema would suggest in order to avoid triggering the schema. Waller tried to describe the ways how eating disordered people cope with schemas. He claims that restrictive disorders (e.g. anorexia nervosa) are associated with schema compensation, while bulimic disorders (e.g. bulimia nervosa) are associated with schema avoidance. For example, self-starvation in anorexia nervosa may be the answer to the schema overweight-self. By refusing to eat, the anorexia sufferer is trying to avoid triggering the schema. She is trying to prove herself and to those around her that she doesn't need any food. In her mind, the thinner she becomes the safer she is from becoming overweight. On the other hand, binge-eating and purging in bulimia nervosa illustrate impulsive attempts to reduce negative views about their body once the overweight schema has been triggered. Drugs and alcohol abuse, often observed in bulimic patients, may also represent an attempt to block negative feelings. Such behaviour helps to numb feelings, leading an individual to a temporary relief from compulsive thoughts about her weight and the risk of being overweight.

Problems with Schema-Based Models of Eating Disorders

The application of the term "schemata" in the field of eating disorders encourages the researchers to design new methods, allowing the hypothesis in this field to be tested.

According to Segal (Segal, 1988), schema-based information processing is usually assessed only indirectly through the use of paper-and-pencil methods in which the tested subjects read questions and answer by writing (e.g. personality inventories). The author states "the strategy of relying on negative self-reports to validate a construct whose operation is intended to explain these self-reports becomes increasingly circular unless additional external referents can be provided to demonstrate schematic processing" (p. 147). Unfortunately, the success of cognitive-behavioural therapy in eating disorders may have encouraged a tendency to uncritically accept its foundation theories (see Mogg, Stopa, & Bradley, 2001).

Mogg, Stopa, & Bradley (Mogg, Stopa, & Bradley 2001) claim that it is not their intention to prove that cognitive schema models are useless. However, one cannot deny there is an uneasy tension between cognitive psychogical treatments for eating disorders and the imperfect cognitive models they rely on. Demonstration of treatment effectiveness does not provide evidence supporting the validity of underlying models by itself,. Thus we come to the question: how well do contemporary schema-based models of eating disorders fulfil experimental precision? Wells and Matthews (Matthews, 1994) claim that "currently, there is a proliferiation of schema-like concepts (see, e.g. Schank, 1982) but little data to distinguish their validity, except within a few specific, highly constrained laboratory paradigms" (p. 48). For this reason, the authors claim that using notions such as schemata in cognitive theories is somewhat speculative. At the same time, they ask for an explanation about the mechanism of the schema-driven selection. They state: "We would like to know whether schema function is constrained by the processing architecture, the level of control of selection, and whether selection guided by complex knowledge and expectancy is essentially the same as selection of the traditional targets of attentional research, features, categories and objects" (p.49).

In conclusion, understanding the mechanism of the schema-driven information-selection in mood disordered individuals appears to be the main challenge to both the authors and the supporters of the majority of cognitive theories of eating disorders. This is due to the existing "gap" between theory and its scientific verification. The lack of researchers' consensus on the exact mechanisms behind the schema-driven information processing in mood disordered people contributes to the problem.

How to Overcome Controversies?

According to Vitousek and Hollon (Vitousek and Hollon, 1990), in eating disordered individuals, latencies in judging whether some kinds of schema-related material (e.g. food-related words and photos of overweight bodies) apply to the self, differ from latencies in judging neutral material (e.g. words related to a household and photos of animals), and they differ from latencies in judging the former material in healthy individuals. For example, during the Stroop colour naming test (Stroop, 1935), eating disordered patients are significantly slower in naming the colors of the ink in which food-related words are printed than in naming the ink color of neutral words, and are also slower than healthy subjects in responding to the former stimuli.

Markus, Hamill and Sentis (Markus, Hamill and Sentis 1987) have pioneered the research in this field. They showed that overweight young adult women who indicated that being overweight was an important part of their self-definition (i.e. overweight schematics) processed self-relevant information differently from those with no self-schema in this domain (i.e. the aschematics). Individuals belonging to the first group rated more overweight adjectives as self-descriptive (i.e. "me" vs. "not me" judgments) and were faster in "me" judgments, and slower in "not me" judgments of overweight adjectives than people in the second group. Overweight schematics were also more likely to judge silhouettes of overweight women as self-descriptive and were faster in those judgments than the schematics. On the other hand, although he does not use the term "self-schemata", Higgins é Higgins, 1990) claims that the available knowledge may be chronically accessible, and it will influence peoples' selective attention. Markus et al. (Markus, 1987) and Higgins (Higgins, 1990) published their research results twenty years ago.

Nowadays, research increasingly uses cognitive psychology not only in testing latencies in judging some words and images, but also in exploring attentional focus in eating disordered individuals. Researchers have access to more advanced and varied research methodologies to study the attentional focus on different types of stimuli in eating disordered people. After a period of initial fascination by the Stroop colour naming test (Stroop, 1935), and particularly its modified version testing selective attention in mood disordered individuals, the method appeared to be an insufficient tool to measure attentional bias. Among other limits, the method does not allow to discriminate between different types of attentional bias, such as vigilance to a given stimulus, difficulty in disengaging attention and attentional avoidance (Cisler & Koster, 2010).

Koster, Verschuere, Crombez and van Damme (Koster, Verschuere, Crombez and van Damme, 2004) modified the dot probe task (MacLeod, Mathews, & Tata, 1986), so they could test all three components of attentional bias (Koster et al. 2004). During the test assorted pairs of stimuli (negative and neutral, positive and neutral and just neutral) were presented. Monitoring the changes of attentional biases through time enables to test the way in which the individual processes the particular stimuli. Regrettably, to the author's best knowledge, the modified dot probe task has not been applied in the research of the eating disorders yet.

According to the author of the chapter, applying the modified dot probe task in the testing of the three attentional components would substantiate, and perhaps even improve, the Waller model. As a matter of fact, the model assumes that subjects with restrictive and bulimic behaviors experience certain schema processes (schema compensation and schema avoidance, accordingly), both of which represent a way to cope with overweight schema. However, Waller does not consider the chance that the processes change with time. Such hypothesis seems plausible if we combine the two suggestions of Waller and Koster et al. (Waller and Koster, 2004) together. The first model deals with the three types of dysfunctional styles of copying with schemas (schema surrender, schema avoidance and schema overcompensation). The second model focuses on rigorous research of attentional biases (vigilance, avoidance and difficulty in disengaging attention). The combination of the two models may suggest that a given attentional bias could reveal a specific dysfunctional type of copying with schemas. A reliable analysis of the changes of attentional biases through time would allow establishing if and at what stage (preconscious or conscious, and if conscious, after how long exposure duration) eating disordered people make use of particular coping schemas such as that of overweight self. As a result, the vigilance towards a given negative stimulus related to eating disorder (e.g. a photo of an overweight girl) and difficulty in disengaging attention away from it would confirm surrendering to the negative schemata of overweight self, which triggers the eating disorder. On the other hand, avoiding the stimulus would provide the evidence of the avoidance of overweight self schemata. Again, vigilance towards positive stimulus and difficulty in disengaging attention away from it would confirm the schema compensation. Nonetheless, it is important to test whether vigilance towards a given stimulus and difficulty in disengaging attention away from it do not reflect different schema processes.

Conclusion

The modern experimental paradigms assessing attentional bias, in particular the dot probe task, can offer helpful insights into the mechanism of the schema-driven information-processing in eating disorders. This suggestion might be criticized, according to Wells and Matthews (Wells and Matthews, 1994) who wondered "whether selection guided by complex knowledge and expectancy is essentially the same as selection of the traditional target of attentional research" (p. 49), which is a remarkable issue. However, we should remember that modern paradigms of experimental psychology are somehow able to access the patient's thoughts and emotions, mainly due to computer readings of subtle changes of the reaction times and analysing data below the threshold of conscious perception. Detecting the automatic vigilance towards some emotional messages is possible when stimuli are quite simple In the future we should consider the possibility of designing some experimental paradigms aimed at testing attentional bias in specific circumstances, e.g. in anxiety inhibiting situation (i.e. when the tested subjects are asked to suppress anxiety). The on-going progress in the field of cognitive psychology will certainly contribute to the development of further experimental opportunities capable to support the research of eating disorders.

References

Beck, A. T. (1976). *Cognitive therapy and the emotional disorders.* New York: International Universities Press.

Cash, T. F. (2002). Cognitive-behavioral perspectives on body image. In. T.F. Cash, & T. Pruzinsky (Eds.), Body image. *Body image: A handbook of theory, research, and clinical practice,* (38-46). New York: Guilford Press.

Cash, T. F. & Labarge, A. S. (1996). Development of the Appearance Schemas Inventory: A new cognitive body-image assessment. *Cognitive Therapy and Research, 20,* 37-50.

Cisler, J. M. & Koster, E. H. W. (2010). Mechanisms of attentional biases towards threat in anxiety disorders: An integrative review. *Clinical Psychology Review, 30,* 203-216.

Eiber, R., Mirabel-Sarron, C. & Urdapilleta, I. (2005). Cognitions in eating disorders and their assessment. *Encephale, 31,* 643-652.

Fairburn, C. G., Cooper, Z. & Shafran, R. (2003). Cognitive behaviour therapy for eating disorders: a "transdiagnostic" theory and treatment. *Behaviour Research and Therapy*, *41*, 509-528.

Higgins, E. T. (1990). Personality, social psychology, and person-situation relations: Standards and knowledge activation as a common language. In L. A. Pervin (Ed.), *Handbook of personality: Theory and research*, (301-338). New York, NY: The Guilford Press.

Johansson, L. (2006) *The role of schema processes in eating pathology.* Uppsala Universitet.

Koster, E. H. W., Verschuere, B., Crombez, G. & van Damme, S. (2005). Time-course of attention for threatening pictures in high and low trait anxiety. *Behaviour Research and Therapy*, *43*, 1087-1098.

Lamoureux, M. M. H. & Bottorff, J. L. (2005). "Becoming the real me": Recovering from anorexia nervosa. *Health Care for Women International*, *26*, 170-188.

Luck, A., Waller, G., Meyer, C., Ussher, M. & Lacey, H. (2005). The Role of Schema Processes in the Eating Disorders. *Cognitive Therapy and Research*, *29*, 717–732.

MacLeod, C., Mathews, A. & Tata, P. (1986). Attentional bias in emotional disorders. *Journal of Abnormal Psychology*, *95*, 15 - 20.

Markus, H. (1977). Self-schemata and processing information about the self. *Journal of Personality and Social Psychology*, *35*, 63-78.

Markus, H., Hamill, R. & Sentis, K. P. (1987). Thinking fat: Self-schemas for body weight and the processing of weight relevant information. *Journal of Applied Social Psychology*, *17*, 50-71.

Mogg, K., Stopa, L. & Bradley, P. B. (2001). From the conscious into the unconscious": What can cognitive theories of psychopathology learn from Freudian theory? Commentary. *Psychological Inquiry*, *12*, 139-143.

Power, M. & Dalgleish, T. (1997). *Cognition and emotion. From order to disorder*. UK: Psychology Press.

Rieger, E. & Touyz, S. (2006). An investigation of the factorial structure of motivation to recover in anorexia nervosa using the anorexia nervosa stages of change questionnaire. *European Eating Disorders Review*, *14*, 269-275.

Schank, R. C. (1986). *Explanation Patterns: Understanding Mechanically and Creatively*. Hillsdale, NJ: Erlbaum.

Segal, Z. V. (1988). Appraisal of the self-schema construct in cognitive models of depression. *Psychological Bulletin*, *103*, 147-162.

Schmidt, U. & Treasure, J. (2006). Anorexia nervosa: valued and visible. A cognitive-interpersonal maintenance model and its implications for research and practice. *British Journal of Clinical Psychology*, *45*, 343-366.

Stroop, J. R. (1935). Studies of interference in serial verbal reactions. *Journal of Experimental Psychology*, *18*, 643 -

Tan, J. O. A., Hope, T. & Steward, A. (2003). Anorexia nervosa and personal identity: The accounts of patients and their parents. *International Journal of Law and Psychiatry*, *26*, 533-548.

Vandereycken, W. (2006). Denial of illness in anorexia nervosa – a conceptual review: Part 1 Diagnostic significance and assessment. *European Eating Disorders Review*, *14*, 341-351

Vitousek, K. B. & Hollon, S. D. (1990). The investigation of schematic content and processing in eating disorders. *Cognitive Therapy and Research*, *14*, 191-214.

Wells, A. & Matthews, G. (1994). *Attention and emotion. A clinical perspective.* Hove, England: Erlbaum.

Williamson, D. A., Stewart, T. M., White, M. A. & York-Crowe, E. (2002). An information-processing perspective on body image. In. T.F. Cash, & T. Pruzinsky (Eds.), Body image. *Body image: A handbook of theory, research, and clinical practice,* (47-54). New York: Guilford Press.

Young, J. E. (1999). *Cognitive therapy for personality disorders: A schema focused approach.* Sarasota, FL: Professional Resource Exchange.

Young, J. E., Klosko, J. & Weishaar, M. E. (2003). *Schema therapy: A practitioner's guide.* New York: Guilford.

Index

D

I

Q

R

S

T

U

V

W

Y